PILE FOUNDATION

SUBSTRUCTURE
ANALYSIS AND DESIGN

By

PAUL ANDERSEN, Ph.D.

Professor of Structural Engineering
University of Minnesota

SECOND EDITION

THE RONALD PRESS COMPANY   •   NEW YORK

Library of Congress Catalog Card Number: 56-6804

PRINTED IN THE UNITED STATES OF AMERICA

PREFACE

Nearly eight years have elapsed since the first edition of this book appeared. The many developments in the field of foundation engineering during this time have necessitated a revision of the subject matter, but the plan of organization of the first edition has not been changed.

The pedagogical objective of the first edition, to present the various phases of substructure analysis and design, clearly and logically for the benefit of the student, has been retained. In the second edition a further objective, to make the book more useful to the practicing engineer, has received added attention. New design information has been included in nearly every chapter. It is believed that this additional material together with the many new problems at the end of each chapter, will make the book more interesting as well as more useful to the student.

Most texts on foundations treat the subject either from the viewpoint of the soil technician or from that of the construction engineer. The soil technician is primarily interested in the probable behavior of the soil at a particular site under the proposed loading, while the engineer in the field has the greater interest in the constructional phases of the project.

The designer of foundations is less concerned with the above aspects and more interested in the methods and procedures for determining the stresses developed in the various parts of the substructure. For this reason the author believes that this book, which deals with analysis and design, will prove most useful in the field of structural engineering and will meet the needs of teachers giving courses in conventional methods of structural design.

The first chapter is devoted to methods for evaluating lateral earth pressures—the classical methods by Rankine and Coulomb, supplemented by the modern conceptions of the effects of surcharge, cohesion, and pore pressures. In the second chapter, direct applications of these theories are made to the design of flexible bulkheads. The third chapter on "Soil Bearing Power" deals with allowable soil bearing pressures and their dependence on such factors as size, shape, and depth of the contact area. The following chapter discusses the current practice in footing design. Piles and groups of piles are discussed at length and applications are made to typical examples. The last seven chapters are devoted to specialized phases of substructure analysis, extending into the fields of pier, dock, and breakwater design.

Throughout the book, emphasis has been placed on applications to the problems of the designing engineer. Facility in setting up mathematical relationships to express stresses in the substructure is best achieved

iii

by studying practical examples, and the various illustrative problems form an integral part of the text.

The author acknowledges his indebtedness to Professor Cyril D. Jensen for his constructive criticism of the manuscript and his many valuable suggestions. Thanks are also due to the late Mr. A. E. Cummings of Raymond Concrete Pile Company, and to Mr. C. B. Spencer, Vice President of Spencer, White and Prentis, Inc., for their permission to reproduce photographs of various phases of construction work on substructures.

PAUL ANDERSEN

University of Minnesota
    January, 1956

TABLE OF CONTENTS

CHAPTER 1. EARTH PRESSURES

CHAPTER 2. SHEET PILING

CHAPTER 3. SOIL BEARING POWER

Chapter 6. Pile Groups

Chapter 7. Cellular Cofferdams

Chapter 8. Single-Wall Cofferdams

Chapter 9. Open and Pneumatic Caissons

Chapter 10. Floating Caissons

TABLE OF CONTENTS

CHAPTER 11. BREAKWATERS

CHAPTER 12. WHARVES AND PIERS

CHAPTER 13. BRIDGE PIERS AND ABUTMENTS

APPENDIX

SUBSTRUCTURE ANALYSIS AND DESIGN

CHAPTER 1

EARTH PRESSURES

1-1. Introduction. It is impossible to make an exact determination of the pressure intensities throughout an earth mass. So many uncertain elements which can neither be anticipated nor determined are involved that it becomes difficult to assemble enough information upon which to base a satisfactory solution giving the correct pressures at any time during the existence of the structure.

By making certain assumptions regarding the proportion of the earth mass, by treating it as an ideal material, it is possible, though, to arrive at certain definite expressions for the various pressure intensities. Although these pressures may not be the right ones, they will indicate the relative variations and furnish a framework upon which to superimpose the modifications experimentally determined. The analysis of an ideal earth mass may show the maximum pressures that can be expected to occur in the commonly used fills, which the actual pressures may approach as the properties of the fill or earth mass approach that of the ideal one. Thus, the probable maximum value of earth pressures may be established and a safe design arrived at.

1-2. Definitions. When a mass of earth is held back by means of a retaining structure, a lateral force is exerted on the structure. If this

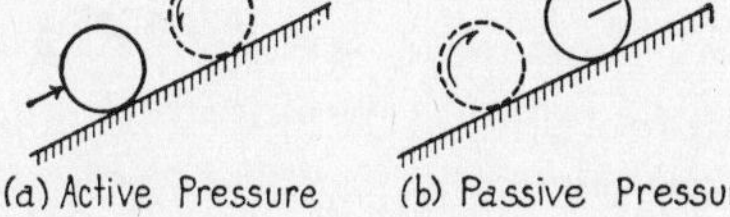

(a) Active Pressure   (b) Passive Pressure

Fig. 1-1. Earth pressure analogy.

force is not effectively resisted, the earth mass will fail and a portion of it will move sideways and downward. The pressure exerted by the earth on the wall is called the *active earth pressure.*

If the wall resists forces which tend to compress the soil or fill behind it, then the earth must have sufficient internal resistance to transmit these forces. Failure to do this will result in rupture; a portion of the earth will move sideways and upward away from the wall. This resistance of the earth against outside forces is called *passive earth pressure.*

The passive pressure or passive resistance is always greater than the active pressure. This is illustrated by an analogy in Fig. 1-1. Here a steel ball is placed on an incline and will, due to the action of gravity, tend to roll downward. In order to keep the ball at rest a force must be applied, the magnitude of which will depend, for any given angle of slope, on the friction between the ball and the incline; the greater this friction, the smaller the force needed to prevent downward motion. If, however, it is desired to roll the ball upward, a still greater force is required because, in this case, the friction will not assist in preventing movement but must be overcome in order to move the ball. Thus it is seen that the greater the internal friction of a soil the greater the difference between active and passive pressures. And a material entirely lacking cohesion and internal friction, as do liquids, will have identical active and passive pressures.

In all theories of earth pressures the chief factors are the frictional resistance of the earth's particles, its cohesion, and its unit weight. There is still some uncertainty as to whether friction and cohesion act at the same time, or whether friction comes into action after the cohesion has been destroyed.

The *angle of internal friction* is a measure of the frictional resistance between individual particles of the soil and is most satisfactorily defined by Coulomb's equation, to which reference will be made in the following.

The *angle of repose* may be defined as the angle of inclination of slope at which a cohesionless material will come to rest, if deposited to form an unrestrained heap. As the angle of internal friction of sand depends to a large extent on the initial density, it will not equal the angle of repose except for material in its dry and loose state. For dry and loose fill, the angle of internal friction will be approximately equal to the angle of repose. The angle of internal friction is usually increased if the material is saturated and also if it is inundated.*

The *cohesion* of any substance is its property of resistance to separation independent of any normal pressure which may exist on the plane of rupture. In the cohesionless soils (such as sand and gravel), this resistance is due solely to frictional resistance. In cohesive soils (such as clay), the friction between the particles is augmented by the resistance to shearing of the material. Both friction and cohesion are tangential forces, but, whereas the former is proportional to the normal pressure between the particles, the latter is assumed to be independent thereof. Cohesion in earth varies with the nature of the soil, there being a great deal in compact clay and only very little in dry sand and gravel.

The *unit weight of earth* will depend on the specific gravity of the individual particles and the amounts of void, filled either by air, water,

---

*There are many conflicting statements on this subject. See D. P. Krynine, *Soil Mechanics* (New York, 1941), p. 172; and also H. DeB. Parsons, "Some Soil Pressure Tests," *Trans. A.S.C.E.* (1935), Vol. 100, p. 12.

or both; it is the one factor that varies the least and will usually lie some-where between 90 and 100 lb/cu ft.

In addition to the internal friction in an earth mass, friction will also exist between the earth and the retaining structure at their surface of contact. This is known as *wall friction* or *external friction*. An important question is whether frictional resistance between the back of a retaining wall and the adjacent earth should be included in the computations for stability. Inclusion of the friction will affect the direction of the thrust and its magnitude. The wall friction will depend on the type of material used for the retaining structure. It is much less for a steel sheet-piling wall than for a concrete retaining wall; and it may be considerably reduced, and even completely eliminated, by water draining down the back of the wall.

1-3. Historical Data. The first rational theory of earth pressures was presented in the year 1773 by the French scientist, C. A. Coulomb.* It is noteworthy that Coulomb wrote before the invention of the trigonometric symbols and computed all ratios as algebraic fractions. He stated that resistance known as friction is proportional to pressure, that cohesion is a measure of the resistance which a solid body opposes to rupture into two parts, and that this cohesion is independent of the normal pressure and proportional to the area of the section.

Coulomb's theory of earth pressure considers the total pressure exerted by earth against a retaining wall (either solid or flexible), and arising from wedge action (downward motion of a wedge-shaped body of soil). Due to this wedge action, the weight of a particle causes a pressure against adjacent particles, which is transmitted through the mass of earth to the wall. The Coulomb theory gives the amount and point of application of the total pressure, but not its direction. The direction is usually assumed to be horizontal or to make an angle with the wall equal to the angle of external friction between the earth and the wall.

The Coulomb method was subsequently given geometrical interpretations by the French mathematician J. V. Poncelet† (1788–1867) and the German engineer Karl Culmann‡ (1821–1881), that of Professor Culmann's being the most general.

The Scottish physicist W. J. M. Rankine§ (1820–1872) considered

*"Essai sur une Application des Regles des Maximis et Minimis a Quelques Problemes de Statique Relatifs a l'Architecture," *Mem. Acad. Roy. Pres. Divers Savants* (Paris), Vol. 7.

†"Memoir sur la Stabilité des Revetments et de leur Fondations," *Mem. de L'Officier du Genie* (1840), Vol. 13.

‡*Graphische Statik* (Zurich, 1886).

§"On the Stability of Loose Earth," *Phil. Transactions Royal Society* (London, 1857), Vol. 147.

a mass of loose earth of indefinite extent, having a plane top surface, and subjected to its own weight. He assumed that the earth is incompressible, homogeneous, and granular; and that the particles of which it is composed are without cohesion, but are held in place by friction. It follows that, for stability, the direction of the pressure on any plane surface within the mass cannot make an angle with the normal to that surface greater than the angle of internal friction; otherwise, slipping will result.

The Rankine method of analysis starts with an infinitesimal prism of earth and by summation arrives at expressions for thrusts of an entire earth mass. The final algebraic expressions for the thrust, as determined by either the Coulomb method or the Rankine method, are similar in form; and, when certain modifications are placed upon the Coulomb method, are identical.

In 1915 the Rankine formulas were adapted to allow for cohesion by the British engineer, A. L. Bell.*

Finally additional researches on earth pressures have been published by Karl Terzaghi and C. F. Jenkin. References to their work will be made in the following.

1–4. Pressures of Cohesive Soils. Fig. 1–2 shows an apparatus which tests the resistance to displacement by sliding along a given plane in a

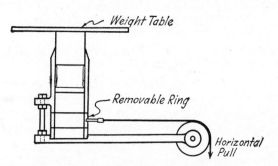

FIG. 1–2. Shear test apparatus.

loose granular material or cohesive material. Such a device may consist of a solid cylindrical cast-iron plunger with machined faces working inside a brass cylinder which is cut through horizontally along two parallel planes, the cut surfaces being perfectly smooth. The removable ring is therefore free to slide easily in horizontal direction.

To make a test, the ring is placed in the position shown and the cylinder thus formed is filled with the soil, care being taken to keep the material undisturbed as far as possible. The plunger is inserted and

---

*"On the Lateral Pressure and Resistance of Clay and the Supporting Power of Clay Foundations," *Proc. Inst. of Civil Engineers* (London, 1915), Vol. 199.

weights are placed on the table, which forms the upper part of the plunger, until the soil has been subjected to the desired degree of compressive stress. Another set of weights is then used to produce and measure a pull in the wire, connecting to the removable ring, sufficient to start sliding of the ring and soil sample. In this way, by making successive tests with different specimens of the same material placed under varying degrees of compressive stress, the law may be determined which governs the relation between the ultimate shearing resistance and the normal pressures on the plane of shear.

Fig. 1–3 shows typical shear-pressure curves for a cohesionless material and a cohesive material. Both can be represented with approximate

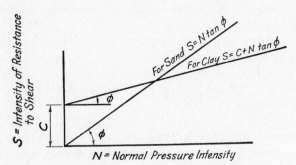

FIG. 1–3. Typical shear-pressure curves showing relation of shearing resistance to normal pressure.

accuracy by straight lines. For a cohesionless material, such as sand, the straight line passes through the origin and is inclined to the horizontal at an angle ϕ, which may be defined as the angle of internal friction. For a cohesive material, such as clay, the shear-pressure relationship can also be represented by a straight line which, however, will not pass through the origin and generally will make an angle with the horizontal considerably smaller than those for cohesionless materials. The relationship between normal pressure intensity N and the intensity of resistance to shear S can be expressed by the relationship, known as Coulomb's equation,

$$S = C + N \tan \phi. \qquad (1-1)$$

In the following are developed the theoretical expressions for active and passive earth pressures based on the law of shearing resistance expressed by Eq. (1–1). Fig. 1–4 shows a small unit volume of a cohesive soil subjected to normal stresses only in the vertical and horizontal directions. These stresses are termed principal stresses and the planes upon which these stresses are normal are readily found by methods discussed in textbooks on theory of elasticity.* For earth masses whose upper

---

*See Stephen Timoshenko, *Theory of Elasticity* (New York, 1934), pp. 15–17.

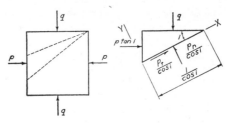

Fig. 1–4. Soil pressures.

boundaries are planes, Rankine has shown that the principal planes are parallel and normal to the upper boundary plane. The following symbols will be used:

q = stress intensity on horizontal plane,
p = stress intensity on vertical plane,
p_n = normal stress intensity on oblique plane,
p_t = tangential stress intensity on oblique plane,
c = unit cohesion,
ϕ = angle of internal friction.

From Coulomb's equation it follows that a cohesive material will fail if, at some point, the total shear becomes greater than the sum of the internal friction and cohesion; thus,

$$p_t > p_n \tan \phi + c. \tag{1–2}$$

Consider next an arbitrary section, through the unit volume in Fig. 1–4, making an angle i with the horizontal. Static equilibrium requires that

$$\Sigma X = 0; \quad \frac{p_t}{\cos i} + p \tan i \cos i - q \sin i = 0, \tag{1–3}$$

$$\Sigma Y = 0; \quad \frac{p_n}{\cos i} - p \tan i \sin i - q \cos i = 0. \tag{1–4}$$

Solving for p_t and p_n,

$$p_t = \tfrac{1}{2}(q - p) \sin 2i, \tag{1–5}$$

$$p_n = \tfrac{1}{2}(q + p) + \tfrac{1}{2}(q - p) \cos 2i. \tag{1–6}$$

Rupture will not occur as long as the unit cohesion, c, is greater than

$$p_t - p_n \tan \phi = \tfrac{1}{2}(q-p) \sin 2i - \left[\tfrac{1}{2}(q+p) + \tfrac{1}{2}(q-p) \cos 2i\right] \tan \phi. \tag{1–7}$$

The angle i which will give the maximum value of (1–7) can be found by equating to zero the first derivative. Thus,

$$\frac{d}{di}(p_t - p_n \tan \phi) = (q - p) \cos 2i + (q - p) \sin 2i \tan \phi = 0. \tag{1–8}$$

Solving,

$$\tan 2i = \frac{-1}{\tan \phi}; \quad i = \frac{\pi}{4} + \frac{\phi}{2}. \tag{1-9}$$

As this value for i will locate the most dangerous section, the value of the horizontal pressure p necessary to prevent rupture can now be found thus:

$$p_t - p_n \tan \phi - c =$$
$$\tfrac{1}{2}(q - p) \cos \phi - \left[\tfrac{1}{2}(q + p) - \tfrac{1}{2}(q - p) \sin \phi\right] \tan \phi - c = 0. \tag{1-10}$$

Reducing and solving for p gives

$$q(1 - \sin \phi) - p(1 + \sin \phi) - 2c \cos \phi = 0,$$

$$p = q \frac{1 - \sin \phi}{1 + \sin \phi} - 2c\sqrt{\frac{1 - \sin \phi}{1 + \sin \phi}}. \tag{1-11}$$

Eq. (1-11) can also be written as

$$p = q \tan^2 \left(45° - \frac{\phi}{2}\right) - 2c \tan \left(45° - \frac{\phi}{2}\right). \tag{1-12}$$

Solving for q gives

$$q = p \tan^- \left(45° + \frac{\phi}{2}\right) + 2c \tan \left(45° + \frac{\phi}{2}\right). \tag{1-13}$$

In case of a cohesionless material $c = 0$ and Eqs. (1-12) and (1-13) become

$$p = q \tan^2 \left(45° - \frac{\phi}{2}\right), \tag{1-14}$$

$$q = p \tan^2 \left(45° + \frac{\phi}{2}\right). \tag{1-15}$$

Eqs. (1-14) and (1-15) give, for a cohesionless soil, the relationship between the principal intensities of stress when the angle of internal frictions ϕ is known and the upper surface is a horizontal plane. It is readily seen that the pressure intensity q is equal to the weight of the earth mass above the unit volume under consideration. If the depth to this plane is h and the unit weight of the material is w, then $q = wh$ and Eq. (1-14) becomes

$$p = wh \tan^2 \left(45° - \frac{\phi}{2}\right), \tag{1-16}$$

and expresses the active earth pressure intensity for an ideal cohesionless material at a depth h below the horizontal top surface.

1-5. Numerical Example. Fig. 1-5 illustrates an open-cut excavation in a cohesive soil. This excavation has been carried down without any lateral support to a depth x and then, by means of braced sheet piling, to a depth y and finally, by a second section of sheet piling inside the first, down to rock. It is desired to find x and y; the properties of the soil are given in Fig. 1–5.

It should be possible to omit lateral support to such depth where no horizontal pressure is necessary to prevent failure. In other words in Eq. (1–12), p should be equated to zero and q to the weight of the overlying soil. Thus,

$$100x \tan^2 (45° - \tfrac{1}{2}20°) - 2 \times 400 \tan (45° - \tfrac{1}{2}20°) = 0,$$

$$x = 11.4 \text{ ft.}$$

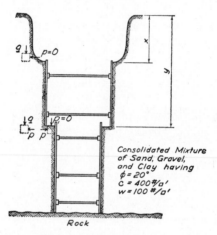

FIG. 1–5. Trench wall.

In the case of the depth y, the lateral movement has been prevented but not the upward movement of the earth between the two sections of sheet piling. Therefore,

$$p = 100y \tan^2 35° - 800 \tan 35°,$$

$$p_1 = p \tan^2 35° - 800 \tan 35° = 0.$$

Eliminating p gives

$$100y \tan^3 35° - 800 \tan^2 35° - 800 = 0; \quad y = 34.8 \text{ ft.}$$

As a second example on application of Rankine's theory consider the retaining wall shown in Fig. 1–6, which produces a drop in elevation between upper and lower surface equal to $H - h$. It is evident that instability of this wall will result in a movement from right to left. Hence the surface H must be subject to active earth pressure and the surface h to passive pressure. It will be assumed that the earth around the wall is without any cohesion.

According to Eq. (1–16) the active pressure intensity at the foot of the wall is

$$p_A = wH \tan^2 (45° - \tfrac{1}{2}\phi), \qquad (1–17)$$

and the total active pressure acts a distance of $\tfrac{1}{3}H$ from the bottom and equals

$$P_A = \tfrac{1}{2}wH^2 \tan^2 (45° - \tfrac{1}{2}\phi). \qquad (1–18)$$

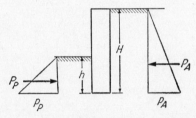

FIG. 1–6. Earth pressures on retaining wall.

On the side of the retaining wall facing the lower surface passive pressure will develop. At the bottom the resisting pressure will be

$$wh = p_P \tan^2 (45° - \tfrac{1}{2}\phi).$$

Solving for p_P

$$p_P = wh \tan^2 (45° + \tfrac{1}{2}\phi). \qquad (1–19)$$

The total passive pressure acts a distance $\tfrac{1}{3}h$ from the bottom and equals

$$P_P = \tfrac{1}{2}wh^2 \tan^2 (45° + \tfrac{1}{2}\phi). \qquad (1–20)$$

A loaded top surface as shown in Fig. 1–7 will increase the earth pressure developed below it. Thus for the wall shown in Fig. 1–7, the active earth pressure diagram will be trapezoidal having the following intensities:

$$p_1 = p \tan^2 (45° - \tfrac{1}{2}\phi); \quad p_2 = (p + wH) \tan^2 (45° - \tfrac{1}{2}\phi). \quad (1–21)$$

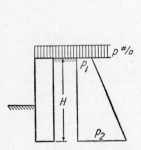

FIG. 1–7. Effect of surcharge.

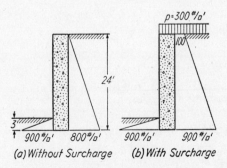

FIG. 1–8. Earth pressure diagrams.

In order to illustrate the magnitudes of earth pressures usually encountered in design of retaining walls, assume the following numerical values for the wall shown in Fig. 1–6: $\phi = 30°$; $w = 100$ lb/cu ft; $H = 24$ ft; $h = 3$ ft. Substituting in Eqs. (1–17) to (1–20) gives the pressure diagrams shown in Fig. 1–8(a), with total pressures as follows: $P_A = 9600$ lb and $P_P = 1350$ lb. If a surcharge of 300 psf is assumed, the pressure diagrams will be as shown in Fig. 1–8(b); the passive pressure being unchanged and the active pressure increased to $P_A = 12{,}000$ lb. These examples illustrate the comparatively slow rate of increase in the active earth pressure and the very rapid rate of increase with depth of the passive pressure.

1–6. Coulomb's Theory. It was shown in the foregoing how the pressure exerted by a soil on a vertical wall can be found as the sum of the pressures exerted by an infinite number of small elements lying on a vertical line. The case treated was that of a vertical wall retaining an earth mass having a horizontal top surface (Fig. 1–6). Also, friction existing between the earth and its contact surface of the wall was disregarded. An investigation of a much more general case will be made in the following.

The approach to the general case is the one which is often called "Coulomb's theory." This theory assumes that the resultant pressure on the back of a wall makes an angle with the normal to the wall equal to the angle of friction between the wall and the fill. The theory further assumes that the pressure exerted by the cohesionless fill arises from wedge action, that there is a wedge of earth having the wall on one side, the top surface as an upper boundary, and a plane of rupture as the third side. Of all possible planes of rupture, the one which gives the maximum thrust is selected. The plane of rupture will always be found to lie between the back of the wall and a line which makes an angle with the horizontal equal to the angle of internal friction.

Fig. 1–9(a) shows a retaining wall having a vertical height of h and an inside face, AB, which makes an angle of α with the horizontal. The earth mass behind this wall has a sloping top surface (angle with horizontal

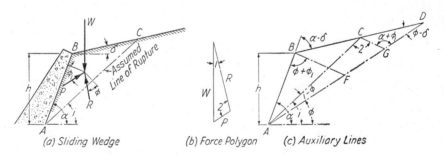

(a) Sliding Wedge   (b) Force Polygon   (c) Auxiliary Lines

FIG. 1–9. General formula for active earth pressure.

is δ). It will be assumed that the earth mass is cohesionless, has an angle of internal friction equal to ϕ, and an angle of external friction with the retaining wall equal to ϕ_1.

If it is assumed that the surface of rupture is represented by the straight line AC, it is seen that the earth prism ABC will be subjected to the action of three forces, namely:

(1) The weight, W, of the prism.
(2) A force, P, equal and opposite to the earth pressure on the wall.
(3) The reaction, R, from the surface of rupture AC; this force is the resultant of infinitesimal shearing forces and normal forces acting on this line prior to rupture.

If the prism is just on the verge of moving, the angle between R and the perpendicular to AC must be equal to ϕ, and the angle between P and the perpendicular to the wall must be equal to ϕ_1.

It is possible to draw an infinite number of potential rupture lines. The actual angle of rupture, i, is the one which will result in the maximum pressure, P, on the wall. The wall must be strong enough to resist this maximum force.

The critical angle, i, will first be determined by differentiating a general expression for P, which can be obtained in terms of W from the force polygon in Fig. 1–9(b). It is seen that the angle between R and W must equal

$$1 = i - \phi,$$

and the angle between R and P must be

$$2 = \alpha + \phi + \phi_1 - i.$$

In order to simplify the computations additional lines and angles are introduced in Fig. 1–9(c). Line AD makes an angle with the horizontal equal to the angle of internal friction ϕ. Line CG is drawn so that angle ACG is equal to the angle between R and P in the force polygon. It is seen that the angle CAD must equal the angle between R and W in the force polygon. It is now evident from similar triangles that

$$\frac{P}{W} = \frac{CG}{AG}.$$

The weight, W, of the prism ABC is equal to the area of the triangle multiplied by the unit soil weight; thus,

$$W = \tfrac{1}{2}w \times AB \times BC \times \sin(\alpha - \delta). \qquad (1\text{–}22)$$

Substituting in Eq. (1–22) gives

$$P = \tfrac{1}{2}w \times \sin(\alpha - \delta)\,\frac{AB \times BC \times CG}{AG}. \qquad (1\text{–}23)$$

Next, draw BF parallel to CG; then,

$$\frac{CG}{BF} = \frac{GD}{FD} \qquad CG = \frac{BF \times GD}{FD},$$

$$\frac{BC}{BD} = \frac{FG}{FD} \qquad BC = \frac{BD \times FG}{FD}.$$

Substituting the values for CG and BC in Eq. (1–23) gives

$$P = \tfrac{1}{2}w \sin (\alpha - \delta) \frac{AB \times BF \times BD}{FD \times FD} \left[\frac{FG \times GD}{AG} \right]. \qquad (1\text{–}24)$$

The quantities appearing between the brackets are functions of the variable angle i; all other quantities are independent of i. The three variable quantities can be expressed in terms of $AG = x$, thus

$$FG = x - AF; \quad GD = AD - x,$$

or for the bracketed quantity in Eq. (1–24)

$$y = \frac{(x - AF)(AD - x)}{x},$$

$$\frac{dy}{dx} = \frac{AF \times AD - x^2}{x^2} = 0$$

$$x = \sqrt{AF \times AD} = AG. \qquad (1\text{–}25)$$

Substituting in Eq. (1–24)

$$P = \tfrac{1}{2}w \sin (\alpha - \delta) \frac{AB \times BF \times BD}{(AD - AF)^2}$$

$$\times \frac{(\sqrt{AF \times AD} - AF)(AD - \sqrt{AF \times AD})}{\sqrt{AF \times AD}}$$

$$= \tfrac{1}{2}w \sin (\alpha - \delta) \frac{AB \times BF \times BD}{(\sqrt{AD} + \sqrt{AF})^2}$$

$$= \tfrac{1}{2}w \sin (\alpha - \delta) \frac{AB \times BF \times BD}{AD\left(1 + \sqrt{\dfrac{AF}{AD}}\right)^2}.$$

The lengths in this equation can all be expressed in terms of AB; thus,

$$BF = AB \frac{\sin (\alpha - \phi)}{\sin (\alpha + \phi_1)} \qquad BD = AB \frac{\sin (\alpha - \phi)}{\sin (\phi - \delta)}$$

$$AD = AB \frac{\sin (\alpha - \delta)}{\sin (\phi - \delta)} \qquad AF = AB \frac{\sin (\phi + \phi_1)}{\sin (\alpha + \phi_1)}.$$

And

$$\left(1 + \sqrt{\frac{AF}{AD}}\right)^2 = \left[1 + \sqrt{\frac{\sin(\phi + \phi_1)\sin(\phi - \delta)}{\sin(\alpha + \phi_1)\sin(\alpha - \delta)}}\right]^2$$

$$\frac{AB \times BF \times BD}{AD} = (AB)^2 \frac{\sin^2(\alpha - \phi)}{\sin(\alpha + \phi_1)\sin(\alpha - \delta)}.$$

But $AB = h \div \sin \alpha$, which gives

$$P_A = \frac{wh^2}{2} \frac{\sin^2(\alpha - \phi)}{\sin^2 \alpha \sin(\alpha + \phi_1)\left[1 + \sqrt{\frac{\sin(\phi + \phi_1)\sin(\phi - \delta)}{\sin(\alpha + \phi_1)\sin(\alpha - \delta)}}\right]^2}. \qquad (1\text{-}26)$$

Because the total pressure can be expressed as a function of the square of the height, it follows that the increment (which can be expressed as a first derivative) is a linear function of the height or that the resultant acts on the back of the wall at a distance from A equal to $\frac{1}{3}AB$.

In the case of a vertical wall the angle α will equal 90°. If any friction existing between wall and backfill is disregarded ($\phi_1 = 0°$, a safe assumption) the formula for the active pressure is (see Fig. 1-10)

$$P_A = \frac{wh^2}{2} \left[\frac{\cos \phi}{1 + \sqrt{\sin \phi(\sin \phi - \cos \phi \tan \delta)}}\right]^2. \qquad (1\text{-}27)$$

If the top surface slopes down from the top of the wall as shown in Fig. 1-11, a negative value should be given to the angle of slope δ.

FIG. 1-10. Notation for active pressure.   FIG. 1-11. Active pressure, δ negative.

A general formula for passive earth pressure can be derived by considering the lower portion of a wall, shown in Fig. 1-12, subjected to active pressure on the right side and prevented from moving toward the left by an earth mass the upper surface of which makes an angle with the horizontal equal to δ. Proceeding as for the active earth pressure, the following formula for passive pressure is arrived at

$$P_P = \frac{wh^2}{2} \times \frac{\sin^2(\alpha - \phi)}{\sin^2 \alpha \sin(\alpha + \phi_1)\left[1 - \sqrt{\frac{\sin(\phi + \phi_1)\sin(\phi - \delta)}{\sin(\alpha + \phi_1)\sin(\alpha - \delta)}}\right]^2}. \qquad (1\text{-}28)$$

It follows from the above formula that the passive pressure intensity varies with the depth according to a straight line. In the case of a vertical wall the angle α will equal 90°. If any friction existing between the wall and the earth is disregarded ($\phi_1 = 0$°, a safe assumption) the formula for the passive pressure is (see Fig. 1–13)

$$P_P = \frac{wh^2}{2}\left[\frac{\cos\phi}{1 - \sqrt{\sin\phi\,(\sin\phi - \cos\phi\,\tan\delta)}}\right]^2. \qquad (1\text{–}29)$$

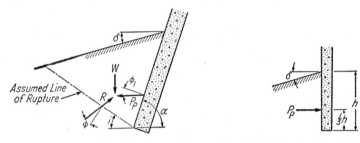

FIG. 1–12. General formula for passive earth pressure.

FIG. 1–13. Notation for passive pressure.

1–7. Poncelet's Construction. A graphical determination of earth pressures, known as "Poncelet's construction," can be used for active and passive pressures for top surfaces of straight lines. It will be explained in the following discussion first for the general case of active pressure.

Fig. 1–14 shows a sloping retaining wall, which sustains the active pressure from a cohesionless earth mass having an angle of internal friction

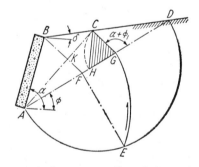

FIG. 1–14. Active pressure, Poncelet's construction.

of ϕ and an angle of external friction at the wall of ϕ_1. The top surface of the earth mass makes an angle with the horizontal equal to δ. The angle between the back of the wall and the horizontal is α.

The graphical construction of the active pressure is as follows: Draw a line through A making an angle with the horizontal equal to ϕ; intersect this line at D with the top surface; construct a semicircle over AD as diameter; draw BF so that angle $BFD = \alpha + \phi_1$; draw FE perpendicular to AD; make AG equal to AE; draw CG parallel to BF; make HG equal to CG. The total active pressure on AB will then be equal to the unit soil weight multiplied by the area of triangle CGH. The proof of this follows.

It is seen from similar triangles that

$$\frac{CG}{BF} = \frac{GD}{FD} = \frac{AD - AG}{AD - AF},$$

$$\frac{CG}{KF} = \frac{AG}{AF}.$$

If CG is eliminated between the above two equations, it is seen that

$$\frac{BF}{KF} = \frac{AD - AF}{AD - AG} \times \frac{AG}{AF}; \quad 1 - \frac{KF}{BF} = 1 - \frac{AD - AG}{AD - AF} \times \frac{AF}{AG},$$

$$\frac{BF - KF}{BF} = \left(\frac{AG}{AF} - \frac{AD - AG}{AD - AF}\right)\frac{AF}{AG}. \tag{1-30}$$

Because $AG = AE$ and AE is a side in the right triangle AED, it follows that

$$AG^2 = AF \times AD; \quad \frac{AG}{AF} = \frac{AD}{AG} \tag{1-31}$$

Substituting Eq. (1–31) in Eq. (1–30) gives

$$\frac{BK}{BF} = \left(\frac{AD}{AG} - \frac{AD - AG}{AD - AF}\right)\frac{AG}{AD}$$

$$= \left(\frac{AD^2 - AD \times AF - AD \times AG + AG^2}{AG(AD - AF)}\right) \times \frac{AG}{AD}$$

$$= \frac{AD^2 - AD \times AG}{AD(AD - AF)}$$

$$= \frac{AD - AG}{AD - AF}$$

$$BK = BF \frac{GD}{FD}. \tag{1-32}$$

From the similar triangles CDG and BDF

$$\frac{GD}{FD} = \frac{CG}{BF}; \quad CG = BF \frac{GD}{FD}. \tag{1-33}$$

From Eqs. (1–32) and (1–33) it follows that

$$BK = CG. \tag{1-34}$$

Because these two lines are also parallel it follows that the perpendicular distances from B and G to line AC must be equal and that the two triangles ABC and ACG must have equal areas.

In Fig. 1-9 it was found that

$$P = W \frac{CG}{AG}. \tag{1-35}$$

Comparing Fig. 1-9 and Fig. 1-14 it is seen that in both cases line AC will represent the surface of rupture because $AG^2 = AF \times AD$ [Eqs. (1-25) and (1-31)]. It is seen that

$$W = w \times \text{triangle } ABC = w \times \text{triangle } ACG.$$

The latter area can be expressed in terms of two sides and the included angle or

$$W = w\tfrac{1}{2}AG \times GC \times \sin (\alpha + \phi_1). \tag{1-36}$$

Substituting Eq. (1-36) in Eq. (1-35) gives

$$P = w\tfrac{1}{2}CG^2 \sin (\alpha + \phi_1), \tag{1-37}$$

or the soil weight times the area of the isosceles triangle CGH.

The graphical determination of the passive pressure is shown in Fig. 1-15. It is assumed that due to active pressure on the right side of AM,

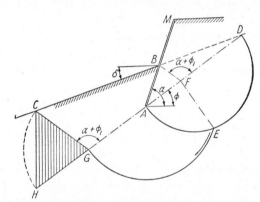

FIG. 1-15. Passive pressure, Poncelet's construction.

passive pressure is exerted on the left side of AB. The construction is the same as outlined in Fig. 1-14 with the exception that AE is swung to the left instead of to the right. The total passive pressure on AB will equal the soil weight multiplied by the area of triangle CGH. The surface of rupture will be the line connecting A and C. The proof of this construction is similar to the one given above for the active pressure.

Considerable simplification of Poncelet's construction will result from special values of the various angles. Fig. 1-16 shows the construction of active and passive pressures in the case of a vertical wall, horizontal top surfaces and an angle of external friction equal to zero. The upper triangle at C_1 will represent the total active pressure on AC, while the lower triangle at B_1 will represent the total passive pressure on AB.

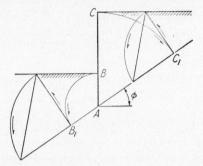

Fig. 1–16. Special case of earth pressures.

It is evident from Poncelet's construction that the assumption of zero for the angle of external friction between the earth and the wall is on the safe side. The omission of the angle of external friction will result in a larger numerical value for the active earth pressure and also a larger lever arm with respect to the bottom of the wall, hence a larger overturning moment. In the case of the passive pressure disregard of the angle of external friction will result in a smaller numerical value of the pressure and also a smaller lever arm with respect to the bottom of the wall, or a smaller moment resisting overturning. This also is on the safe side.

1–8. Numerical Example. In the case of a vertical wall and horizontal surfaces (Fig. 1–17) the expressions for active [Eq. (1–26)] and passive [Eq. (1–28)] pressures, become

$$ P = \frac{wh^2}{2} \times \frac{\cos^2 \phi}{\cos \phi_1 \left[1 \pm \sqrt{\dfrac{\sin (\phi + \phi_1) \sin \phi}{\cos \phi_1}} \right]^2}. \qquad (1\text{-}38) $$

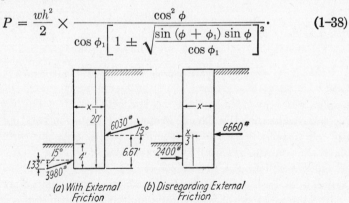

(a) With External Friction (b) Disregarding External Friction

Fig. 1–17. Numerical example, retaining wall.

As a numerical example let it be desired to find the active and passive pressures on the retaining wall shown in Fig. 1–17. The properties of the cohesionless soil are as follows: $w = 100$ lb/cu ft; $\phi = 30°$; $\phi_1 = 15°$. If these values are substituted in Eq. (1–38) the values appearing in Fig. 1–17(a) will result: 6030 lb for the active pressure and 3980 lb for the passive pressure inclined to the perpendicular to the wall as shown.

If complete absence of external friction is assumed ($\phi_1 = 0$), Eq. (1–38) becomes

$$P = \frac{wh^2}{2} \frac{1 \mp \sin \phi}{1 \pm \sin \phi}, \qquad (1\text{–}39)$$

where the upper sign corresponds to the active pressure and the lower sign to the passive pressure. Substituting, $w = 100$ lb/cu ft, $\phi = 30°$, and 20 ft and 4 ft for the height, h, gives 6660 lb for the active pressure (an increase of 10 per cent) and 2400 lb for the passive pressure (a decrease of 40 per cent).

In order to demonstrate the much greater degree of safety which results from the pressures in Fig. 1–17(b) and their assumed horizontal directions, let it be desired to find the thickness of wall x, which will be required for stability. The criterion for stability is the absence of tension stresses under the base, or zero moment of all external forces about the third point.

In the case of Fig. 1–17(b) it is seen that equality of moments give

$$6660 \times 6.67 = 2400 \times 1.33 + 20 \times 150x\tfrac{1}{6}x,$$

$$x = 9.1 \text{ ft},$$

while for Fig. 1–17(a)

$$6030(6.67 \cos 15° - \tfrac{2}{3}x \cos 75°)$$

$$= 3980\left(1.33 \cos 15° + \frac{x}{3} \cos 75°\right) + 500x^2$$

$$x = 7.0 \text{ ft}.$$

Thus it is seen that disregard of friction between wall and earth is always on the side of safety.

1–9. Culmann's Graphical Method. By this method active and passive earth pressures can be determined for any irregular top surface, either curved or broken, with or without surcharge.

The construction will be explained first for the basic case of a vertical retaining surface without wall friction and with a horizontal top surface.

In Fig. 1–18(a), a given wedge OAB will exert a pressure ad on the vertical plane OA; this pressure can be found by replacing the force ab

(representing the weight of the wedge) by two components—namely, the lateral pressure and a force ac that makes an angle with the perpendicular to OB equal to the angle of internal friction ϕ. The active pressure can be found by comparing the lateral components ad for various values of the angle v; the maximum of these represents the active earth pressure.

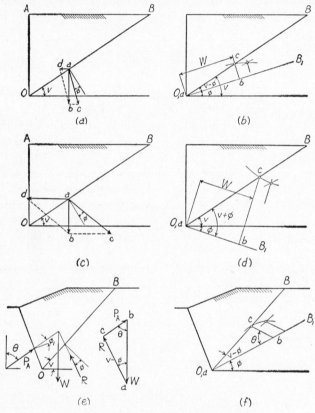

Fig. 1–18. Culmann's graphical method.

In Fig. 1–18(b), the point a has been moved to point O and the triangle abc has been rotated through an angle equal to $90° + \phi$ in the counterclockwise direction. This operation makes point c fall on the line OB.

The comparison of active pressures for the various possible sliding surfaces can now be made by computing the weights of the corresponding prisms and, to any convenient scale, laying them off in order on the line through O, making an angle ϕ with the horizontal equal to the angle of internal friction. Lines are then drawn through each of these points perpendicular to OB_1 and intersected with the sloping sides of the corresponding prisms. Finally, a smooth curve is drawn through the points of intersection c. The maximum ordinate to this curve, measured from OB_1, represents the active pressure against OA.

The passive earth pressure can also be determined graphically by a similar procedure. In Fig. 1–18(c), the weight of the prism OAB, as represented by ab, is replaced by the components ad and ac, the problem being to find the angle v, for which ad becomes a minimum.

In Fig. 1–18(d), the point a has been moved to point O and the triangle abc has been rotated through an angle equal to $90° - \phi$ in the counterclockwise direction. The graphical construction of the passive earth pressure is similar to that already explained for the active pressure, except that the weights of the prisms are laid off on a line OB_1, located below the horizontal through O. The minimum ordinate to the curve through the points c will indicate the passive earth pressure.

Culmann's construction can readily be applied to the general case of a fill with an irregular top surface, retained by a wall having a sloping back and an angle of external friction ϕ_1. Fig. 1–18(e) shows the three forces which must maintain equilibrium if sliding along OB is not to occur. In Fig. 1–18(f) the triangle, formed by these forces, has been rotated through an angle equal to $90° - \phi$ in the clockwise direction. It is seen that the construction differs from the previous one only in that cb is no longer perpendicular to OB_1, but makes an angle with this line equal to the angle θ between a vertical and the direction of the earth pressure. The direction of the earth pressure makes an angle ϕ_1 with the normal to the back of the wall.

The graphical determination of the total active earth pressure for the case of a broken earth line is shown in Fig. 1–19. The angle of internal

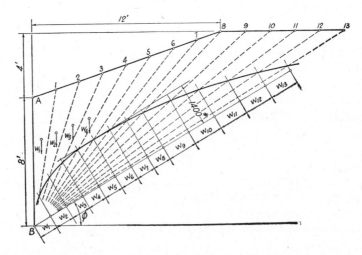

FIG. 1–19. Graphical construction of active earth pressure.

friction is assumed to be 30°, and the wall friction is disregarded. In Fig. 1–20 is shown the construction of the total passive earth pressure for similar soil conditions and for a broken top surface line.

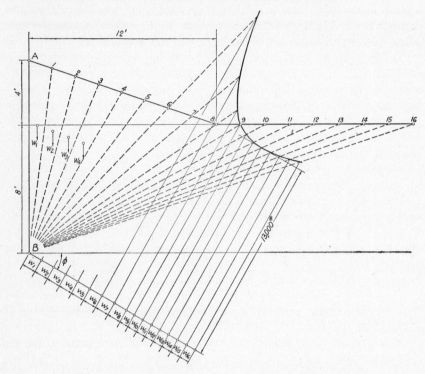

FIG. 1–20. Graphical construction of passive earth pressure.

1–10. General Wedge Theory. The Coulomb theory may be applied with some confidence to retaining walls whose lateral resistance is independent of their amount of yield. For timbering of excavations in sand, the following theory, first presented by Karl Terzaghi,* may be applied.

In the general wedge theory, the shape of the surface of sliding is assumed to be a logarithmic spiral with the polar equation

$$r = r_0 e^{\alpha \tan \phi}, \qquad (1\text{–}40)$$

in which r = length of a vector through the center of the spiral,

r_0 = length of arbitrarily selected reference vector,

e = base of natural logarithms,

α = angle between r and r_0,

ϕ = angle of internal friction.

---

*"General Wedge Theory of Earth Pressure," *Trans. A.S.C.E.* (1941), Vol. 106, p. 68.

Fig. 1–22 shows such a spiral according to Eq. (1–40). It has the property that a vector, passing through the center of the spiral and any arbitrary point on the spiral, intersects the normal to this point at an angle equal to the angle ϕ of internal friction. If, therefore, the surface of rupture BC in Fig. 1–21 is assumed to be a portion of a logarithmic spiral, the reactions on all its elements at the moment of failure must

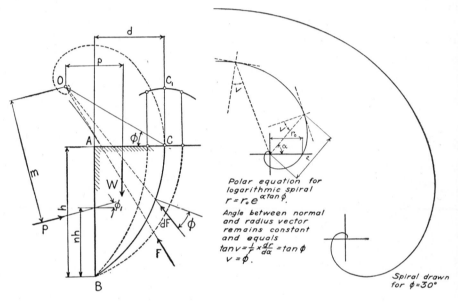

FIG. 1–21. General wedge theory. FIG. 1–22. Spiral for wedge theory of earth pressures.

pass through a common point—namely, the center of the spiral. The determination of the active earth pressure P can thus be made from the weight of the wedge ABC.

The general wedge theory assumes that the frictional resistance is fully mobilized over the entire surface of sliding. As a consequence the reaction dF on each element of the sliding surface intersects the normal to this surface at an angle ϕ. Hence all the reactions dF and the resultant reaction F must pass through this point. If the point of application and direction of lateral pressure are now known, then it is seen that its magnitude can be found by taking moments about the center of the spiral; thus,

$$P = W \frac{p}{m} , \qquad (1\text{–}41)$$

where p and m are the distances from the spiral center to the vector W representing the weight of the wedge and the vector P representing the lateral pressure, respectively.

The remainder of the investigation is similar to Culmann's graphical solution. Several spirals are assumed to intersect the horizontal surface of the bank at different distances from the rim of the cut. The resulting active earth pressures are plotted to form a curve, the maximum ordinate of which, CC_1, will represent the active earth pressure on surface AB.

The general wedge theory is based on the empirical facts that the surface of sliding intersects the horizontal surface of the bank at a right angle and that the center of the lateral pressure on the timbering of a cut, with a depth h in sand, is somewhere between an elevation of $0.5h$ and $0.6h$ above the bottom of the cut. This ratio has been designated by n in Fig. 1–21 and must be known or assumed. Likewise the angle of internal friction ϕ must also be known or assumed. An assumption of complete absence of friction between the wall and the earth will be on the safe side.

In order to reduce the work of tracing the spirals, one spiral, representing the angle of internal friction ϕ of the sand under consideration, may be drawn on tracing cloth (Fig. 1–22) and then superimposed on the bank (Fig. 1–21), always intersecting this at a right angle and passing through point B. In this manner the various locations of O may be determined and the lever arms m and p scaled. The magnitude of W can be taken, with sufficient accuracy, as

$$W = \tfrac{2}{3}AB \times AC$$

and its distance from the bank as four-tenths of the distance AC.

As a numerical example, let it be desired to determine the active earth pressure on the timbering of a cut in a sand with a depth $h = 10$ ft. It can be assumed that the sand is cohesionless and has an angle of internal friction $\phi = 30°$ and that the angle of external friction between sand and timber is $\phi_1 = 15°$. It is further assumed that the center of the pressure is at midheight or $n = 0.5$.

The spiral in Fig. 1–22, which was traced for an angle $\phi = 30°$, can be used for determining the spiral centers for the various distances AC. The most dangerous surface of rupture appears to be for $AC = 4.5$ ft, and the locations of the spiral center and the lever arm are shown in Fig. 1–23.

The magnitude of the reaction dF in Fig. 1–21 will increase from zero at the top to some definite value at the bottom, and the variation will generally be proportional to the distance from the top. The resultant F of all these reactions dF will therefore act somewhere close to that point on the spiral which is two-thirds of the height h from the top. It is readily seen that this will raise the point of application of the lateral pressure above the two-thirds point.

According to the general wedge theory for the pressure of sand on timbering in excavations, the distribution of the pressure over the lateral support should be more or less parabolic, with a maximum pressure at approximately half the depth of the cut.

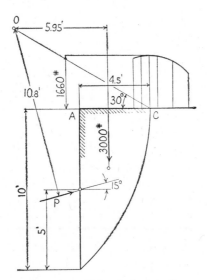

FIG. 1–23. Numerical example.

1–11. Practical Considerations.   It has already been pointed out that an exact evaluation of earth pressures under all circumstances is not possible.   The presence of cohesion and the effects of percolating water will materially affect the pressures.   But, as the construction of a retaining wall or a sheet-piling bulkhead will usually necessitate filling up behind the structure with cohesionless material, an evaluation of active earth pressures can ordinarily be made under the assumption of cohesionless soil. The correct angle of internal friction for such material should be the result of a shear test.

Table 1–1 lists some approximate properties of typical cohesionless soils and can be used only as a rough guide to the actual behavior of the materials.   The values listed compare favorably with similar information in current textbooks.*

It is important to know the percentage of voids for evaluating submerged weights and pressures.   Where the percentage of voids is not known, it may be obtained fairly closely by remembering that the specific gravity

---

*See D. H. Lee, *Sheet Piling, Cofferdams, and Caissons* (London, 1945), p. 37.

of the soil constituents seldom varies much from that of quartz (2.7). Thus, if the loose weight of a material is say 105 lb/cu ft, the percentage of voids v may be found as follows:

$$2.7 \times 62.5 \frac{100 - v}{100} = 105; \quad v = 38 \text{ per cent.}$$

TABLE 1-1

| MATERIAL | DRY | | | | |
| | Loose | | | Compacted | |
	w^*	$v\dagger$	$\phi\ddagger$	w^*	$v\dagger$
Coarse sand............	100	40	32–38	115	31
Fine sand..............	90	46	30–35	105	37
Gravel................	110	34	35	120	28
Broken stone...........	90	46	45	110	34

$*w$ = unit weight (lb/cu ft).
$\dagger v$ = percentage of voids.
$\ddagger\phi$ = angle of internal friction (degrees).

Careful thought should be given to the possible effects of vibrations on earth pressures. In most cases these are absent; but, in the vicinity of railroad tracks, cranes, and other machinery, there is likely to be an increase of the earth pressure in the fill behind the retaining structures. For cases where it is known that vibrations are likely to occur, it is recommended that the angle of internal friction ϕ be decreased somewhat from the values determined by tests. This decrease should be from 10 to 15 per cent.* If friction between wall and earth is taken into account, this should be reduced also; for simplicity; it may be taken as zero over the upper half of the wall and at its full static value over the lower half of the wall.

The question, whether frictional resistance between the back of the wall and the adjacent earth is or is not a permissible factor to be included in the computations of earth pressures, is an important one. In the case of a vertical steel sheet-piling wall, the external friction will amount to very little and should be disregarded. The results of investigations† would indicate that, for concrete retaining walls, the angle between the resultant of the active earth pressure and the normal to the wall may vary considerably during the test.

In no case should the angle of external friction be assumed greater than the angle of internal friction of the backfill; usually it is between 50

---

*See H. Krey, *Erddruck, Erdwiderstand, und Tragfahigheit des Baugrundes* (Berlin, 1932).

†Karl Terzaghi, "Large Retaining Wall Tests. I. Pressure of Dry Sand," *Engineering News-Record* (February 1, 1934), p. 136.

and 75 per cent of this value. It has been shown that the omission of wall friction will always provide additional safety against failure, and because it simplifies the analysis, it is often neglected.

The results of experimental investigations* show that the actual lateral pressure of earth is usually somewhat less than that deduced by the Coulomb theory. For a concrete wall sustaining a cohesionless backfill, this theory can ordinarily be relied upon to give a thrust which will not be exceeded.

In the practical analysis and design of retaining walls such as the one

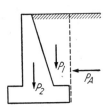

FIG. 1–24.
Retaining wall
analysis.

shown in Fig. 1–24, it is generally assumed that the pressure acts against a vertical plane drawn upward through the heel of the structure. In other words, instead of considering two forces—the weight of the wall and the thrust acting upon its slope—three are taken into account, namely: the auxiliary thrust against a prism of earth, P_A, the weight of the prism itself, P_1, and the weight of the wall, P_2.

Another important problem concerns the earth pressure exerted on steel sheet-piling walls, also known as flexible bulkheads. The total thrust can be expected to be equal to that which acts on the back of a rigid concrete retaining wall; but, the distribution of this thrust will be quite different due to the lateral bulging which tends to relieve the pressures where the deflections are large and to increase them at, and adjacent to, the upper and lower support. The pressure diagram generally is assumed as shown in Fig. 1–25(b), while the pressure distribution which is in accordance with the probable action of sheet-piling walls in average soils is shown in (c). It is seen that

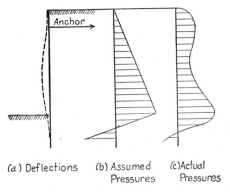

(a) Deflections   (b) Assumed   (c) Actual
                      Pressures   Pressures

FIG. 1–25. Flexible bulkhead.

---

*H. De B. Parsons, "Some Soil Pressure Tests," *Trans. A.S.C.E.* (1935), Vol. 100, p. 1.

the assumptions, although apparently fairly seriously in error, are in fact safe for design and simplify the analysis which would otherwise be too involved for work other than that of exceptional importance.

1-12. Combined Pressures. In a majority of retaining structures, such as those made of sheet piling, the lateral pressures are caused by a combination of earth pressures and water pressures. In the case of earth submerged in water, two assumptions are in general use:

(a) The total pressure of earth and water is taken as the pressure of the earth only, where the weight of the earth per cubic foot is equal to the weight of a cubic foot of earth saturated with water.

(b) The total pressure of earth and water is taken as the full water pressure, plus the earth pressure based on the submerged weight of the material (dry weight minus the weight of the displaced water).

As an illustration of the above, let it be desired to find the pressure diagram for the steel sheet-piling wall shown in Fig. 1–26. The top surface

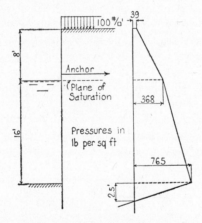

FIG. 1–26. Combined pressures.

is loaded with a surcharge of 100 psf. It is also known that the dry earth weighs 105 lb/cu ft and contains 34 per cent voids; its angle of internal friction is 26° in a dry condition and, although there usually is an increase in this quantity due to submergence, it will be assumed that the angle of internal friction remains unchanged under water.

The active pressure diagram is now computed as follows: The pressure intensity at the top will be

$$100 \tan^2 \left(45° - \frac{26}{2} \right) = 39 \text{ psf.}$$

The pressure 8 ft below the top at the plane of saturation will be

$$(100 + 8 \times 105) \tan^2 \left(45° - \frac{26}{2}\right) = 368 \text{ psf.}$$

Assumption (b) gives the higher value for the total pressure; but it appears the logical one because it is impossible to insure against water penetrating between the piling wall and the earth, no matter how impervious, and such penetration brings a corresponding development of hydrostatic pressure in addition to earth pressure.

Lateral pressures exerted by submerged soils can be computed by the theories used for dry materials. The physical characteristics of most soils, however, are affected by the change of the surrounding medium. Thus, the angle of internal friction generally assumes a higher value due to the presence of water.* In the following example this possible increase will be disregarded since it is on the side of safety. The weight of the submerged earth is obtained by subtracting from its dry weight a quantity equal to its displaced volume. Thus,

$$105 - \frac{100 - 34}{100} 62.5 = 63.7 \text{ lb/cu ft.}$$

The pressure at a distance of 24 ft below the top will be

$$(100 + 8 \times 105 + 16 \times 63.7) \tan^2 \left(45° - \frac{26}{2}\right) = 765 \text{ psf.}$$

Passive earth pressure is present below this level, and the depth at which unit passive pressure intensity will equal unit active intensity is readily determined. To allow for the additional resistance due to the undisturbed and naturally compact soil into which the sheet piling is usually driven (see statement at the end of this section), the passive pressure intensity is sometimes multiplied by a so-called "efficiency" factor. If this factor is assumed to be 2, the distance x to the point of equal passive and active pressure intensities can be found to be

$$765 + x\, 63.7 \tan^2 \left(45° - \frac{26}{2}\right) = 2x\, 63.7 \tan^2 \left(45° + \frac{26}{2}\right),$$

$$x = 2.5 \text{ ft.}$$

It will be shown in the next chapter that the pile should be driven to a depth considerably below this level and also that, as far as bending stresses in the pile are concerned, these can be determined with sufficient accuracy by applying the pressure diagram, thus found, to a beam assumed simply supported at the anchor point and at the point where unit active pressure equals unit passive pressure.

*See J. Feld, "Lateral Earth Pressure," *Trans. A.S.C.E.* (1923), Vol. 86, p. 1545.

If the assistance of friction to the passive resistance of the soil is not taken into account, a substantial increase in the passive resistance has been ignored. For earth on steel, the angle of external friction ϕ_1 is probably between one-third to one-half of the angle of internal friction ϕ. A considerable amount of cohesion is also present in the undisturbed soil below the lower level of a bulkhead wall. For these reasons the steel manufacturing companies recommend that the passive earth pressures figured by the Coulomb or Rankine formulas be multiplied by 2.

1–13. Effect of Pore Pressures. If a fully saturated soil is pervious, as are most cohesionless materials, its consolidation under a static load will be almost instantaneous, because excess water will have no difficulty in escaping from the voids. If on the other hand, the saturated soil is a cohesive material, such as a clay with low permeability, it will consolidate slowly, because excess water in its voids will be squeezed out slowly toward pervious boundaries of the clay stratum.

When a load is applied to a completely saturated cohesive soil in its plastic range of consistency, the entire compressive stress caused by the load is at first carried by the water in the voids, and the lateral pressure is immediately increased by the same amount. This pressure is called pore pressure.

The mechanics of pore pressures can be illustrated by an analogy. Fig. 1–27 illustrates a cylinder with a piston supported on springs. The

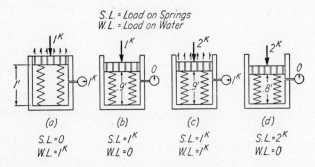

FIG. 1–27. Pore pressure analogy.

cylinder is filled with water; the piston has some exceedingly small holes passing through it vertically, which will allow water, under pressure in the cylinder, to escape at a very low rate. The cross section of the cylinder is 1 sq ft.

To begin with, the external load is zero and a small hydrostatic pressure, varying from zero to 62.4 psf, is present in the water. An external load of 1 kip is then applied to the piston, as shown in Fig. 1–27(a). The perfora-

tions in the piston are assumed to be so small that only a minimal amount
of water can immediately escape. Since water is incompressible the 1-kip
load is, at the outset of loading, carried on the water and the pressure gage
will indicate a lateral pressure of 1000 psf (plus, of course, the small
original hydrostatic pressure). The water begins immediately to escape
through the minute holes in the piston, and simultaneously the springs
begin to compress slowly, permitting a gradual downward movement of
the piston, until the entire 1-kip load is carried on the springs and none on
the water. This stage is shown in Fig. 1–27(b) where the pressure gage
records zero hydrostatic pressure.

Assume next that the external load is increased to 2 kips. The first
increment will be carried on the springs, but the second part (1 kip) will
at the outset be carried by the water and the pressure gage will again
register 1 kip until escape of the water through the small perforations
brings the springs into action as shown in Fig. 1–27(c) and (d).

As a numerical example of the evaluation of pore pressures, consider

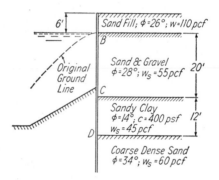

FIG. 1–28. Numerical example of pore pressure.

the bulkhead or retaining wall shown in Fig. 1–28. Four different strata
are indicated. The top layer AB will be placed after the bulkhead has
been constructed. It is considered likely that the layer CD will develop
pore pressure when the top layer is placed.

Fig. 1–29(a) shows the lateral pressures if pore pressure is not present.
The pressure intensities just above and just below are evaluated by Eq.
(1–16); thus,

$$110 \times 6 \tan^2 (45° - \tfrac{1}{2}26°) = 257 \text{ psf,}$$

$$110 \times 6 \tan^2 (45° - \tfrac{1}{2}28°) = 238 \text{ psf.}$$

Between B and C, the submerged soil weight should be used and pressure
intensity at C will be equal to

$$(6 \times 110 + 20 \times 55) \tan^2 (45° - \tfrac{1}{2}28°) = 635 \text{ psf.}$$

The soil layer between C and D is cohesive and according to Eq. (1–12) the pressure intensities at these levels will be

$$(6 \times 110 + 20 \times 55) \tan^2 (45° - \tfrac{1}{2}14°)$$

$$- 2 \times 400 \times \tan (45° - \tfrac{1}{2}14°) = 449 \text{ psf.}$$

$$(6 \times 110 + 20 \times 55 + 12 \times 45) \tan^2 (45° - \tfrac{1}{2}14°)$$

$$- 2 \times 400 \tan (45° - \tfrac{1}{2}14°) = 779 \text{ psf.}$$

Finally, the lateral pressure intensity in the coarse dense sand just below D is, from Eq. (1–16),

$$(6 \times 110 + 20 \times 55 + 12 \times 45) \tan^2 (45° - \tfrac{1}{2}34°) = 650 \text{ psf.}$$

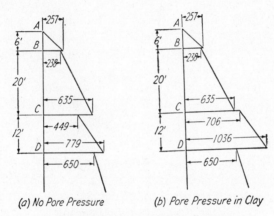

(a) No Pore Pressure   (b) Pore Pressure in Clay

FIG. 1–29. Earth pressure diagrams.

The diagram in Fig. 1–29 represents the values which the pressures will eventually reach as the water drains from the clay stratum, but immediately after the sand fill AB has been placed the pressures in the cohesive layer CD will be greater. Before the sand is deposited the pressures at C and D, respectively, will be (Eq. 1–12)

$$20 \times 55 \times \tan^2 (45° - \tfrac{1}{2}14°) - 2 \times 400 \times \tan (45° - \tfrac{1}{2}14°) = 46 \text{ psf,}$$

$$46 + 12 \times 45 \tan^2 (45° - \tfrac{1}{2}14°) = 376 \text{ psf.}$$

The placing of the top sand layer will impose an additional overburden equal to 6×110, which will be transmitted directly to the pore water in the clay, producing a lateral hydrostatic pressure of the same amount, thus giving total pressures at C and D, respectively,

$$46 + 660 = 706 \text{ psf} \quad \text{and} \quad 376 + 660 = 1036 \text{ psf.}$$

The final pressure diagram, including pore pressures, is shown in Fig. 1–29(b).

1-14. Applications of the Theory of Elasticity. The pressure intensities computed by the methods of Rankine and Coulomb can usually be relied upon at the depths encountered in ordinary construction. These theories have been developed for earth masses and surcharges extending for considerable distances behind the retaining member. The effects of load concentrations can also be evaluated by these theories; usually by substitution of equivalent earth lines and the use of Culmann's graphical method. Or these effects can be determined by applying stress distribution as found by the theory of elasticity for semi-infinite solids.*

The theory of elasticity has been chosen as a starting point by many investigators of earth pressures and, although it is generally recognized that an exact determination of stress is not possible by this method, no discussion of lateral pressures on retaining walls would be complete without an account of solutions suggested by this theory.

The underlying assumptions of the application of the theory of elasticity are as follows. The earth mass can be considered as an elastic (power of recovery from strain) and isotropic (uniform in all directions) medium, which obeys Hooke's law of proportionality of stress and strain, and to which the principle of superposition can be applied (strain produced by a composite state of stress is equal to the sum of the strains produced by each one of the stresses individually).

The fill behind a retaining wall or flexible bulkhead cannot ordinarily be assumed to behave as an elastic medium. Strains in a sand mass can be continuous only if isolated particles are so pressed against each other that no mutual displacement of grains is possible. It is evident that particles at the surface of a granular mass are not so restrained. They can move freely and, therefore, do not form a body in the sense used in mechanics. The discussion and numerical examples, which follow, should therefore be regarded as means for acquainting the reader with an interesting approach to the subject of lateral earth pressures, which has repeatedly been brought to the attention of the engineering profession.

It is known from the theory of elasticity that, if a portion AB of the boundary of a semi-infinite elastic body is subjected to the action of a strip loading of an intensity w per square unit, as shown in Fig. 1-30, then the principal stresses at point C will be

$$\sigma_1 = \frac{w}{\pi}(\beta + \sin \beta),$$

$$\sigma_2 = \frac{w}{\pi}(\beta - \sin \beta), \qquad (1\text{-}42)$$

---

*See I. White and G. Paaswell, "Lateral Earth and Concrete Pressures," *Trans.* A.S.C.E. (1939), Vol. 104, p. 1685.

where β is the angle ACB in radians—sometimes called the *angle of visibility* because it is the angle under which the loaded strip is seen from the point C.* The direction of the major principal stress σ_1 bisects the angle β. The

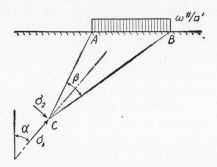

Fig. 1-30. Principal stresses in semi-infinite solid.

maximum shearing stress at point C will equal one-half of the difference between the two principal stresses or

$$\tau_{\max} = \frac{w}{\pi} \sin \beta.$$

It is interesting to note that there are some points within the mass where the value of the shearing stress is greater than at others. These are the points where $\beta = 90°$. The locus of these points is the semicircle having AB for its diameter. The maximum value of $\tau_{\max}$ is w/π, or approximately one-third of the load intensity.

The value of the angle α between the major principal stress and a vertical line can readily be found and the unit horizontal pressure p, as shown in Fig. 1-31, can be found by

$$p = \sigma_1 \sin^2 \alpha + \sigma_2 \cos^2 \alpha. \tag{1-43}$$

As a numerical example, let it be desired to find the horizontal pressure intensities on the back of a retaining wall (Fig. 1-32) due to a loaded railroad track running parallel to the wall and transmitting to the fill a uniform pressure of 1000 psf over a strip 10 ft wide.

In order to plot the pressure diagram, six points are selected on the vertical wall and lines are drawn to the edges of the loaded strip. The angles between these lines and the back of the wall are readily computed from the known dimensions and are found by subtraction and by bisection.

*S. Timoshenko and J. N. Goodier, *Theory of Elasticity* (New York, 1951), p. 95.

Thus for point ② located 10 ft below the top surface, the computations will be as follows:

$$\beta = \frac{2\pi}{360}(63°26' - 45°00') = 0.3216,$$

$$\sin \beta = 0.3162,$$

$$\sigma_1 = \frac{1000}{3.1416}(0.3216 + 0.3162) = 203,$$

$$\sigma_2 = \frac{1000}{3.1416}(0.3216 - 0.3162) = 1.7,$$

$$\alpha = \tfrac{1}{2}(63°26' + 45°00') = 54°13',$$

$$\sin^2 \alpha = 0.6581, \qquad \cos^2 \alpha = 0.3419.$$

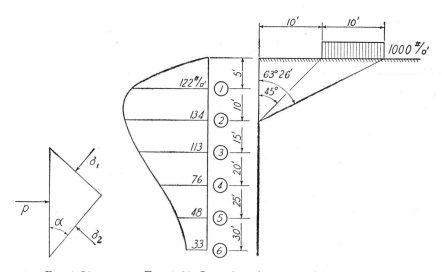

FIG. 1–31.   FIG. 1–32. Lateral earth pressure due to strip loading.

In accordance with Eq. (1–43) the pressure intensity on the back of the wall at a distance 10 ft below the top surface will be

$$203 \times 0.658 + 1.7 \times 0.342 = 134 \text{ psf.}$$

It is interesting to note that the maximum pressure occurs close to the intersection of the wall and a 45° line drawn from the edges of the loaded strip.

If the entire top surface is covered by a unit load w, then, for all points on the back of the enclosing wall, $\beta = 90°$ and the bisecting lines will all make angles $\alpha = 45°$ with the vertical. Hence the effect of the surcharge will be constant for all depths and, according to Eqs. (1–42) and (1–43), will equal

$$\frac{w}{\pi}\left(\frac{\pi}{2} + 1\right)\sin^2 45° + \frac{w}{\pi}\left(\frac{\pi}{2} - 1\right)\cos^2 45° = \frac{w}{2}. \tag{1–44}$$

The effect of the surcharge w is, according to Eq. (1–44), a constant increase for all depths of the lateral pressure intensity. This is in agreement with the conventional Rankine's theory which gives the following increase for this additional pressure:

$$w \tan^2\left(45° - \frac{\phi}{2}\right). \tag{1–45}$$

Equating (1–44) and (1–45) gives

$$\tan^2\left(45° - \frac{\phi}{2}\right) = \frac{1}{2},$$

$$\phi = 19°30'. \tag{1–46}$$

The effect on the lateral earth pressure of a uniformly loaded ground surface is then, according to the theory of elasticity, the same as found by Rankine's theory for a cohesionless mass having an angle of internal friction equal to 19°30'.

1–15. Boussinesq Formula. In the case of a single concentrated load acting on the top surface, pressure intensities on a vertical enclosure can be found by the following formula. Referring to Fig. 1–33 the normal

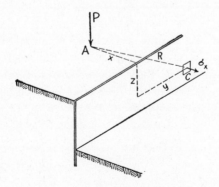

Fig. 1–33. Boussinesq formula.

pressures at a point C in a semi-infinite solid due to a concentrated load P at A will be*

$$\sigma_x = \frac{3Px^2z}{2\pi R^5} , \qquad (1\text{–}47)$$

$$\sigma_y = \frac{3Py^2z}{2\pi R^5} , \qquad (1\text{–}48)$$

$$\sigma_z = \frac{3Pz^3}{2\pi R^5} , \qquad (1\text{–}49)$$

where x, y, and $z =$ coordinates to point C and $R =$ distance from A to C.

Eqs. (1–47) and (1–48) have been given for the special case when Poisson's ratio (transversal strain divided by axial strain) is one-half, while Eq. (1–49) is applicable for any value of Poisson's ratio. Poisson's ratio will usually average about 0.30 for sand and about 0.40 for clay.†

Extensive experiments have been made to check the lateral pressures on retaining walls due to concentrated loads.‡ The experimental evidence confirms the applicability of the Boussinesq formula to the qualitative distribution of pressure. Quantitatively, however, the experimental pressures were much greater than the theoretical ones (sometimes twice as great). As to the position of the maximum pressure, there appears to be a good agreement between test data and theory. The maximum pressure occurs at a point whose distance below the plane at which the load is applied is about one-half the distance from the wall to the load.

1–16. Earth Pressure Specifications. The primary object of design specifications is to insure uniformity of proportions of various structures, as well as reasonable safety and economy. A secondary object is to insure fair competition—that is, to make certain that all designs have as their starting point the same basic loads and forces. Thus, specifications do not necessarily give a picture of the true state of loads and stresses but rather endeavor to give a consistent account of simplified and safe assumptions.

An examination of earth pressure requirements in current use in the United States reveals an extensive use of the so-called "classical" theories for evaluation of lateral earth pressures, with special emphasis on Rankine's theory.

The theory of earth pressures is based, to some extent, on the soil acting as a liquid. As the internal friction between its particles decreases, the active pressure will increase and the passive resistance will decrease,

---

*See H. M. Westergaard, "Effects of a Change of Poisson's Ratio Analyzed by Twinned Gradients," *Journal of Applied Mechanics* (1940), Vol. 62, p. A-113.

†D. P. Krynine, *Soil Mechanics* (New York, 1941), p. 125.

‡M. G. Spangler, "Horizontal Pressures on Retaining Walls Due to Concentrated Surface Loads," *Bulletin No. 140* (Iowa Engineering Experiment Station, 1938).

and both will tend to become horizontal. The term *equivalent liquid pressure* is used in specifications to indicate a hydrostatic pressure increment of the same intensity as the horizontal earth pressure at a unit distance below the surface.

The specifications of the American Association of Highway Officials require that:[*]

(1)   Structures designed to retain fills shall be proportioned to withstand pressure as given by Rankine's formula; provided, however, that no structure shall be designed for less than an equivalent fluid pressure of 30 lb/cu ft.

(2)   When highway traffic can come within a distance from the top of the structure equal to one-half its height, the pressure shall have added to it a live load surcharge pressure equal to not less than 2 ft of earth.

The specifications of the Ohio State Highway Department supplement the above requirements with the demand that, in cases where it is anticipated that the fill may be saturated by long periods of high water, the design shall provide for greater equivalent fluid pressure, varying from 30 to 60 lb/cu ft, the amount depending upon the estimated influence of the porous backfill in reducing the saturated condition of the embankment.[†] It is stipulated in these specifications that, for retaining walls sustaining a

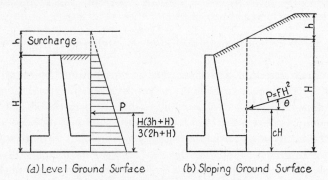

(a) Level Ground Surface   (b) Sloping Ground Surface

FIG. 1–34. Earth pressures according to
Ohio State Highway Department.

fill with a level ground surface as shown in Fig. 1–34(a), the pressure diagram shall be computed in accordance with Rankine's theory. The total overturning will be horizontal and acting at a height of one-third of the height of the wall, if no surcharge is assumed; and at the centroid of the trapezoid representing the pressure distribution, if surcharge is present.

---

[*]*Standard Specifications for Highway Bridges*, Adopted by American Association of Highway Officials (1953), p. 167.

[†]*Specifications for Design of Highway Structures*, State of Ohio, Department of Highways (1946), p. 25.

In the case of a sloping embankment, as shown in Fig. 1–34(b), the total active earth pressure is assumed to be acting on a vertical plane through the rear edge of the heel and to have an angle of inclination with the horizontal depending on the extent and degree of the surface slope. Furthermore, the location of the total pressure is higher than the customary one-third point for intermediate heights of the sloping portion of the embankment. Table 1–2 gives requirements for the case of an embankment

TABLE 1–2

EARTH PRESSURES IN FIG. 1–34(b)*

$\dfrac{h}{H}$	F	c	θ
0.00	15.00	0.333	0°
0.02	15.62	0.339	9°35′
0.05	16.44	0.345	14°30′
0.10	17.65	0.349	18°55′
0.20	19.51	0.349	23°15′
0.33	21.09	0.344	25°40′
0.50	22.05	0.336	26°55′
0.65	22.30	0.333	27°10′
∞	22.30	0.333	27°10′

*Based on equivalent fluid pressure of 30 lb/cu ft. Embankment slope 2:1.

slope of 26°30′ with the horizontal, and an equivalent liquid pressure of 30 lb/cu ft.

The American Railway Engineering Association, in specifications adopted in 1953, makes exclusive use of the Rankine–Coulomb theories and stipulates that the lateral pressures shall be assumed to act parallel to the ground surfaces and, if no surcharge is present, through the third points of the distances measured vertically from the bottom of the rear edge of the wall to the ground surface.* For cases of irregular top surfaces, with or without surcharge, the AREA recommends the trial-wedge method of earth pressure computation which will be explained in the following paragraphs.

Fig. 1–35 shows a retaining wall which provides lateral support for an earth embankment carrying a railroad track.† The cohesive soil which makes up the embankment is assumed to have the following properties:

$w = 120$ lb/cu ft,

$c = 200$ psf,

$\phi = 30°$.

Since this soil possesses cohesion it is possible for it to develop tension cracks to a depth [see Eq. (1–12)] of

*A.R.E.A. Manual (1953), Vol. I, Chapter 8 (Masonry), pp. 8-5-9.
†Ibid., pp. 8-5-13.

$$h_0 = \frac{2c}{w} \tan\left(45° + \frac{\phi}{2}\right) = 5.77 \text{ ft}$$

and it is assumed that down to this depth no lateral pressure will develop. The earth above this level will simply act as surcharge for the soil below. The earth pressure on the vertical plane DF will be found and the AREA specifications assume that the direction of this pressure is the same as that of line AC, which has a horizontal projection equal to twice the height of the wall.

A number of trial wedges are next considered. Fig. 1–35 shows four such wedges: $FDbB, FDb_2B_2B, FDb_3B_3B$, and FDb_4B_4B. The total weights

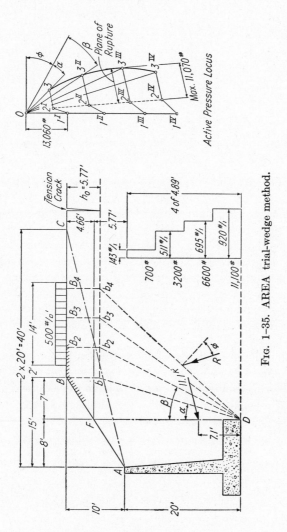

Fig. 1–35. AREA trial-wedge method.

for each of these are found. Thus, for $FDbB$:

$$W_1 = \tfrac{1}{2}7(5.77 + 25.34) \times 120 = 13{,}060 \text{ lb,}$$

and for the remaining three wedges ($bb_2 = b_2b_3 = b_3b_4 = 5$ ft) in succession:

$$W_2 = 13{,}060 + 120 \times 5(5.77 + \tfrac{1}{2}24.23) + 3 \times 500$$

$$= 13{,}060 + 10{,}740 + 1500$$

$$= 25{,}300 \text{ lb,}$$

$$W_3 = 25{,}300 + 10{,}740 + 2500 = 38{,}540 \text{ lb,}$$

$$W_4 = 38{,}540 + 10{,}740 + 2500 = 51{,}780 \text{ lb.}$$

Acting along the sloping surfaces Db, Db_2, Db_3, and Db_4 are cohesive forces which at the time of rupture will equal

$$c_1 = 25.22 \times 200 = 5044 \text{ lb,}$$

$$c_2 = 27.04 \times 200 = 5408 \text{ lb,}$$

$$c_3 = 29.60 \times 200 = 5920 \text{ lb,}$$

$$c_4 = 32.73 \times 200 = 6546 \text{ lb.}$$

There are four forces acting on each wedge of soil:

(1) The weight, W, of the whole wedge.
(2) The reaction, R, on the plane of rupture.
(3) The resulting pressure, P, on DF (direction assumed same as AC).
(4) The cohesion, c, along the surface of rupture.

The directions of all four forces are known, and also the magnitudes of two, W and c. It is, therefore, possible to construct force polygons for each wedge and plot a curve which will give the variation of pressure for the various wedges. This has been done in Fig. 1–35, which shows the active pressure locus. The maximum ordinate is equal to 11,070 lb. It is interesting to note that points 1^{I}; 1^{II}; 1^{III} $\cdots$, which represent the ends of the cohesion vectors, will lie on a straight line.

In order to find the point of application of the pressure, the AREA specifications recommend plotting the variation of pressure intensity along DF. In order to do this it is necessary to find the total pressure at various levels under F. Again it is assumed that there is a neutral or ineffective zone of depth 5.77 ft below this point. The remaining part of DF is divided into four equal parts and the graphical construction just outlined is repeated at distances 4.89 ft, 9.78 ft, and 14.67 ft above D. The values found are indicated.

Approximate pressure intensities are next found thus:

$$700 \div 4.89 = 143 \text{ lb/ft}$$

$$(3200 - 700) \div 4.89 = 511 \text{ lb/ft}$$

$$(6600 - 3200) \div 4.89 = 695 \text{ lb/ft}$$

$$(11,100 - 6600) \div 4.89 = 920 \text{ lb/ft}$$

and the pressure diagram is plotted as shown. While the correct diagram should be plotted with ordinates parallel to AC, its purpose (locating the position of the resulting pressure of 11,100 lb) is served equally well by horizontal ordinates. If static moments are taken about the bottom of the diagram it is seen that

$$
\begin{aligned}
700 \times 17.12 &= 11,900 \\
2500 \times 12.23 &= 30,600 \\
3400 \times 7.34 &= 24,900 \\
4500 \times 2.45 &= \underline{11,000} \\
78,460 &\div 11,100 = 7.1 \text{ ft.}
\end{aligned}
$$

PROBLEMS

1-1. Find the maximum distance, X, for the trench excavation shown, if the soil properties are as follows: $c = 200$ psf, $\phi = 18°$, $w = 95$ lb/cu ft. (*Ans.*: 24 ft.)

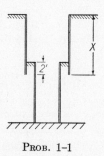

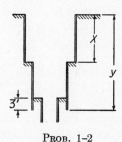

PROB. 1-1   PROB. 1-2

1-2. Find the maximum distances X and y for the trench excavation shown. The soil properties are as follows: $c = 300$ psf, $\phi = 14°$, $w = 100$ lb/cu ft. (*Partial Ans.*: $X \div y = 0.725$.)

1-3. Find the total active pressure, P_1, on AC and the total passive pressure, P_2, on BC. The soil is cohesionless and the angle of internal friction is $20°$, and the angle between the two parallel sloping surfaces and the horizontal is $15°$. Check by Poncelet's construction. (*Ans.*: $P_1 \div P_2 = 1.29$.)

1–4. Use Poncelet's construction for finding the active earth pressure on AB if $\delta = \phi = 30°$.   (*Ans.*: 15 kips.)

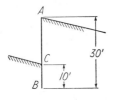

PROB. 1–3

PROB. 1–4

1–5. For what angle δ will the active earth pressure be exactly equal to the passive pressure on AB?   (*Ans.*: $\delta = \phi$.)

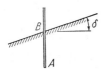

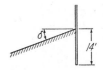

PROB. 1–5

PROB. 1–6

1–6. A cohesionless soil has an angle of internal friction $\phi = 20°$ and a unit weight $w = 102$ lb/cu ft. For a height $h = 14$ ft, find the angle δ with the horizontal which will produce a passive pressure of: (a) 18 kips; (b) 20 kips; (c) 25 kips. (*Ans.*: 5°, −8°.)

1–7. Find the percentage of voids in a soil which weighs 110 lb/cu ft in air and 70 lb/cu ft submerged in water.   (*Ans.*: 36 per cent.)

DRIVING STEEL SHEET PILING

CHAPTER 2

SHEET PILING

2-1. Introduction. Sheet piling consists of special shapes of interlocking piles, driven so as to form a continuous and reasonably tight wall. The structural function of sheet piling is to resist lateral pressures due to earth and water, the successful accomplishment of which depends, for a straight wall, on sufficient depth of penetration and capacity to sustain the bending moments and, for a curved wall, on tensile strength of the interlocks.

2-2. Steel Sheet Piling. Steel is, by far, the most frequently used material for sheet piling. It is extensively used not only for temporary

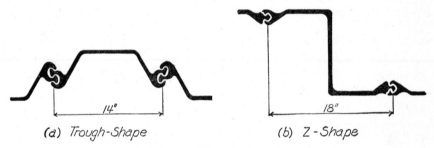

(a) Trough-Shape   (b) Z-Shape

FIG. 2-1. Steel sheet piling.

construction such as cofferdams, but also for permanent structures such as bulkheads, sea walls, wharves, and piers. This wide application of steel sheet piling for heavy lateral loads and long spans can be attributed to two factors: First, it is generally recognized that steel, if properly protected, is well adapted for subsurface and marine construction in both fresh and salt waters. Numbers of steel sheet-piling structures exist today, built twenty and thirty years ago, which testify to this. Secondly, the simplicity, strength, and economy of steel sheet piling are very considerable.

Fig. 2-1(a) shows the most commonly used type of American steel sheet piling. The section is rolled in a number of sizes. The width, also called the driving distance of the pile, varies (14 in. being the minimum); depth, weight per linear foot, and section modulus also vary. The section is symmetrical and is provided with interlocks that are continuous throughout the entire length of the unit in both horizontal and lateral direction. This style of interlock, often called the *thumb-and-finger* type of joint, provides a maximum number of points of contact and insures a maximum of interlock strength with minimum weight. The flexibility of this interlock permits the piling to be driven in a curved line; a swing of as much as 10° is possible between adjacent units. This feature, together with the high tensile strength of the interlock, makes the straight web section of this type adaptable for cellular cofferdam construction. The disadvantage of the thumb-and-finger type is the fact that earth and small stones fill up the groove and resist the downward motion of the adjacent section. The resistance of this entrapped earth often becomes so large that torn interlocks result from driving.

Fig. 2–1(*b*) shows a Z-shaped section which has certain advantages over the trough-shaped section. It has much greater section modulus for its weight. In addition, the interlocks of a Z-pile are located where the longitudinal shear is zero. As a consequence, the section modulus of the single uninterlocked pile is the same as when interlocked with the adjoining pile. The Z-section has a *ball-and-socket* type of interlock which reduces to a minimum the friction in the interlock during driving. The section should be driven with the ball end leading so that the socket slides down over the ball of the previous section. In this way no soil can become trapped in the interlock; such soil would, if present, tend to force open the interlocks during driving, due to packing of this soil. The flexibility or swing in the interlock has been reduced to an absolute minimum. This limits the twist of the pile during driving or after load is applied.

The Z-pile section is especially suitable for deep water structures such as docks, wharves, piers, canal locks, breakwaters, and deep cofferdams.

2–3. Timber Sheet Piling. Sheet piling of timber is used for short spans and light lateral loads. The simplest type of timber sheet piling consists merely of planks with ordinary planed tongue and groove. Positive interlocks can also be made of wood but the limited use of timber sheet piling rarely justifies expensive units.

2–4. Reinforced Concrete Sheet Piling. Sheet piling of reinforced concrete is used occasionally for permanent work, but only where the lengths are comparatively short. The interlock is generally a tongue-and-groove arrangement as shown on Fig. 2–2. The tongue may extend the full length of the pile or for only that portion below the waterline, the groove above being grouted to insure watertightness.

The bottom of the pile is usually beveled on one side (Fig. 2–2) so that it will be forced against the adjacent pile and will maintain contact during driving.

In order to combine the positive interlock of the steel sheet piles with the high permanency of concrete piles, sheet-pile units have been built in which a steel pile is cut longitudinally through the web and the two

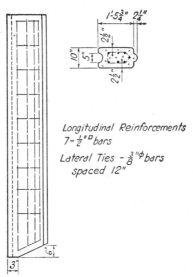

FIG. 2-2. Reinforced concrete
sheet piling.

halves are cast into a concrete pile on opposite edges. After the piles
are driven, the grooves containing the steel interlock are cleaned and
filled with grout.

2-5. Cantilever Sheet Piling. Sheet piling which depends for stability
solely on the embedment of the lower portion is called cantilever piling
or unanchored piling. In the following it will be assumed that active
and passive earth pressures are governed by Coulomb's theory. Expressions for depth of penetration and maximum bending moment can then
be derived by the principles of statics.

Fig. 2-3 shows a cantilever pile subjected to the action of a concentrated load L, acting at a distance h above the ground. In order to main-

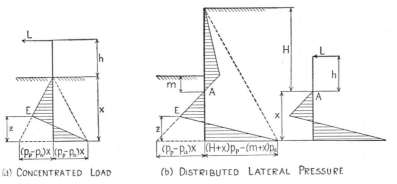

(a) CONCENTRATED LOAD   (b) DISTRIBUTED LATERAL PRESSURE

FIG. 2-3. Cantilever sheet piling.

tain equilibrium, lateral earth pressures must act in opposite directions just below this ground surface and in the same direction farther down. These pressures are brought about by movements of the pile against the earth; the resulting pressures can therefore be evaluated as the difference between passive and active pressure. It is now assumed that this passive resistance will be fully mobilized down to point E, which is a distance z from the bottom; and also fully mobilized in the opposite direction at the bottom of the pile. The change in pressure between point E and the bottom is assumed to vary according to a straight line.

Equating to zero, the sum of all forces gives

$$L - \tfrac{1}{2}(p_p - p_a)x^2 + (p_p - p_a)xz = 0, \qquad (2\text{-}1)$$

or

$$z = \frac{(p_p - p_a)x^2 - 2L}{2(p_p - p_a)x} . \qquad (2\text{-}2)$$

Taking moments about the bottom of the pile gives

$$L(h + x) - \tfrac{1}{6}(p_p - p_a)x^3 + \tfrac{1}{3}(p_p - p_a)xz^2 = 0. \qquad (2\text{-}3)$$

Substituting in Eq. (2–3) the value of z from Eq. (2–2) gives

$$x^4 - \frac{8L}{p_p - p_a} x^2 - \frac{12Lh}{p_p - p_a} x - \left[\frac{2L}{p_p - p_a} \right]^2 = 0. \qquad (2\text{-}4)$$

With load and soil properties known, the depth of penetration can be determined from Eq. (2–4), which is solved quite readily by trial. Eq. (2–2) gives the shape of the load diagram from which, in turn, can be determined shears and moments.

The case of a cantilever pile subjected to distributed lateral pressure on the portion above ground is shown in Fig. 2–3(b). The passive resistance on the left side is the same as for the concentrated load; but, due to the greater overburden, the passive resistance at the bottom of the pile has been increased. By equating to zero the sum of all forces and taking moments about the bottom of the pile, the following four equations, revised for the case of distributed load, can be obtained:

$$L - \frac{x^2}{2}(p_p - p_a) + \frac{z}{2}\left[(H + 2x)p_p - (m + 2x)p_a\right] = 0, \quad (2\text{-}1\text{a})$$

$$z = \frac{(p_p - p_a)x^2 - 2L}{2(p_p - p_a)x + Hp_p - mp_a}, \qquad (2\text{-}2\text{a})$$

$$L(h + x) - \frac{x^3}{6}(p_p - p_a) + \frac{z^2}{6}\left[(H + 2x)p_p - (m + 2x)p_a\right] = 0, \quad (2\text{-}3\text{a})$$

and, eliminating z,

$$6L(h + x) - x^3(p_p - p_a) + \frac{\left[(p_p - p_a)x^2 - 2L\right]^2}{2(p_p - p_a)x + Hp_p - mp_a} = 0. \qquad (2\text{-}4\text{a})$$

In these last equations the symbol L represents the resultant of all forces above the point A where the pressure intensity becomes zero, h de-

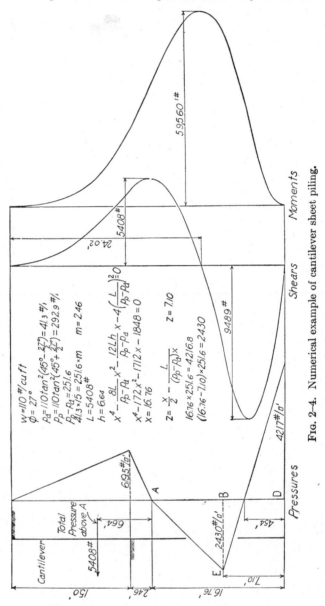

Fig. 2-4. Numerical example of cantilever sheet piling.

notes the distance from the resultant to this point, and H is the distance from the top surface to the point A.

It should be noted that the difference in penetration, which results from the application of either Eqs. (2–1) to (2–4) or Eqs. (2–1a) to (2–4a) to the case of distributed load, is very small; and, inasmuch as the former are simpler and always on the safe side, they are often applied to all cantilever piles regardless of manner of loading.

In Fig. 2–4 is shown an unanchored sheet-pile wall driven into the ground and resisting, over a height of 15 ft, lateral pressure resulting from fill on one side. It is assumed that the soil properties of fill and ground are the same. Fig. 2–4 lists these properties in the form of unit weight and angle of internal friction. It is desired to find total length of piling, maximum shear, and maximum bending moment. The Eqs. (2–1), (2–2), (2–3), and (2–4) that were developed for cantilever piles subjected to a concentrated load have been applied.

First is located the point A of zero lateral pressure; then Eq. (2–4) is used for determining the necessary depth below this point; finally Eq. (2–2) is used for finding the distance $BD = z$, and diagrams for shears and moments are drawn.

If, for comparison, Eqs. (2–1a), (2–2a), (2–3a), and (2–4a) are applied to the example in Fig. 2–4, then $H = 17.46$ and the depth of penetration below point A is found to be $x = 15.3$ ft, compared to 16.8 ft as found by the more approximate method.

2–6. Anchored Sheet Piling. In laterally loaded sheet piling, total length and unit weight can be materially reduced by anchorage of the top or some other part of the pile near the top. As will be shown in the subsequent paragraphs, however, minimum penetration consistent with static equilibrium will not necessarily be the most economical. Additional depth will be accompanied by further reduction in bending stresses.

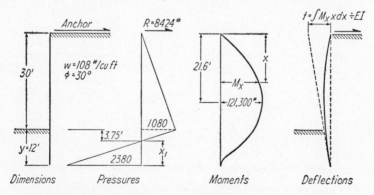

FIG. 2–5. Anchored sheet piling, minimum penetration, Case A.

Fig. 2–5 shows a sheet-piling wall anchored at the top and resisting lateral pressure that is caused by a 30-ft difference in elevation between two earth surfaces. The soil is assumed to be cohesionless with a unit weight of 108 lb/cu ft and an angle of internal friction equal to 30°. The increments of active and passive pressures will equal

$$p_a = 108 \tan^2 (45° - \tfrac{1}{2}30°) = 36 \text{ lb/ft,}$$

$$p_p = 108 \tan^2 (45° + \tfrac{1}{2}30°) = 324 \text{ lb/ft.}$$

The active pressure will be a triangle between the two surfaces; below the lower surface it will decrease due to the presence of passive pressure, and at a distance of 3.75 feet below it, active and passive pressure intensities will be equal, found thus,

$$1080 + 36x = 324x; \quad x = 3.75 \text{ ft.}$$

Below this point there will be an excess of passive pressure and if the distance to the bottom is called x_1 it is seen that the pressure intensity here will be $(324 - 36)x_1$. Taking moments about the anchor rod, which is assumed placed at the top, gives

$$\tfrac{1}{2}30 \times 1080 \times 20 + \tfrac{1}{2}3.75 \times 1080 \times 31.25 = 144x_1^2(33.75 + \tfrac{2}{3}x_1),$$

or

$$x_1^3 + 50.6x_1^2 - 4033.5 = 0.$$

Solving gives $x_1 = 8.25$ or a total length of 42 ft for the minimum penetration of this sheet-piling wall. The anchor tension is readily found by subtracting total passive pressure from total active pressure; thus,

$$R = \tfrac{1}{2}1080 \times 33.75 - \tfrac{1}{2}8.25 \times 8.25 \times 288 = 8424 \text{ lb.}$$

Maximum bending moment is found by locating first the point of zero shear; thus,

$$8424 = \tfrac{1}{2}36x \times x; \quad x = 21.6 \text{ ft,}$$

$$M_{\text{max}} = 8424 \times \tfrac{2}{3}21.6 = 121{,}300 \text{ ft-lb.}$$

It is known from mechanics that the deflection, t, of the tangent to the bottom of the stressed wall with respect to the top is equal to

$$t = \frac{1}{EI} \int M_x x \, dx. \tag{2-5}$$

Substituting the values for Case A gives

$$t = \int_0^{42} (8424x - \tfrac{1}{2}36x^2\tfrac{1}{3}x)x \, dx + \int_0^{12} \tfrac{1}{2}324x^2\tfrac{1}{3}x(x \not{+} 30) \, dx,$$

$$t = 62 \times 10^6. \tag{2-6}$$

which should, of course, be divided by EI (product of modulus of elasticity and moment of inertia) in order to give the actual displacement.

Fig. 2-6 shows the same sheet-piling wall extended 5 ft deeper, resulting in a total length of 47 ft. It is evident that the pressure diagram for the upper portion (42 ft from the top) must be identical to that for Case *A*. It is also evident that maintenance of static equilibrium requires additional pressure to the right of the toe. The pressure intensity at the very bottom

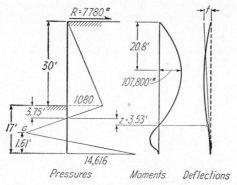

FIG. 2–6. Anchored sheet piling, Case B.

is assumed to be equal to passive pressure resulting from a 47-ft over-burden reduced by active pressure caused by 17 ft of overlying soil.

Fig. 2–7 shows how point *a* is established. The line *ea* is assumed to

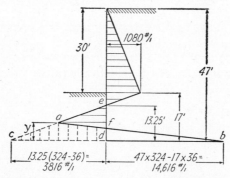

FIG. 2–7. Pressure diagram, Case B.

extend down to the bottom of the wall, necessitating subtraction of pressure corresponding to the quadrangle *acdf*. This quadrangle added to triangle *bdf* gives a total triangle *abc*. Thus in Fig. 2–7, while actual pressures are indicated by horizontal crosshatching, it is proposed to simplify computations by adding and subtracting pressures indicated by vertical cross-hatching. Taking moments about the anchor at the top gives

$\frac{1}{2}1080(30 \times 20 + 3.75 \times 31.25) - \frac{1}{3}3816 \times 13.25 \times 42.58$

$$+ \tfrac{1}{2}y(3816 + 14{,}616)(47 - \tfrac{1}{3}y) = 0,$$

$$y = 1.61 \text{ ft.}$$

Anchor tension is found again as the difference between pressures; thus,

$$R = \tfrac{1}{2}1080 \times 33.75 + \tfrac{1}{2}1.61 \times 18{,}432 - \tfrac{1}{2}13.25 \times 3816 = 7780 \text{ lb.}$$

Points of zero shear are next established and the maximum moments found. The moment diagram discloses a point of contraflexure which lies a distance $z = 3.53$ ft below the point of equal active and passive

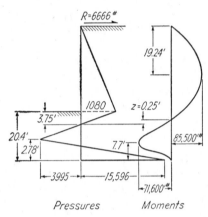

Fig. 2–8. Anchored sheet piling, favorable penetration.

intensities. The maximum bending moment is 107,800 ft–lb. The displacement of the tangent to the toe of the wall is

$$t = \int_0^{47} (7780x - 6x^3)x \, dx + \int_0^{17} 54x^3(x + 30) \, dx$$

$$- \int_0^{1.61} (18{,}432 \div 1.61)x\tfrac{1}{2}x\tfrac{1}{3}x(x + 45.4) \, dx, \qquad (2\text{–}7)$$

$$t = 43 \times 10^6.$$

Thus it is seen that anchor tension, maximum bending moment, and angle of rotation at the bottom all have decreased as a result of deeper penetration of the sheet-piling wall.

If still deeper penetrations are investigated it will be found that these quantities continue to decrease until a depth has been reached at which the quantity t will equal zero. This means that at this depth the angle of rotation will equal zero, or that the surrounding soil will provide complete fixity. The variations of t, R, and M are shown on Fig. 2–9. Also indicated in this diagram is the variation of the distance z between the point of equal active and passive pressure intensities in the pressure diagram and the point of contraflexure in the moment diagram.

The penetration at which no angle of rotation is developed at the bottom is called favorable penetration. Penetrations beyond this level will not change the pressure diagram because no displacements will occur and no passive pressures can be invoked if the position of the sheet-piling wall is not altered. Fig. 2–9 indicates that for a pile length of 50.4 ft this favorable

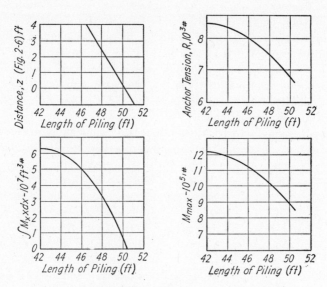

FIG. 2–9. Theoretical investigation of anchored piling.

penetration has been reached. The pressure and moment diagrams for this length are shown in Fig. 2–8.

It will be shown in the following that the amount of material required for favorable penetration is a minimum compared to shorter lengths of the sheet piling.

The weights of structural shapes will always increase with their resisting moments, M, or, what amounts to the same, with their section moduli, S. In the case of a rectangle this increase in weight will be proportional to the square root of the resisting moment. If conventional nomenclature is used, thus,

$$M_1 = fS_1 = f\tfrac{1}{6}bd_1^{\,2} = \frac{f}{6b}\,b^2d_1^{\,2} \sim W_1^{\,2}$$

$$M_2 = fS_2 = f\tfrac{1}{6}bd_2^{\,2} = \frac{f}{6b}\,b^2d_2^{\,2} \sim W_2^{\,2}$$

$$\frac{W_1}{W_2} = \sqrt{\frac{M_1}{M_2}}. \qquad (2\text{–}8)$$

In the case of rolled steel sheet-piling sections this relation will either hold as for the following:

$$\text{MP110} - 32\ \text{psf} - 15.3\ \text{in.}^3/\text{ft} \qquad \frac{32}{27} = \sqrt{\frac{15.3}{10.7}},$$

$$\text{MP116} - 27\ \text{psf} - 10.7\ \text{in.}^3/\text{ft}$$

or the increase will be greater than indicated by Eq. (2–8). The material utilization factor is

$$F = l\sqrt{M} \qquad (2\text{–}9)$$

where l = total length of piling, and M = maximum bending moment. This quantity has been plotted in Fig. 2–10 for the anchored steel sheet-piling wall in Fig. 2–9. It is seen that as the depth of the wall increases there is first an increase in material, with a maximum reached at about 46 ft. The amount of material will then decrease, and at a depth of penetration of 20.4 ft, it is approximately the same as for the much shorter length of minimum penetration.

The utilization factor is thus nearly the same in both alternatives, with or without constraining action. There would be very little difference

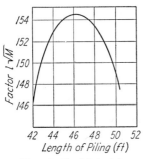

FIG. 2–10. Material utilization factor.

between the required amounts of material. There is, according to Figs. 2–5 and 2–8, considerable difference between anchor tensions, which for the favorable penetration will result in savings in the cost of wales, tie rods, and anchorage. The greatest advantage, however, of the favorable depth lies in its smaller deflections and its greater actual safety. If the sheet piling is driven to only minimum depth (Case A), then the factor of safety against pushing out is only unity;* if the passive pressure is less than its assumed value, the toe of the pile will move outward and the wall will collapse. In Fig. 2–8, if the passive earth pressure should become smaller than was originally assumed, the only effect will be a reduction in the constraining moment and a corresponding increase in the active moment; the greater depth of the piling will prevent failure of the wall.

The sheet-piling wall with favorable penetration will, with its anchorage, require less material than other lengths. For this reason it is also called *economic penetration.*

2–7. Equivalent Beam Method. Fig. 2–9 indicates that as the depth of the sheet piling increases the point of contraflexure will move up, and for the most economical depth, this point of contraflexure will almost coincide with the point of equal active and passive pressure intensities immediately under the lower surface. For computation purposes, therefore, the upper portion of the constrained sheet-piling wall, where the maximum bending moment occurs, can be replaced by a beam simply supported at the

---

*Actually, it is considerably more, because external friction between wall and soil has been disregarded.

point of anchorage and the first point of zero pressure intensity. The shears and moments of this equivalent beam will approximate very closely the shears and moments in the constrained beam.

Fig. 2–11 shows the equivalent beam corresponding to Fig. 2–8. Anchor tension and maximum bending moment have been computed. A comparison with the values for the constrained beam indicates that those for the equivalent beam are excellent approximations (errors are smaller than 2 per cent) and also on the side of safety.

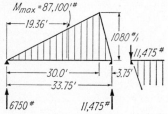

FIG. 2–11. Equivalent beam.   FIG. 2–12. Economic penetration.

An approximate expression for the penetration, y, can be derived from Fig. 2–12. Taking moments about the bottom of the pile, it is seen that

$$\tfrac{1}{2}(y - x)(y - x)(p_p - p_a)\tfrac{1}{3}(y - x) = P(y - x),$$

$$y = x + \sqrt{\frac{6P}{p_p - p_a}}.$$

The errors involved in disregarding the two crosshatched areas (including one and excluding the other), and in assuming concurrence of point of contraflexure and point of equal pressure intensities, are small and can be compensated for by increasing the value of y by 10 per cent. Hence the expression for the desired penetration

$$y = 1.1\left(x + \sqrt{\frac{6P}{p_p - p_a}}\right), \qquad (2\text{--}10)$$

where x = distance to point of equal pressures,
    P = equivalent beam reaction,
    p_p = passive pressure increment,
    p_a = active pressure increment.

If Eq. (2–10) is applied to the equivalent beam in Fig. 2–11, it is seen that

$$y = 1.1\left(3.75 + \sqrt{\frac{6 \times 11,475}{324 - 36}}\right) = 21.1 \text{ ft.}$$

This compares favorably to the depth of 20.4 ft found in Fig. 2–8.

2–8. Numerical Examples. Fig. 2–13(a) shows a sheet-piling wall with a supporting anchor placed 3 ft below the top surface. If the soil properties are assumed to be the same as those in Fig. 2–5 it is seen that the distance from the lower surface to the point of equal intensities is found thus,

$$(324 - 36)x = 35 \times 36; \quad x = 4.38 \text{ ft.}$$

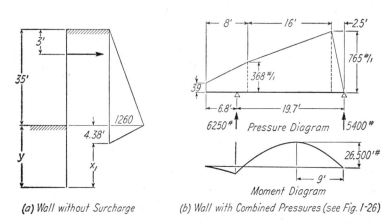

(a) Wall without Surcharge   (b) Wall with Combined Pressures (see Fig. 1-26)

FIG. 2–13. Numerical examples.

The distance from this point to the bottom of the wall with minimum penetration is found by taking moments about the anchor rod; thus,

$$\tfrac{1}{2}1260(35 \times 20.33 + 4.38 \times 33.46) = 144x_1^2(36.38 + \tfrac{2}{3}x_1),$$

$$x_1 = 9.36 \text{ ft.}$$

The anchor tension and maximum bending moments corresponding to the minimum penetration will be, respectively, 12,110 lb and 173,100 ft-lb.

If favorable or economic penetration is desired the shear at the lower end of the equivalent beam should be evaluated thus,

$$p = \tfrac{1}{2}1260(35 \times 20.33 + 4.38 \times 33.46) \div 36.38 = 14,860 \text{ lb,}$$

and the distance to the bottom of the wall will be

$$y = 1.1\left(4.38 + \sqrt{\frac{6 \times 14,860}{324 - 36}}\right) = 24.1 \text{ ft.}$$

The maximum bending moment is found to be 126,030 ft-lb and the anchor tension 9950 lb per lin ft. The latter figure should, of course, be multiplied by the anchor rod spacing in order to give amount of tension in one rod.

It is of interest to compare the above quantities with the corresponding ones arrived at by the exact method of plotting diagrams similar to Fig. 2–9. The comparison has been made in Table 2–1.

As a second numerical example, consider the sheet-piling wall in Fig. 1–26. If the distance from the top surface to the anchor rod is 6 ft, $9\frac{1}{2}$ in., then the equivalent beam will be as shown in Fig. 2–13(b) and the reactions

TABLE 2–1

ECONOMIC PENETRATION (Fig. 2–12)

	Exact Method	Equivalent Beam Method
Maximum monent, M	125,800 ft-lb	126,030 ft-lb
Anchor tension, T	9,930 lb	9,950 lb
Penetration, y	23.1 ft	24.1 ft
Distance to point of contraflexure, z	0.2 ft	0

can be readily found. The point of zero shear is located by solving the following equation:

$$39 \times 8 + \tfrac{1}{2}\,329 \times 8 + 368x + \tfrac{1}{2}x\,\frac{765 - 368}{16}\,x = 6250,$$

$$x = 9.5 \text{ ft.}$$

The bending moment at this point is found to be approximately 26,500 ft-lb. The economic penetration of this sheet-piling wall will be, according to Eq. (2–9),

$$y = 1.1\!\left(2.5 + \sqrt{\frac{6 \times 5400}{2 \times 63.7 \tan^2 58° - 63.7 \tan^2 32°}}\,\right) = 14.1 \text{ ft.}$$

The case of anchored sheet piling driven into a sloping bank is illustrated in Fig. 2–14. The passive earth pressure has been evaluated by means of Eq. (1–29). If it is assumed that the bank consists of uncon-

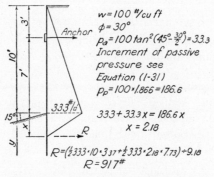

FIG. 2–14. Sheet piling in sloping ground.

solidated material and no efficiency factor can be used, the penetration should be

$$y = 1.1\left(2.18 + \sqrt{\frac{6 \times 971}{186.3 - 33.3}}\right) = 9.16 \text{ ft.} \qquad (2\text{--}11)$$

For anchored sheet piling, the tie rods connect to the sheet-pile wall through a horizontal girder generally called a *wale*. The wale is usually placed at or slightly below the waterline in order to keep the tie rods in the area of saturation, thereby preserving them against rust and rot. As shown in Fig. 2–15, the wale can be made of timber or steel and it can

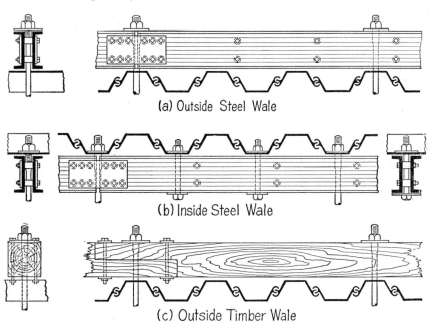

(a) Outside Steel Wale

(b) Inside Steel Wale

(c) Outside Timber Wale

Fig. 2–15. Typical structural arrangement for wales.

be placed on the outside or on the inside of the wall. It has been pointed out in Chap. 1 (Fig. 1–25) that, for flexible bulkheads, the assumed straight-line variation of the earth pressure intensity will result in too large bending moments and too small anchor pulls.

2–9. Design Procedures. Current procedures for bulkhead computations originated about twenty-five years ago. Since that time the knowledge of the physical properties of earth materials and of the mechanics of earth pressures has increased vastly, yet the methods of design remain practically unaltered.*

---

*See Karl Terzaghi, "Anchored Bulkheads," *Proc. A.S.C.E.* (September, 1953), Vol. 79, Separate No. 262.

The Bureau of Yards and Docks of the United States Navy has constructed many types of sheet-piling walls, which have been designed to meet a large variety of soil and site conditions. It has been the practice of the Bureau of Yards and Docks to compute earth pressures in the following manner.*

(1) The active pressures and passive pressures for granular material are both computed by the Rankine–Coulomb formulas, neglecting the effect of wall friction.

(2) For fine-grained and cohesive materials, the earth pressures are based on both frictional and cohesive resistance, with allowance for pore pressure (due to tide range) in unconsolidated material.

(3) Uniform surcharges are converted to equivalent heights of the backfill material.

The designs of the Bureau of Yards and Docks are predicated on providing an actual safety factor of from 1.5 to 2.0 for the passive resistance. By the use of the pressures computed as outlined above, the minimum depth of penetration required for stability of the sheet pile is determined. This minimum depth is considered sufficient to give the required factor of safety for sheet piling driven into natural undisturbed soils.

The anchor rod, which supports a sheet-piling wall, usually terminates in an anchorage that must be able to resist the tension in the rod. Several forms of typical anchorages are shown in Fig. 2–16. The anchorage shown in Fig. 2–16(a) is especially suitable in locations where the existing grade

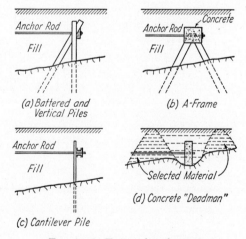

FIG. 2–16. Types of anchorages.

*See W. Ayers and R. C. Stokes, "The Design of Flexible Bulkheads," *Proc A.S.C.E.* (January, 1953), Vol. 79, Separate No. 166.

is low, because it does not depend on the passive resistance of the material which will be placed over the natural surface. This also applies to the types shown in Figs. 2–16(b) and (c). The latter of these consists of a cantilever pile which may be an ordinary pile, a pair of steel-sheet piling units, or a continuous row of sheet piles.

The anchorage shown in Fig. 2–16(c) is effective at a site where the existing ground elevation is above the level of the anchor rod. It is usually called a *deadman* and consists of a vertical concrete wall which derives its resistance from the passive pressure developed in front of it. The concrete should preferably be cast in a trench in undisturbed and well-consolidated soil. If this is not possible, then it becomes necessary to place selected quality material around the deadman, deposit it in layers, and thoroughly compact it.

The proper location of an anchorage is of great importance. Anchorages which depend on batter piles for resistance should be placed behind the portion of the earth developing active pressure on the wall. This means behind a line drawn through the point of intersection of the wall and the lower ground level, and making an angle with the horizontal equal to the angle of repose of the material behind the bulkhead. In the case of anchorages which depend on passive earth pressure, the location should be in a region which can develop this pressure independently of the active pressure that exists immediately behind the wall. Anchorages of this type should not be closer to the bulkhead than from two to three times the distance from mean tide level to the dredged bottom.

The presence of soft materials or the use of hydraulic fills may cause unduly large earth pressures behind flexible bulkheads. Several methods are used for the reduction of active pressures and the increase of passive pressures. The use of a sand blanket is an economical method of improving poor bottom conditions at deep-water sites. Likewise a sand dike behind the wall will reduce the high pressures resulting from poor quality backfill. Fig. 2–17 illustrates a combination of sand blanket and sand dike.

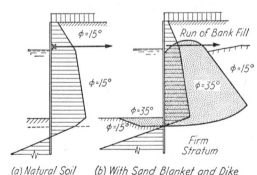

(a) *Natural Soil*   (b) *With Sand Blanket and Dike*

FIG. 2–17. Method of reducing earth pressures.

It was shown in Fig. 1–25 that lateral earth pressures will deflect a flexible bulkhead in such a manner that the pressure intensities are increased near the supports and reduced on the unsupported portion. It is readily seen that this modification of the pressure diagram will tend to increase the pull in the anchor rod and decrease the bending moment in the sheet piling. This has been taken into account by specifications used by designers of port structures in Great Britain.* For sheet-pile wharves it is required that Rankine's formula be used and that a straight-line distribution be assumed for obtaining the toe thrust, and a parabolic distribution for finding the tie rod pull. It is also required that the bending moments in the sheet piling, as figured from the straight-line distribution, can be reduced by multiplying them by the factor 0.6.

2–10. Numerical Example. In order to illustrate the method of design used in the case of a sheet-piling wall with a sand dike [similar to Fig. 2–17(b)], consider the wall shown in Fig. 2–18.

It is assumed that behind this wall will be placed a hydraulic fill which immediately after its placing will exert a hydrostatic pressure. To reduce the lateral forces acting on the sheet piling a sand dike in the form of a triangle will be placed prior to the pumping in of the hydraulic fill. Angles of internal friction and submerged weights are given in Fig. 2–18(a).

The active earth pressure, P_A, exerted on the wall by the combination of sand and hydraulic fill can be found as the resultant of forces acting on a wedge ABCD. Various angles of rupture, v, are assumed and the maximum value of P_A is determined by graphical construction. The forces acting on the wedge in Fig. 2–18(b) are as follows:

W_1 = weight of liquid triangle BCD,
W_2 = weight of sand triangle ABD,
P = hydrostatic pressure on CD due to fill while liquid,
R = resultant of normal and shearing forces on potential surface of rupture, making an angle with perpendicular equal to the angle of internal friction of sand.

Fig. 2–18(d) indicates the method of constructing force polygons, including the forces listed above and the active earth pressure P_A. The latter has a maximum value of 9650 ft-lb, which is the active earth pressure on AB. For comparison the omission of the sand dike would result in a total pressure from the hydraulic fill equal to

$$\tfrac{1}{2}50 \times 30^2 = 22{,}500 \text{ lb.}$$

---

*See N. D. Morgan, "The Design of Wharves on Soft Ground," *Journal Inst. of Civil Eng'rs* (March, 1944), p. 24.

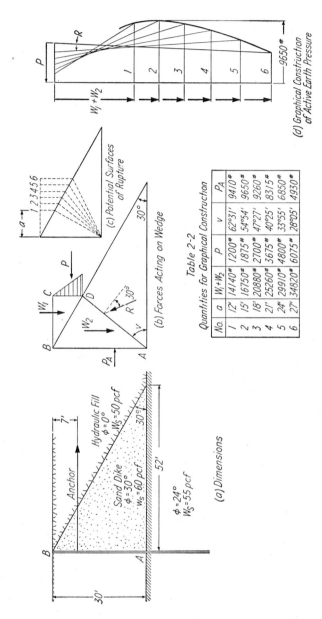

Table 2-2
Quantities for Graphical Construction

No.	a	$W_1 + W_2$	P	v	P_A
1	12'	14140#	1200#	62°31'	9410#
2	15'	16750#	1875#	54°54'	9650#
3	18'	20880#	2700#	47°27'	9260#
4	21'	25260#	3675#	40°25'	8315#
5	24'	29910#	4800#	33°55'	6850#
6	27'	34820#	6075#	28°05'	4930#

Fig. 2-18. Bulkhead with sand dike.

The sand dike alone would, according to Eq. (1–27), exert a pressure of 6950 lb.

The completion of the analysis is shown in Fig. 2–19. The Rankine's coefficients for the lower stratum are first determined thus

$$p_A = w \tan^2 (45° - \tfrac{1}{2}\phi) = 55 \tan^2 (45° - \tfrac{1}{2}24°) = 23.2 \text{ psf},$$

$$p_P = w \tan^2 (45° + \tfrac{1}{2}\phi) = 55 \tan^2 (45° + \tfrac{1}{2}24°) = 130.4 \text{ psf}.$$

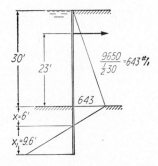

Fig. 2–19. Completion of analysis.

Next is found the point of equal active and passive intensities; thus,

$$643 + 23.2x = 130.4x,$$

$$x = 6 \text{ ft},$$

and finally the distance, x_1, from this point to the level of minimum penetration thus,

$$\tfrac{1}{2}x_1(130.4 - 23.2)x_1(29 + \tfrac{2}{3}x_1) = 9650 \times 13 + \tfrac{1}{6} \times 643 \times 25,$$

$$x_1 = 9.6 \text{ ft}.$$

The method of minimum penetration (often called *free earth support method*) will of course result in increased anchor tension and bending moment. For the above example these quantities will be, respectively, 6640 lb and 63,750 ft-lb.

PROBLEMS

2–1. It is known that the minimum penetration for this sheet-piling wall is 12 ft and that the maximum bending moment corresponding to this minimum penetration is 145,000 ft-lb. Find the angle of internal friction, ϕ, and the unit soil weight, w. The efficiency factor for the passive pressure is 1 and there is no water on either side of the sheet-piling wall. The anchor rods coincide with the top surface of the soil. (*Ans.*: $\phi = 33°$, $w = 92$ lb/cu ft.)

2–2. There is no water on either side of the sheet-piling wall shown and the active and passive pressures are according to Rankine's theory (efficiency factor is 1). It is known that the economical (or favorable depth) is 11.84 ft. Find distance from top surface to anchor rod when $\phi = 32°$ and $w = 100$ lb/cu ft. (*Ans.*: 8.86 ft.)

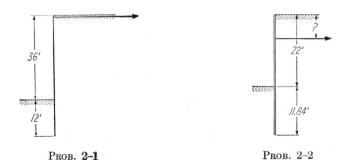

Prob. 2–1   Prob. 2–2

2–3. There is no water on either side of this anchored sheet-piling wall; the efficiency factor for the passive pressure is unity. Find minimum penetration, anchor tension, and corresponding maximum bending moment. (*Ans.*: 6290 ft-lb.)

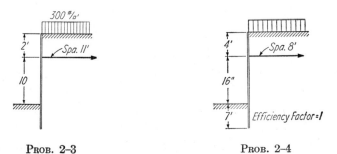

Prob. 2–3   Prob. 2–4

2–4. The surcharge on the top surface of this sheet piling wall has an intensity of 4.75 times the unit soil weight, w. It is known that the minimum penetration is 7 ft and that the corresponding anchor tension is 43,900 lb per rod. Find the soil weight, w, and the angle of internal friction, ϕ. (*Ans.*: $w = 105$ lb/cu ft, $\phi = 34°$.)

2–5. The sheet-piling units of a wall consist of MZ32 reinforced with four plates 4 in. $\times \frac{5}{8}$ in. welded to the flanges in the following manner: two on the outside away from the neutral axis, and two on the inside toward the neutral axis. Find the maximum bending moment that can be resisted by 1 lin ft of this wall if the allowable stress in bending is 21,000 psi. (*Ans.*: 108,500 ft-lb.)

2-6. There is no water on either side of the sheet-piling wall and the active and passive pressures are according to Rankine's theory. The angle of internal friction is 28° and the unit soil weight is 104 lb/cu ft. Find: (a) minimum penetration and corresponding maximum bending moment; (b) favorable penetration and its corresponding maximum bending moment. (*Ans.*: (a) 75,200 ft-lb, (b) 52,500 ft-lb.)

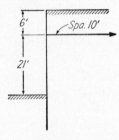

PROB. 2–6

CHAPTER 3

SOIL BEARING POWER

3–1. Introduction. The controlling factor in selection of the size of the contact area between a footing and the supporting soil may be either resistance to soil failure (transition from the state of plastic equilibrium to that of plastic flow) or resistance to excessive settlements. Examples of the first type of design are such substructures as bridge piers carrying statically determinate girders or trusses; no stresses in these would result from differential settlements of the piers, and the safety of the superstructure would depend on the safety against failure of the supporting soil. On the other hand, certain types of buildings, such as those having masonry walls and inadequate frames, may collapse completely because of differential settlements caused by normal consolidation of underlying strata.

Failure of an earth mass may be defined as loss of continuity due to the action of a shearing stress. The deeper the footing is placed, the less the danger of shear failure. Likewise, an increase in the size of the footing will always reduce the shearing stresses, even though the load intensity remains the same.

The settlement of foundations is due to two major causes: (1) a consolidation of the soil in place resulting from a decrease in volume of voids, and (2) a lateral flow of soil particles from under the substructure sometimes causing a bulge of the surrounding top surface. For the same load intensity, larger footings will generally settle more than smaller ones.

3–2. Types of Soil. Soil terminology has not been standardized and there is, at the present time, no definitely established engineering soil classification.

Subgrade materials upon which footings can be constructed may be divided into three main groups: rocks, granular soils (if uncemented also called cohesionless soils), and cohesive soils. The following classification is taken from the building code of Boston, Massachusetts.*

(1) Rocks:

Shale—A laminated, fine-textured, soft rock composed of consolidated clay or silt, which cannot be molded without the addition of water, but which can be reduced to a plastic condition by moderate grinding and mixing with water.

Slate—A dense, very fine-textured, soft rock which is readily split along cleavage planes into thin sheets and which cannot be reduced to a plastic condition by moderate grinding and mixing with water.

---

*See *Boston Building Code*, 1944, Sec. 2904.

Schist—A fine-textured, laminated rock with more or less wavy cleavage, containing mica or other flaky minerals.

(2) Granular Soils:

Gravel—An uncemented mixture of mineral grains $\frac{1}{4}$ in. or more in diam.

Sand—A type of soil possessing practically no cohesion when dry and consisting of mineral grains smaller than $\frac{1}{4}$ in. diam.

Coarse sand—A sand consisting chiefly of grains which will be retained on a 65-mesh sieve.

Find sand—A sand consisting chiefly of grains which will pass a 65-mesh sieve.

Compact gravel, compact sand—Deposits requiring picking for removal and offering high resistance to penetration by excavating tools.

Loose gravel, loose sand—Deposits readily removable by shoveling only.

(3) Cohesive Soils:

Hardpan—A thoroughly compact mixture of clay, sand, gravel, and boulders, for example boulder clay; or a cemented mixture of sand or of sand and gravel with or without boulders, and difficult to remove by picking.

Clay—A fine-grained, inorganic soil possessing sufficient cohesion when dry to form hard lumps which cannot readily be pulverized by the fingers.

Hard clay—A clay requiring picking for removal, a fresh sample of which cannot be molded in the fingers or can be molded only with the greatest difficulty.

Medium clay—A clay which can be removed by spading, a fresh sample of which can be molded by a substantial pressure of the fingers.

Soft clay—A clay which, when freshly sampled, can be molded under relatively slight pressure of the fingers.

Rock flour (inorganic silt)—A fine-grained, inorganic soil consisting chiefly of grains which will pass a 200-mesh sieve, and possessing sufficient cohesion when dry to form lumps which can readily be pulverized with the fingers.

It is readily seen that the definitions of the cohesive soils according to the Boston Building Code are somewhat indefinite. Other building codes are more specific. A notable example is that of the Chicago Building Code* which has the following definition of clay:

Clay. Cohesive soil, plastic within wide range of water content. The consistency of a clay shall be defined by the strength of a fairly undisturbed cylinder whose length is from 1.5 to 2 times its diameter, as follows:

Consistency	Unconfined Compressive Strength (psf)
Very soft	less than 700
Soft	700– 1180
Stiff	1200– 1980
Tough	2000– 3800
Very tough	4000– 7800
Hard	8000–15800

*Municipal Code of Chicago relating to Buildings, 1953, Sec. 70-2.1-(g).

A soil may consist of just one constituent part. It may be a pure sand, a pure silt, or a pure clay; or, it may consist of a mixture of two constituents in varying proportions; or, it may be made up of three constituent parts. Each of these parts may contribute certain physical properties to the mixture in much the same way as cement, water, and aggregates contribute to the properties of concrete.

A soil having a relatively even mixture of the different grades of sand and of silt and clay is called loam. According to the proportion of these ingredients, there are sandy loams, silty loams, and clayey loams.

Gumbo is a fine-grained soil, devoid of sand and rich in alkaline compounds. When fully saturated, it becomes impervious.

Quicksand is a condition and not a soil. Any fine-grained granular material carrying water under head is called quicksand. Since, in this case, sand grains lose weight because of buoyancy, they are very mobile and will flow from under a superimposed load. For equal conditions of upward flow of moisture the greatest loss of stability occurs in sands consisting of very small grains of uniform size.

In order to understand correctly the behavior of sand and clay under load, it is well to keep in mind the distinction between the internal structure of these soil types.

Sand is made up of comparatively large grains of angular shape; the pores in a sand mass are large and the volume of voids is relatively small.

Clay consists of minute and scaly grains; the pores are extremely small and the volume of voids is large. The internal surface area of a clay is extremely large, while a sand has a relatively small surface area.

3–3. Soil Properties. The stability and hence the structural properties of soil are determined to a large extent by the combined effects of internal friction and cohesion, which combine, in most subgrade materials, to make up the shearing resistance of soil. The combined effects are influenced by other factors such as capillarity, compressibility, and elasticity.

The internal friction has already been defined in Chap. 1 as the resistance of soil grains sliding over each other. If frictional resistance is plotted against the load on the sliding plane, the result is a straight line. The coefficient of internal friction is the ratio of sliding resistance to pressure upon the sliding plane. This slope is the tangent of the angle of internal friction.

Sands possess internal friction in appreciable amount. When sand grains are subjected to pressure with restrictions to lateral flow, each grain becomes more intimately embedded with surrounding grains and the number of points of contact is increased. Hence, the internal friction increases with pressure. Clays, with their small, smooth, and scalelike grains, do not possess any appreciable internal friction.

Cohesion may be defined as the binding force which holds soil grains together. There are two kinds of cohesion in soils: (1) true cohesion, caused by the mutual attraction of particles due to molecular forces, as in rocks; (2) apparent cohesion due to the presence of water films, as in fine wet sand. As a general rule, true cohesion is not present in ordinary soils and may be ignored. Hence, the cohesive force in a particular soil will vary with its moisture content. Cohesion is very high in clay, but of little or no significance in silt and sand.

Typical values for the angle of internal friction have already been given in the first chapter of this volume. The cohesion in clay may vary from 200 to 3000 psf.

Capillarity may be defined as the property of soil to transmit water through its pores in all directions, even counter to the direction of the force of gravity. Capillarity results from capillary pressure, which is the pressure exerted by the surface tension of water at the end of a soil tube, or pore.

Since capillary pressure is inversely proportional to the diameter of the pore, and since the diameter of the pore is dependent upon the diameter of soil grains, it follows that capillarity will vary inversely as the diameter of the grain. The rate of transmission of capillary water depends on the ratio of the internal surface area in the pores to the area of the opening.

Sands, with their very large grain diameters and, likewise, large pore diameters, possess very low surface tension or capillary pressure. Therefore, they have no appreciable capillarity. Cohesive clay soils, having the smallest particle size and hence the smallest pore diameter, possess high capillarity.

Compressibility may be defined as the decrease in volume resulting from an increase of pressure. The decrease in volume of a soil mass is, almost entirely, due to a reduction in its volume of voids. Sands are the least compressible, while clays possess a much higher degree of compressibility.

Elasticity may be defined as the ability of a soil to return to its original volume after the release of pressure. No soil will ever return completely to its original volume, since soils are not completely elastic in the sense of Hooke's law. Sands have little or no elasticity; silts and some clays have relatively large elastic qualities.

3–4. Methods of Underground Exploration. Knowledge of the soil conditions under and adjacent to a proposed structure must be obtained before any preliminary and final design can be made. This will necessitate some investigation of the site before a preliminary design is made, and a systematic examination before the final plans are prepared. The object of the underground exploration is usually the determination of a cross section of the ground showing the depth to the top of each stratum, its thickness, and the type of soil. Furthermore, the ground water level should be established and shown, as well as the compactness or hardness of each soil stratum encountered.

It is highly desirable to supplement the soil profile with samples representative of each soil stratum. The underground exploration, therefore, often aims not only to provide data relative to the boundaries between essentially different materials but also to obtain samples of the various strata for laboratory analysis and testing. In view of the increased attention being given to the testing of soils, it is important to obtain these samples relatively undisturbed.

Methods of underground exploration can be divided into the following three groups,* soundings, borings, and test pits.

The simplest type of exploration is that done by driving a sounding rod of steel, usually $\frac{3}{4}$ to 1 in. diam, with a sledge hammer or a drop weight. The rod consists of sections, 4 to 5 ft long, connected by couplings, the bottom section being pointed and the top section fitting into a driving cap. In shallow ground, the depths to rock may be explored in this way but the method is extremely limited in its application, as no information is obtained regarding the types of soil passed through. Refusal does not necessarily indicate that rock has been reached. To avoid mistaking a large boulder for bedrock, further soundings should be made nearby.

By making borings in the soil, a relatively small hole is made in the ground and the soil is brought to the surface by means of tools extended to the bottom of the hole. If the soil sample is recovered from wash water used in the operation of the drill, the method is generally called *wash boring*. The removed material is brought to the surface by a stream of water flowing under pressure through the hollow drill. Samples are taken by trapping this material and allowing it to settle in buckets. Wash borings may be useful in some instances to show the elevation of a rock surface, but they are often useless because they give no information about the compactness of the materials. Furthermore, they reveal the materials penetrated only in a very disturbed state, generally with a considerable amount of the finer particles washed away. Also they give no information about underground water conditions.

Samples taken by auger borings are better and more reliable than wash samples. They may be considerably disturbed, but the grains have not been separated by the action of water. Auger borings can be made in cohesive soils and some granular soils above water level. The auger

---

*See H. A. Mohr, "Exploration of Soil Conditions and Sampling Operation," *Bulletin No. 4* (Graduate School of Engineering, Harvard University).

bores the hole and is withdrawn when filled with solid material. Usually a casing is used for lining the hole.

Undisturbed samples may be obtained by sinking a casing of large diameter (say, 6 in.), usually by the wash boring process, and forcing a core barrel into the material at the bottom of the hole.

Complete information about the geological structure of the ground

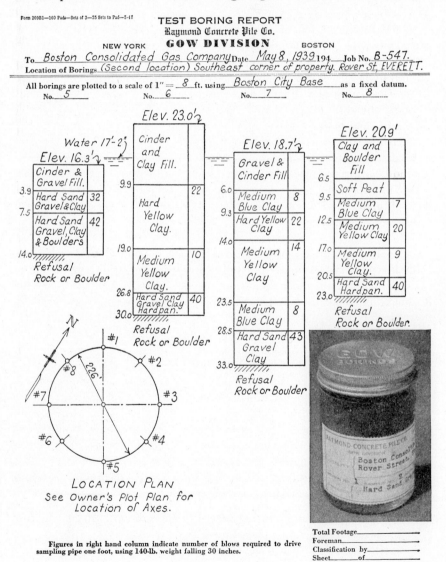

Typical soil exploration report and soil sample. (Courtesy of Raymond Concrete Pile Co.)

can be obtained by means of test pits. These are shafts excavated to a size that a man can dig in them. It will generally be necessary to use wood or steel sheeting. In a test pit the materials can be inspected directly and adequate samples are easily secured. If ground water is encountered during the construction of the test pit, it may be necessary to use a compressed air caisson or some other water-lowering process.

3–5. Interpretation of Boring Data. In interpreting the results of soil exploration it should be remembered that no methods, except core drilling or test pits, afford an opportunity to observe the material in its natural undisturbed condition. Thus wash borings will bring the material to the surface more or less in suspension and have, therefore, a tendency to show the soil coarser than it actually is. Clay may appear as fine sand and sand as fine gravel.

Needless to say, the results of the exploration should be presented in a complete and accurate report, accompanied by a survey plot of the ground locating the positions of the bore holes. Cross sections of the soil strata (soil profiles) are indispensable for a comprehensive study of the data obtained, and often samples from borings at the various elevations are preserved in glass containers and clearly labeled as to location and elevation.

The elevation of the lowest ground water level is of importance, especially if a pile foundation is contemplated, for this elevation fixes the point above which timber piling should not usually extend. In this connection it should be remembered that the ground water table generally slopes upward away from a stream.

From a study of the soil exploration report the substructure designer will decide the type of foundation that in his judgment presents the best solution. In making this decision the field engineer, who conducted the soil exploration, is often called upon to make a definite recommendation. Furthermore, it may be advisable during the actual construction to make field observations relative to the validity of the conclusions drawn from a study of the soil profile. Sometimes discrepancies between assumptions and actual conditions have been discovered, and it has been possible to make appropriate changes in the design before it was too late.*

The ground conditions at a pier or building site will usually be found to be one of the following three types:

(1) Rock may be present very close to the ground surface. In this case footings can be placed directly on it.

(2) Rock may exist at some elevation below the ground surface, but

---

*See Karl Terzaghi, "Recording Results of Field Tests on Soils," *Civil Engineering* (December, 1943), p. 585.

at a distance that can be reached most economically by a special type of substructure such as piles or caissons.

(3) The distance down to the nearest rock stratum may be so great that it cannot be reached by conventional forms of substructures. In this case the foundation must be constructed upon the unconsolidated material overlying the rock.

Fig. 3–1 shows a typical boring section at a proposed building site, where the underlying material is such as to require foundations bearing on rock for the support of a heavy superstructure.* The following is a brief account of the conclusions drawn from the study of several soil profiles similar to the one shown.

The strata above the thick layer of clay were considered incapable of sustaining the anticipated pressures due mainly to the fact that adjacent buildings founded on concrete piles driven into these sand strata had undergone some differential settlements.

The clay stratum varied greatly in thickness and in some cases was almost nonexistent. The layer immediately over the rock consisted of water-bearing sand, gravel, and boulders. For these reasons it was considered imperative that the foundation should be carried down to rock. As the distance to rock was considerable and the intervening material of questionable stability, it required special methods to reach bedrock.

Several types of substructure were considered, outlined briefly as follows:

(1) Steel bearing piles consisting of rolled sections and estimated capable of carrying 65 tons each.

(2) Concrete-filled steel tubes estimated capable of carrying 154 tons each. The proposed dimensions for the steel tubes were 20-in. diam and ½-in. thickness.

(3) Caissons consisting of 5-ft diam shells sunk to rock by pneumatic methods and filled by concrete.

(4) Drilled-in caissons, socketed into the rock and provided with a rolled section inside, the space between the structural steel section and the outside shell being filled with concrete. The diameter of the shell was 30 in. and the structural steel section varied with the load to be transmitted, the maximum load being 1275 tons for one caisson.

The soil profile in the preceding example indicated definitely the desirability of extending the substructure to the elevation of rock. From previous experience the designers were also able to propose four practicable methods of reaching this elevation. Cost estimates favored the use of the drilled-in caissons, which method was finally adopted.

*See C. B. Spencer, "Drilled-in Caissons with Heavy H-Cores Carry 16-Story, Navy Warehouse," *Engineering News-Record* (September 25, 1941), p. 69.

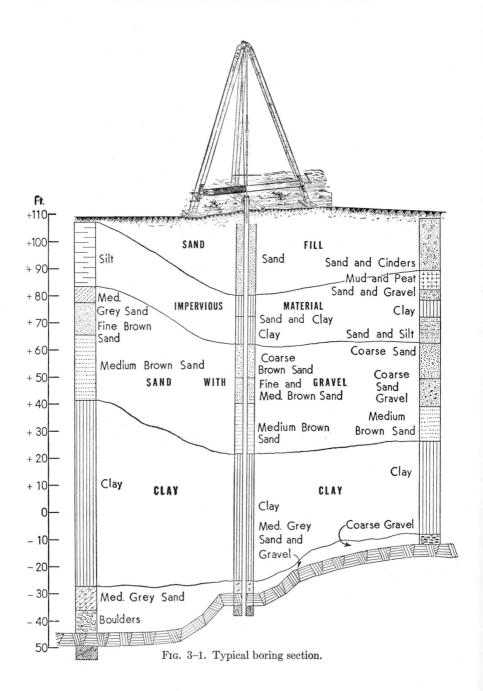

Fig. 3–1. Typical boring section.

3–6. Frost-Free Depth. Most building specifications require that important footings shall be placed at depths to which freezing cannot penetrate. In order to guard against frost action the ground surface should generally be from 3 to 4 ft above the bottoms of the footings, depending of course upon the severity of the climate.

Frost action in soils consists of the following: in winter the frost will raise the ground level in certain places; and in the spring the ground at the same places will soften up and settle back. The first phase of this is called *frost heave* and is caused by the formation of segregated ice layers in the soil. The ice crystals are built up of water drawn from the immediately adjacent soil. It follows that the vertical movements may become particularly aggravated in soils of high capillarity. Observations have revealed that there are practically no heaves in sands or heavy clays, whereas silty soils suffer most from frost action. Large soil particles prevent ice segregation. The critical diameter of particles as far as heave danger is concerned is about 0.02 mm.

Frost action is not limited to the process of heave when the weather again becomes warmer, the frozen soil thaws and the excess water transforms the soil into a liquid mud unable to support the load upon it.

A safe design should place the footings, except for minor structures, at least 4 ft below an adjoining surface exposed to natural or artificial freezing. Artificial freezing may occur under the basement floor in a cold storage warehouse. Foundations for smaller structures, such as garages or buildings of less than 600 sq ft in area and not over one story high, can generally be placed 1 ft below an adjoining surface exposed to freezing, if the underlying soil to a depth of at least 4 ft beneath the surface is clean sand and gravel. No foundation shall, of course, be placed on frozen soil.*

3–7. Soil Bearing Tests. One of the most important problems in connection with substructure design is to determine the safe load which can be applied on a foundation. Methods of evaluating the load-supporting value of soils vary from complex formulas dependent on laboratory tests of cohesion, internal friction, soil weight, and surcharge to simple field loading tests and sometimes only visual inspection of soil samples.

Tests to determine the allowable bearing values of soils are generally made by excavating a test pit down to the elevation on which the foundation is to rest, measuring the settlements due to loads applied to a bearing plate, and determining the ultimate pressure intensity which can be sustained before rupture of the underlying soil occurs.* The safe bearing power of the soil will then equal the ultimate bearing power divided by the safety factor (for instance 1.5 or 2).

Boston Building Code, Sec. 2902(c).

Fig. 3–2 shows a typical arrangement for making soil bearing tests.* The loads are placed on a platform supported on a post, through which the applied loads are transferred to a bearing plate. The platform is held in the proper position by wedges loosely placed against the sheeting. Sand covers the bottom of the test pit in order to protect the subsoil from

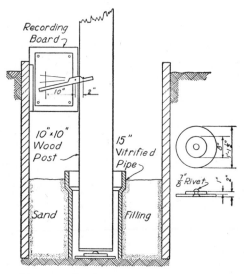

FIG. 3–2. Load-testing apparatus for soil.

drying out and against undue disturbances. Settlements are determined by sighting with an engineer's level on a rod attached to the platform, or by a recording device similar to the one shown in Fig. 3–2. The load is applied in increments and settlements are observed.

Fig. 3–3 shows a typical load-settlement diagram, which generally has

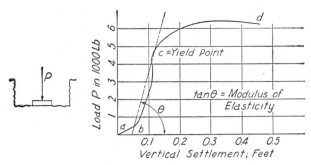

FIG. 3–3. Typical load-settlement diagram.

*Proc. A.S.C.E. (August, 1920), p. 908.

three characteristic parts. Thus, *ab* represents initial compression, caused by reconsolidation of the soil which has been loosened in excavating the pit; *bc* represents the true elastic curve of the soil; while *cd* indicates the breaking down of the soil after the elastic limit is passed. After this full curve has been developed, the test should be repeated with an ultimate load somewhat smaller than the point *c* and this left in place for some time. If this continued application of a load without additional increments causes continued deflection, a still lower load should be tried.

Where it is proposed to impose a certain load per square foot under the foundation, the New York Building Code requires that this load be first applied and allowed to remain undisturbed until no settlement occurs during a period of 24 hr, measurements or readings being taken once each 24 hr or oftener in order to determine the rate of settlement. Thereafter an additional 50 per cent excess load shall be applied and the rate of settlement of this total load similarly determined.

As the value of the shearing stress is proportional to the load intensity on the foundation, it is seen that the values of the shearing stress under the loading platform and the shearing stress under the actual structure are equal. The shearing resistance under the loading platform, however, is smaller than the shearing resistance under the structure, as this quantity is a function of the total load. Hence, the ultimate bearing value as determined by the loading test should be on the safe side.

The lack of restraint around the bearing plate in Fig. 3–2 also tends to make this arrangement yield too conservative values. The effect upon the strains under the bearing plate due to the presence or absence of surrounding restraint is shown in Fig. 3–4. This has been the cause of adopting

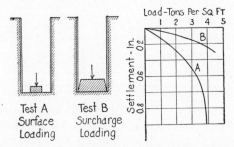

Test A   Test B
Surface   Surcharge
Loading   Loading

FIG. 3–4. Effects of surcharge on bearing capacity of sand.

in some building specifications the provision that the loading area shall be the full size of the pit.

Loading tests are of little value unless properly correlated with other factors. The smaller loads applied in the test will affect a comparatively small region, while the actual foundation pressures will influence a large mass of earth. Soft layers occurring below the test level, while not appreciably changing the deflections during the test, will greatly increase the deformations under the building foundation. Therefore, before the foundation can be designed, it is necessary to know the soil characteristics at depths considerably below the foundation level. Requirements of this nature, as well as of size of loaded area and its depth below the ground surface, have been incorporated in the Boston Building Code. Excerpts from this code dealing with load tests of bearing materials will be given at the end of the succeeding section.

3–8. Other Soil Tests. Of the various laboratory tests made on soils, shear tests are of especial importance to the designer of substructures. From these tests are determined the angle of internal friction and, in case of cohesive soils, also the initial cohesion (see Fig. 1–2).

Shear tests may be made as direct shear tests, in which case the apparatus consists of two sections with the sample placed between. The lower section is held rigidly on a testing platform; the upper section consists of a movable frame and piston. Vertical and horizontal loads are applied to the upper frame and transmitted through the soil sample. The test is repeated for several samples and a diagram is obtained giving the relationship between normal force and shearing resistance.*

The triaxial compression tests can be used as a means of measuring shearing strength. It is analogous to the compression test of concrete cylinders and is made in the same manner. Both cohesionless and cohesive soils can be tested by this method. The soil sample is enclosed in an airtight rubber membrane and placed in a vessel under hydrostatic pressure (usually glycerin); a vertical load is then applied longitudinally until rupture occurs. The state of stress in the soil sample at the point of failure is determined from the relationship between the principal stresses or from Mohr's circle of stress.†

3–9. Theoretical Investigations. Fig. 3–5 shows possible failure lines under a footing resting on an earth mass. Final rupture of the soil may develop as shown in Fig. 3–5(a), where a wedge of earth directly under the base is compressed and moves downward, while the material outside of the wedge moves downward under compression, as well as outward and upward along surfaces on which the shearing resistance has been exceeded. Rupture may also occur, as shown in Fig. 3–5(b), by shearing failure along some curved surface extending from one edge of the footing down through the soil and then up to some point of the top surface.

---

*See D. P. Krynine, *Soil Mechanics* (New York, 1947), p. 151.

†See J. D. Watson, "The Technique of Triaxial Compression Tests," *Civil Engineering* (1939), Vol. 9, p. 731.

The lateral earth pressure theories, which were discussed in the first chapter, can be used for developing relationships involving the allowable bearing pressure and the size and depth below surface of a footing.

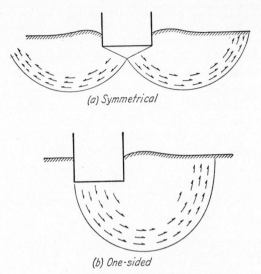

(a) Symmetrical

(b) One-sided

FIG. 3–5. Shear failures under footings.

As a first approximation assume a footing AB resting in a cohesionless soil as shown in Fig. 3–6. Due to the weight of the structure there is a pressure, p, on the contact area. To sustain this direct pressure on the

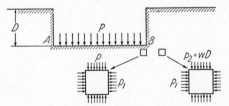

FIG. 3–6. Rankine's method.

earth below the footing, a lateral pressure, p_1, is required which, according to Eq. (1–14), is equal to

$$p_1 = p \tan^2 \left(45° - \frac{\phi}{2}\right) \tag{3-1}$$

where ϕ is the angle of internal friction. The lateral pressure p_1 must in turn be sustained by a third pressure, p_2, at right angles to p_1 as shown in the enlarged view of an element near point B in Fig. 3–6. Therefore,

$$p_2 = p_1 \tan^2 \left(45° - \frac{\phi}{2}\right) = p \tan^4 \left(45° - \frac{\phi}{2}\right) \tag{3-2}$$

The pressure p_2 must be produced by the weight of a column of earth, D in length where D is the depth below the surface. Hence if w denotes the weight of a cubic foot of earth, $p_2 = wD$, or

$$D = \frac{p}{w}\tan^4\left(45° - \frac{\phi}{2}\right), \qquad (3\text{--}3)$$

which will determine for a cohesionless material, such as sand or loose fill, the theoretical minimum depth below the surface.

As a numerical example, let it be desired to find the depth below the top surface of a wall footing supported in loose sand weighing 100 lb/cu ft and having an angle of internal friction equal to 35°. The pressure under the footing is 4000 psf and the factor of safety should be 2. From Eq. (3–3) it is seen that

$$D = 2\,\frac{4000}{100}\tan^4\left(45° - \tfrac{1}{2}35°\right),$$

$$D = 5.87 \text{ ft.}$$

In the case of a cohesive soil, an analysis, similar to the above but based on the relationship expressed for Eq. (1–12), will result in a formula for the minimum depth corresponding to Eq. (3–3), namely,

$$D = \frac{p}{w}\tan^4\left(45° - \frac{\phi}{2}\right) - \frac{2c}{w} \times \frac{\tan\left(45° - \tfrac{1}{2}\phi\right)}{\cos^2\left(45° - \tfrac{1}{2}\phi\right)}, \qquad (3\text{--}4)$$

where c is the unit cohesion of the soil. If in the formula the substitution $\phi = 0$ and $D = 0$ is made, $p = 4c$, which indicates that the bearing capacity of the top surface of a pure clay is equal to four times the unit cohesion. The approximate approach to a theoretical formula for soil bearing pressure as expressed by Eqs. (3–3) and (3–4) is often called Rankine's method.

A closer approximation to actual conditions can be made by taking into account the size of the footing as shown in Fig. 3–7. The resulting formula is called Terzaghi's formula.*

Fig. 3–7 shows a footing of width B resting on top of a deep stratum of cohesive soil and transmitting through its contact surface a pressure of intensity p. Overlying this stratum is another one having a depth D and unit weight w. It is assumed that the manner of failure of the soil is similar to that shown in Fig. 3–5 and that the curved rupture surfaces can be approximated by four straight lines as indicated in Fig. 3–7(a). From an examination of this figure it is seen that failure consists of a downward sliding along SN (active pressure) and upward sliding along NT (passive pressure). When the soil is on the verge of failure the active pressure to

_____

*See C. A. Hogentogler and Karl Terzaghi, "Interrelationship of Load, Road and Subgrade," *Public Roads* (May, 1929), Vol. 10, p. 51.

the left of MN must be exactly equal to the passive pressure to the right of MN.

It was found in the first chapter, Eq. (1–9), that the critical angle for active earth pressure is $45° + \frac{1}{2}\phi$. The distance to point N is, therefore,

$$MN = \frac{B}{2} \tan\left(45° + \frac{\phi}{2}\right) = \frac{B}{2 \tan\left(45° - \frac{1}{2}\phi\right)} \tag{3–5}$$

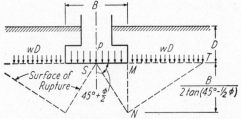

(a) Nomenclature and Manner of Failure

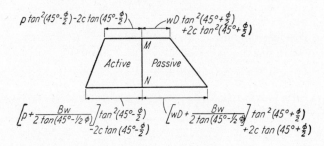

(b) Equality of Active and Passive Pressures

Fig. 3–7. Terzaghi's formula.

The diagrams representing active and passive earth pressures on MN are shown in Fig. 3–7(b), the intensities having been computed from Eqs. (1–12) and (1–13). Because the two trapezoids must have the same area, the sums of the parallel sides must be equal; thus,

$$\left[2p + \frac{Bw}{2 \tan\left(45° - \frac{1}{2}\phi\right)}\right] \tan^2\left(45° - \frac{\phi}{2}\right) - 4c \tan\left(45° - \frac{\phi}{2}\right)$$

$$= \left[2wD + \frac{Bw}{2 \tan\left(45° - \frac{1}{2}\phi\right)}\right] \tan^2\left(45° + \frac{\phi}{2}\right) + 4c \tan\left(45° + \frac{\phi}{2}\right)$$

Solving for p gives

$$p = \frac{Dw}{\tan^4\left(45° - \frac{1}{2}\phi\right)} + \frac{2c}{\tan\left(45° - \frac{1}{2}\phi\right) \sin^2\left(45° - \frac{1}{2}\phi\right)}$$

$$+ \frac{Bw}{4 \tan^5\left(45° - \frac{1}{2}\phi\right)} \left[1 - \tan^4\left(45° - \frac{1}{2}\phi\right)\right] \tag{3–6}$$

A formula similar to the above can be derived if it is assumed that the surface of rupture can be approximated by two 90° arcs as shown in Fig. 3–8, and that movement is prevented by shearing stresses acting in the clockwise direction. The first part of the analysis will deal with the case of cohesionless soil.

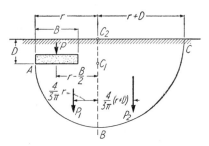

FIG. 3–8. Surface of rupture approximated by 90° arcs.

The shearing resistance of a small element of the failure line (Fig. 3–9) is $N \tan \phi$, N being the normal pressure intensity. If only the unit weight, w, of the overlying soil is considered, it is seen from Fig. 3–9 that the total vertical force acting on an infinitesimal element will be $wr^2 \sin^2 \theta \, d\theta$ and the normal component will be $wr^2 \sin^3 \theta \, d\theta$.

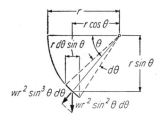

FIG. 3–9. Forces acting on element of rupture surface.

The footing load, P, will further increase the shearing resistance on portions of the surface of rupture immediately below the footing. In computing its effects, cognizance is taken of investigations* which indicate that the radius, r, of arc AB is only slightly smaller than the footing width. It will therefore be assumed that P is uniformly distributed over the horizontal projection of arc AB. The normal component on an infinitesimal element will be $P \sin^2 \theta \, d\theta$.

If moments are taken about the center of arc AB (except that shearing stresses along arc BC are referred to its center), the following equation will result:

$$P\left(r - \frac{B}{2}\right) = \int_0^{\pi/2} wr^3 \sin^3 \theta \tan \phi \, d\theta + \int_0^{\pi/2} P \sin^2 \theta \tan \phi \, r \, d\theta$$

$$+ \int_0^{\pi/2} w(r + D)^3 \sin^3 \theta \tan \phi \, d\theta + \frac{w}{3} [(r + D)^3 - r^3],$$

---

*See Paul Andersen, "Shear Failures under Footings," *Civil Engineering* (1944), Vol. 14, No. 8, p. 360.

in which D is the depth of bottom of footing below the ground surface. The last term represents the difference between the moments of forces P_1 and P_2 (earth weights involved in movement). Completing the integrations and solving for b gives

$$B = r\left(2 - \frac{\pi}{2}\tan\phi\right) - \frac{2w}{3P}\left[r^3(2\tan\phi - 1) + (r + D)^3(2\tan\phi + 1)\right]. \quad (3\text{-}7)$$

To each value of r will correspond a value of footing width B over which the foundation pressure P must be distributed in order to avoid failures along the corresponding circular arcs. The most dangerous failure line is the one which gives the largest value of B. If b is large enough to prevent failure along this line, it will automatically satisfy all other failure lines. Placing the first derivative of b with respect to r equal to zero gives

$$r^2 - \frac{2\tan\phi + 1}{2\tan\phi}Dr + \frac{2\tan\phi + 1}{4\tan\phi}D^2 + \frac{P}{w} \times \frac{\pi\tan\phi - 4}{16\tan\phi} = 0. \quad (3\text{-}8)$$

Eqs. (3-7) and (3-8) can be used to determine for a cohesionless soil the footing width needed to sustain a given load at a given depth when weight of soil and angle of internal friction are known.

In the case of a cohesive soil the shearing resistance along ABC will be increased by cohesive forces. If c is the unit cohesion for the soil, the total moment with respect to the center of the cohesive forces acting tangentially to a 90° arc is

$$\int_0^{\pi/2} cr\,d\theta\,r = \frac{\pi}{2}cr^2.$$

If this expression is added to the right side of Eq. (3-7), for cohesive soils b can be determined from

$$B = r\left(2 - \frac{\pi}{2}\tan\phi\right) - \frac{2w}{3P}\left[r^3(2\tan\phi - 1) + (r + D)^3(2\tan\phi + 1)\right]$$

$$- \pi\frac{c}{P}\left[r^2 + (r + D)^2\right], \quad (3\text{-}9)$$

while r is found from

$$r^2 - \frac{2\tan\phi + 1}{2\tan\phi}Dr + \frac{\pi c}{2w\tan\phi}r + \frac{2\tan\phi + 1}{4\tan\phi}D^2$$

$$+ \frac{P}{w} \times \frac{\pi\tan\phi - 4}{16\tan\phi} + \frac{\pi c}{4w\tan\phi} = 0. \quad (3\text{-}10)$$

3-10. Factor Affecting Soil Bearing Capacity. The formulas derived in the preceding section can be used for illustrating the relative influence exerted by cohesion and internal friction upon the stability of soils without claiming to furnish values suitable for design. The formulas can also be used to demonstrate the influence of such factors as the width of the loaded area and its depth below the ground surface.

In order to ascertain the effect of cohesion, consider a footing resting on the top of a purely cohesive soil. In this case $\phi = 0$; $D = 0$. If these values are substituted in Eq. (3–6) it is seen that

$$p = 4c, \qquad (3\text{–}11)$$

or the bearing capacity, according to Terzaghi's formula, will equal four times the unit cohesion. It also follows from this formula that for a purely cohesive soil the ultimate bearing capacity is independent of the width of the footing.

If in Eqs. (3–9) and (3–10) $\phi = 0$ and $D = 0$ are substituted, it will be found that

$$p = \frac{P}{B} = 2\pi c = 6.3c, \qquad (3\text{–}12)$$

or the bearing capacity, according to the method of circular arcs is somewhat higher (but still of the same order) than found by Terzaghi's formula, and that for a purely cohesive soil the bearing capacity is independent of the size of the footing.

For a cohesionless soil larger footings will sustain higher pressure intensities. The increase in bearing capacity due to an increase in width of footing is shown in Fig. 3–10. In Eq. (3–6) have been substituted $c = 0$, $D = 0$, $w = 100$ lb/cu ft. The results for typical angles of internal

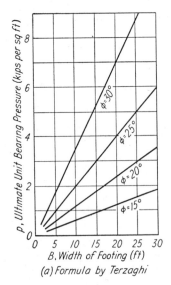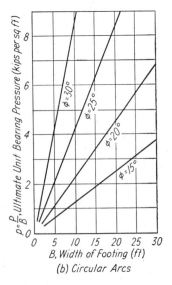

FIG. 3–10. Influence of footing size on soil bearing capacity.

friction have been shown in Fig. 3–10(*a*). If the same values are substituted in Eqs. (3–9) and (3–10) another set of straight lines will result which have been shown in Fig. 3–10(*b*). Thus it is seen that for a cohesionless soil the pressure intensity will be directly proportional to the footing width.

The bearing capacity will also increase with the depth of the footing below the top surface as indicated by both methods.

3–11. Numerical Examples. The angle of internal friction encountered in practice ranges anywhere between $\phi = 2°$ for very soft fat clay and $\phi = 34°$ and more for very well-compacted mixed sands. The angle of internal friction for stiff clays may be represented approximately by $\phi = 9°$. If these values are substituted in Eq. (3–6), it becomes

$$\phi = 2°; \quad p = 1.15Dw + 4.29c + 0.04Bw. \tag{3–13}$$

$$\phi = 9°; \quad p = 1.88Dw + 5.55c + 0.26Bw. \tag{3–14}$$

$$\phi = 34°; \quad p = 12.5Dw + 17.07c + 5.41Bw. \tag{3–15}$$

It should be noted that the first term on the right-hand side contains the weight per unit volume, w. This fact calls to attention the effect of a rise in the ground-water level on the bearing capacity of cohesionless sands. If the water rises near to the surface of the ground, the specific gravity of the sand decreases on account of the hydrostatic uplift; as a consequence, the bearing capacity also decreases. For $D = 0$, $c = 0$ (cohesionless sand, no surcharge), the rise of the ground water to the bottom of the footing should theoretically reduce the bearing capacity by about 38 per cent. This is so because the first two terms in Eq. (3–6) will equal zero, and the value of w for dry material and for wet material will be in the ratio of 2.65 to 1.65. (The specific gravity of sand may be assumed to be 2.65, and it becomes 1.65 when buoyed by water.) This is a reduction of approximately 38 per cent in effective weight and also in bearing value.

The same reduction will result if the method of circular arcs is used. If $D = 0$ is substituted in Eqs. (3–9) and (3–10) the following expression will be found:

$$p = \frac{P}{B} = \frac{18 \tan \phi}{\left(2 - \frac{\pi}{2} \tan \phi\right)^3} \, bw, \tag{3–16}$$

which also indicates direct proportionality between soil bearing power and unit weight.

The formulas developed for pressure intensities give ultimate values at which rupture will occur. If they are applied to design of footings, suitable factors of safety should be used.

Example 1. It is desired to find the footing width for a load $P = 50$ kips resting on top of a cohesive soil possessing the following characteristics: $c = 2$ ksf, $\phi = 9°$, $w = 100$ lb/cu ft. Substituting in Eq. (3–14) gives

$$\frac{50}{B} = 11.1 + 0.026B; \quad B = 4.45 \text{ ft.}$$

Substituting in Eqs. (3–9) and (3–10) gives $r = 3.42$ ft and $B = 3.05$. The load intensity before rupture of soil is, according to Terzaghi's formula, $50,000 \div 4.45 = 11,236$ psf, and according to the method of circular arcs, $50,000 \div 3.05 = 16,393$ psf.

Example 2. The soil characteristics are the same as in the preceding example. Find the footing width for $P = 200$ kips. Substituting again in Eq. (3–14) gives

$$\frac{200}{B} = 11.1 + 0.026B; \quad B = 17.31 \text{ ft,}$$

and substituting in Eqs. (3–9) and (3–10) gives $r = 13.07$ ft and $B = 12.16$ ft. The load intensity for the larger load is $200,000 \div 17.31 = 11,554$ psf, according to Terzaghi's formula, and $200,000 \div 12.16 = 16,452$ psf. Because the soil has relatively small internal friction the pressure intensity increases but slightly for the larger footing according to both methods.

3–12. Building Specifications. It is universally recognized that it is impossible to assign to soils allowable bearing pressures which can be used under all circumstances for small and large footings alike and at all depths below the ground surface. Furthermore, few soils can be placed in any of the classifications listed in Sec. 3–2. A sand is generally clayey or silty and a clay is frequently sandy or stony. Nevertheless, all current building codes contain a table of tentative soil bearing values similar to Table 3–1, which is part of the Boston Building Code. Another table (that of New York City) is part of Appendix 6.

The Boston Building Code takes into account the results of the theoretical formulas which were discussed in Sec. 3–10. The following paragraphs are excerpts from this code:

(1) The tabulated bearing values for rocks of Classes 1 to 3 inclusive shall apply where the loaded area is less than 2 ft below the lowest adjacent surface of sound rock. Where the loaded area is more than 2 ft below such surface, these values may be increased 20 per cent for each foot of additional depth but shall not exceed twice the tabulated values.

(2) The allowable bearing values of materials of Classes 4 to 9 inclusive may exceed the tabulated values by $2\frac{1}{2}$ per cent for each foot of depth of the loaded area below the lowest ground surface immediately adjacent, but shall not exceed twice the tabulated values. For areas of foundation smaller than 3 ft in least lateral dimension, the allowable bearing values shall be one-third of the allowable bearing values multiplied by the least lateral dimension in feet.

TABLE 3–1

Tentative Soil Bearing Values, Boston Building Code

Class	Material	Allowable Bearing Value (Tons/Sq Ft)
1	Massive bedrock without laminations, such as granite, diorite, and other granitic rocks; and also gneiss, trap rock, felsite, and thoroughly cemented conglomerates, such as the Roxbury Puddingstone, all in sound condition (sound condition allows some cracks)........................	100
2	Laminated rocks such as slate and schist, in sound condition (some cracks allowed)...............................	35
3	Shale in sound condition (some cracks allowed)...........	10
4	Residual deposits of shattered or broken bedrock of any kind except shale.......................................	10
5	Hardpan...	10
6	Gravel, sand-gravel mixtures, compact..................	5
7	Gravel, sand-gravel mixtures, loose, sand, coarse, compact..	4
8	Sand, coarse, loose; sand, fine, compact.................	3
9	Sand, fine, loose......................................	1
10	Hard clay...	6
11	Medium clay...	4
12	Soft clay..	1
13	Rock flour, shattered shale, or any deposit of unusual character not provided for herein........................	(Value to be fixed by the Commissioner)

(3)   The tabulated bearing values for Classes 10 to 12 inclusive apply only to pressures directly under individual footings, walls, and piers. When structures are founded on or underlain by deposits of these classes, the total load over the area of any one bay or other major portion of the structure, minus the weight of the excavated material, divided by the area, shall not exceed one-half the tabulated bearing values.

(4)   Where bearing materials directly under a foundation overlie a stratum having smaller allowable bearing values, these smaller values shall not be exceeded at the level of such stratum. Computation of the vertical pressure in the bearing materials at any depth below a foundation shall be made on the assumption that the load is spread uniformly at an angle of 60° with the horizontal; but the area considered as supporting the load shall not extend beyond the intersection of 60° planes of adjacent foundations.

(5)   Where portions of the foundation of an entire structure rest directly upon or are underlain by medium or soft clay or rock flour, and other portions rest upon different materials, or where the layers of such softer materials vary greatly in thickness, the magnitude and distribution of the probable settlement shall be investigated; and, if necessary, the allowable loads shall be reduced or special provisions be made in the design of the structure to prevent dangerous differential settlements.

It is generally recognized that many buildings carry but a small part of the live load for which they are designed, and which is used in the computations of the loadings to be brought upon the foundations. Thus, office buildings are designed for a live load of say 50 psf; there is probably no office building that has half that live load, considering the building as a whole. Apartment houses are often designed for 40 psf, while one-third of that figure would be a much closer approximation of the actual loading. On the other hand structures such as warehouses, garages, and manufacturing plants very often support the live loads for which they were designed and, in some cases, far greater loads.

Building specifications usually require the full live loads to be included in the evaluation of the foundation loads, and sometimes exclude all or parts of the loads caused by wind pressure. Thus, the Boston Building Code* has the following provisions:

(1) The loads to be used in computing the maximum pressure upon bearing materials under foundations shall be the live and dead loads of the structure, including the weight of the foundations, but excluding loads from overlying soil.

(2) Eccentricity of loading in foundation shall be fully investigated and the maximum pressure shall not exceed the allowable bearing values.

(3) Where the pressure on the bearing material due to wind is less than 25 per cent of that due to dead and live loads, it may be neglected in the design. Where this ratio exceeds 25 per cent, foundations shall be so proportioned that the pressure due to combined dead, live, and wind loads shall not exceed the allowable bearing values by more than 25 per cent.

In order to correlate the results made by bearing tests to the actual conditions of the foundation, the Boston Building Code makes the following recommendations relative to load tests of bearing materials;† the soil classification refers to Table 3–1.

(1) For bearing materials of Classes 1 to 5 inclusive, the loaded area shall be at least 1 sq ft and for other classes at least 4 sq ft. For materials of Classes 6 to 13 inclusive, the loaded area shall be the full size of the pit and at such depth that the ratio of the width of the loaded area to its depth below the immediately adjacent ground surface is the same as the larger of the following two values: (a) ratio of the width of any footing to its depth below the immediately adjacent ground surface; (b) ratio of the width of the entire foundation or group of footings to its depth below the average surrounding ground surface. (See Fig. 3–11).

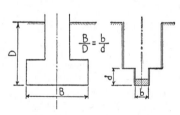

Fig. 3–11. Loading-test arrangement.

(2) When loading tests are made on bearing materials of Classes 10 to 13 inclusive, suitable methods shall be used to prevent evaporation from the materials being tested.

(3) A test load shall be applied which will produce a unit pressure equal to

*Boston Building Code, Sec. 2905.
†Ibid., Sec. 2916.

that for which the proposed foundations are designed. This load shall be allowed to remain undisturbed until no measurable settlement occurs during a period of 24 hr. The load shall then be doubled in increments not exceeding 25 per cent of the design load. At least 4 hr shall elapse between the application of successive increments. The total load shall be allowed to remain undisturbed until no measurable settlement occurs during a period of 24 hr.

(4) Measurements of settlement shall be accurate to $\frac{1}{32}$ in. and shall be taken and recorded every hour during the first 6 hr after the application of each increment, and at least once every 12 hr thereafter.

(5) When the design load upon bearing materials of Classes 1 to 10 inclusive causes settlement of less than $\frac{3}{8}$ in. and twice the design load causes settlement of less than 1 in., the design load shall be allowed; but, if medium or soft clay underlies these materials, the vertical pressure on such clay shall not exceed that allowable in Table 3-1.

Any earth in its natural state has a certain quantity of moisture permanently present in its constituent parts, which is termed its *water content*. The water content of clay, which is one of its chief characteristics, is seldom constant, varying with the depth and with the nature of the various materials with which it may be mixed. The structural properties of a soil will vary with its moisture content and density. For example, a clay soil at low density will have very high load-supporting capacity when dry, but when saturated at this same density will have very low load-supporting power. Hence, when determining the load bearing power of a soil, its moisture content and density must be defined and controlled to permit accurate evaluation of the soil in that particular condition. The next step is to determine the most unfavorable moisture and density condition that will prevail for the soil in field service and then make evaluation of the soil in this moisture and density condition for use in design calculations.

3-13. Practical Examples. In order to illustrate the use and implications of requirements of the Boston Building Code, the following numerical examples are given.

A wall footing, transmitting 13,750 lb/lin ft, will be 2 ft, 6 in. wide. How far below the top of a coarse sand layer (Class 8, Table 3-1) should this footing be placed?

This footing has a least dimension smaller than 3 ft, which necessitates a reduction of the bearing value of 3 tons/sq ft. On the other hand it is possible to increase this value by $2\frac{1}{2}$ per cent for each foot of depth x below the ground surface. Hence,

$$13,750 = 2.5 \frac{2.5}{3} 6000(1 + 0.025x),$$

$$x = 4 \text{ ft.}$$

As a second numerical example let it be assumed that column footings, transmitting 200 kips each and spaced 15 ft on centers, rest on top of a layer of sand and gravel mixture (Class 7). This layer is 12 ft thick and overlays a thick stratum of soft clay (Class 12). Find size of footing contact areas and check vertical pressure on the clay stratum (see Fig. 3–12).

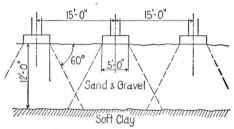

FIG. 3–12. Inferior soil at lower level.

According to Table 3–1, the allowable bearing pressure for the top layer may be taken as 8000 psf, or square footings of 5 ft × 5 ft will be sufficient to transmit the column loads to the soil directly below.

The soft clay has, according to Table 3–1, a permissible bearing pressure of 2000 psf. It is seen from Fig. 3–12 that the planes through the edges of the footing, making angles of 60° with the horizontal, intersect each other. Therefore, each column load must be assumed distributed over an area of 15 ft × 15 ft. In computing the pressure at the lower level, the Boston Building Code excludes the weight of the overlying soil. Thus 200,000 ÷ 225 = 890 psf, or considerably less than the maximum value on the lower level.

3–14. Settlements. A settlement means a vertical displacement of the base of a structure. Differential settlements, or unequal settlements, mean that some parts of the structure settle more than other parts.

Structures do not settle because the foundation has failed, but because the subgrade under the foundation is adjusting itself to new conditions. Settlement cracks in structures occur through unequal or differential settlements. Unequal settlements may be caused by nonuniform soil layers, by large differences in load intensities of individual footings, or by differences in size and shape of the footings.

The settlement of a footing is the result of two general effects produced by the stresses, which result from the application of the pressure to the soil. These effects are: (a) a compression, or consolidation, of the soil directly below the footing; and (b) a lateral movement of the soil from under the footing. The settlement of the footing is the combined result. The consolidation of the soil is due to the normal compressive stresses, which cause the expulsion of some of the water and the compression of the air which occupies the voids in the soil. Thus a change in the unit volume of the soil takes place. Such change of unit volume is, for the most part, of a permanent character, though there is some elastic deformation as well. The lateral movement is also of an only partially elastic character. By artificially preventing the lateral flow, one could somewhat reduce the settlements of a building, but not prevent them entirely.

The duration of the period of settlement varies with the nature of the soil. On sand and gravel the settlement may reach its ultimate value in a few days or weeks after completion of the superstructure. On clay the settlement is generally gradual and may reach its ultimate value after the lapse of years. Typical behavior of cohesionless and cohesive soils is shown in Fig. 3–13. Footings on sand will settle, and the settlement will

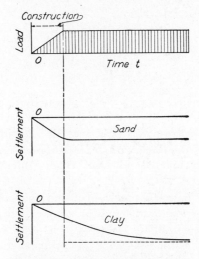

Fig. 3–13. Settlement of structures.

occur almost instantly upon application of load, with no further variation. Application of a load on clay squeezes out water and consequently settlement occurs, not suddenly as in sand, but continuously with decreasing amounts as resistance is built up.

The actual settlement of a structure cannot be evaluated from the settlements observed during a loading test. According to the theory of elasticity, the ratio of settlements produced by two areas A and a, resting on the top boundary of a semi-infinite solid and sustaining equal load intensities, equals

$$\sqrt{\frac{A}{a}}.$$ (3–17)

Thus, for a circular area, the settlement should increase in direct proportion to the radius.

Actually the settlement of the structure will be considerably smaller than indicated by Eq. (3–17); but larger areas will always settle more than smaller areas, and this is especially true of cohesive soils.

Fig. 3–14* represents the interpretation of the results of loading tests

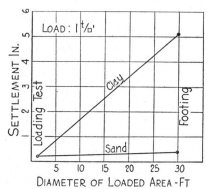

FIG. 3–14. Relation between size of loaded area and settlement.

performed on homogeneous ground (clay of a uniform consistency or sand of uniform density). The upper curve refers to a very cohesive material and the lower curve corresponds to a perfectly cohesionless material. As these materials are seldom met with in actual practice, it becomes evident that no general rules can be established which will cover the behavior of footings in general.

One of the most important questions that the substructure designer has to answer is: Which allowable unit pressure is to be used in the design of spread footings where differential settlements may endanger the safety of the structure? Thus for a statically determinate structure, a comparatively large value (in some cases, several inches) can usually be allowed. On the other hand for a statically indeterminate structure, the allowable intensity of secondary stresses must be selected first, and from this the admissible difference in settlement.

3–15. Housel's Method. It has long been recognized from observations that large areas of soft soil will not support as much weight per unit of surface as more limited areas of the same soil. This has led to an evaluation of critical loads for clay soils, based on an expression made up of two separate strength factors, known as Housel's method. While the basic assumption underlying this method is questionable, it does enable the designer to extrapolate from the available test data; and reliable results

*See Karl Terzaghi, "Modern Conceptions Concerning Foundation Engineering," *Journal of Boston Society of Civil Engineers* (December, 1925), p. 15.

can be expected where the tests are performed on areas which are not too small compared with the actual bearing area.

W. S. Housel* has suggested that, for cohesive soils, the bearing capacity of a footing can be written as the sum of two terms representing, respectively, compressive resistance under the area and the shearing resistance along the edge. Thus,

$$W = Ap + Ps, \qquad (3\text{-}18)$$

where W = total load on bearing area,

A = contact area of footing,

P = perimeter of footing,

p = pressure under area,

s = shear along edge.

As an illustrating example, let it be desired to design a square footing to transmit a load of 94 kips to a cohesive soil without exceeding a settlement of $\frac{1}{2}$ in. Two tests are made with bearing areas of 1 ft $\times$ 1 ft and 2 ft $\times$ 2 ft; they give settlements of $\frac{1}{2}$ in. for loads of 7600 and 20,800 lb, respectively. From Eq. (3-18) simultaneous values of p and s can be found; thus,

$$p + 4s = 7600,$$

$$4p + 8s = 20,800,$$

$$p = 2800 \text{ psf},$$

$$s = 1200 \text{ psf}.$$

Applying Eq. (3-18) to the desired footing, having a side length a, gives

$$2800a^2 + 1200 \times 4a = 94,000,$$

$$a = 5 \text{ ft}.$$

It follows from Eq. (3-18) that the area-perimeter ratio should influence the settlement of a footing. Except for very small areas, this hypothesis is substantiated by experiments.†

3-16. Proportioning Footings. An attempt will be made in the following paragraphs to place on a rational basis the design of spread footings on soft clay. It has already been pointed out that uniformity of pressure does not necessarily insure uniformity of settlements for individual footings. Footings of different sizes will settle unequally, even though the average unit pressure remains the same.

The method is based on work published by the German investigators,

---

*See *Engineering Research Bulletin* (University of Michigan, October, 1929), No. 13.
†See C. A. Hogentogler, *Engineering Properties of Soil* (New York, 1937), p. 225.

Kogler and Scheidig.* A uniform soil will be assumed, the water content of which will be supposed to remain constant. The object is to determine the sizes of the footing areas in plan.

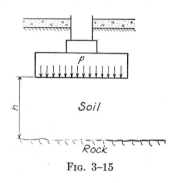

FIG. 3–15

Fig. 3–15 shows a column footing of rectangular shape which supports a column in a building. The bottom of the footing rests below the basement floor. The average vertical unit pressure applied to the soil is p. The settlement of the footing is not only dependent on the soil pressure and on the soil properties, but it is also a function of the size and shape of the footing itself and of the depth h of the soil layer. While a mathematical analysis of the problem is complicated, it can be shown that for approximate settlements the following relatively simple expression can be used:

$$S = \frac{pbk}{E},\qquad (3\text{–}19)$$

where S = settlement,

$\quad p$ = pressure intensity,

$\quad b$ = smallest lateral dimension of footing,

$\quad E$ = modulus of compression of the soil,

$\quad k$ = constant dependent on shape and size of footing and also on depth of the soil to the rock.

Fig. 3–16 shows the variation of k as influenced by the soil depth and shape of footing, while a rough idea of the values of the modulus of compression E can be gained from Table 3–2.†

If equal settlements are to take place for two footings, which are supporting total loads of P_1 and P_2, and if Eq. (3–19) is applied, then

$$\frac{P_1 b_1 k_1}{A_1 E} = \frac{P_2 b_2 k_2}{A_2 E}. \qquad (3\text{–}20)$$

As the modulus of compression E cancels, it is seen that footing areas resting on the same soil can be proportioned by this method without knowledge of the exact value of E. Thus the process for the design on this basis is, after the total loads on the contact areas have been determined, to select the smallest of the footings and, with some allowable soil pressure, determine its required area. Next, all the other footings are

*See F. Kogler and A. Scheidig, *Bauwerk und Baugrund* (Berlin, Wilhelm Ernst and Son, 1929).

†See I. F. Morrison, "The Design of Spread Footings," *Engineering Journal* (Canada, January, 1941), pp. 10–14.

proportioned in accordance with Eq. (3–20). In order to do this the values of k_1 and k_2 must be known and these may be found from Fig. 3–16 by a process of trial and error.

As a numerical example, let it be desired to find the square contact areas for three single footings carrying, respectively, 36, 48, and 72 kips.

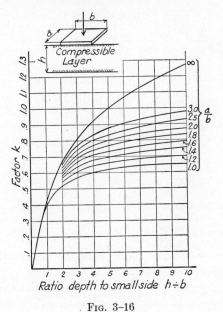

FIG. 3–16

The compressible layer in which the footings are resting extends 6 ft below the contact areas ($h = 6$). It is assumed that a square footing of 9 sq ft will be used for the load of 36 kips and the other footings will be propor-

TABLE 3–2

Soil Type	E (Tons/Sq Ft)
Gravel (dense)	1000–2000
Sand (dense)	500– 800
Sand (loose)	100– 200
Clay (hard)	80– 150
Clay (medium)	40– 80
Clay (soft)	15– 40
Clay (very soft)	5– 30

tioned so that final deflections will be approximately equal for the three loads. For the smallest footing, having

$$\frac{h}{b} = \frac{6}{3} = 2; \quad \frac{a}{b} = 1,$$

it is seen from the diagram in Fig. 3–16 that the corresponding value of the coefficient k equals 0.52. Applying Eq. (3–20) gives

$$\frac{36 \times 3 \times 0.52}{9} = \frac{48 \times b_2 \times k_2}{b_2{}^2} = \frac{72 \times b_3 \times k_3}{b_3{}^2},$$

$$6.24 = 48\frac{k_2}{b_2} = 72\frac{k_3}{b_3}. \qquad\qquad (3\text{--}21)$$

It is now found by trial that Eq. (3.21) is satisfied by

$$b_2 = 3.66; \quad 6 \div 3.66 = 1.64; \quad k_2 = 0.48,$$

$$b_3 = 4.92; \quad 6 \div 4.92 = 1.22; \quad k_3 = 0.43.$$

Thus the three square footings should, for equal deflections, have sides of 3 ft, 0 in.; 3 ft, 8 in.; 4 ft, 11 in. and the pressure intensities become, respectively,

$$36,000 \div (3.0 \ \times 3.0 \ ) = 4000 \text{ psf.}$$

$$48,000 \div (3.66 \times 3.66) = 3583 \text{ psf.}$$

$$72,000 \div (4.92 \times 4.92) = 2974 \text{ psf.}$$

The designer of substructures is generally concerned only with differential settlements of the foundation units, which will produce harmful stresses in the superstructure. No knowledge of the modulus of compression is needed for proportioning footings for equal deflections. If, however, it is desired to evaluate the actual amounts of settlement according to this method, the compression modulus should be determined by tests, and allowance for the small size of the bearing area should be made by application of Eq. (3–19) and Fig. 3–16.

As a numerical example let it be desired to find the modulus of compression from tests made with a bearing plate of 1 sq ft. A pressure of 5 tons resulted in a deflection of $\frac{3}{4}$ in.; the soil layer was more than 15 ft deep. With a value of $k = 0.65$, this test gives

$$E = \frac{0.65 \times 5 \times 12}{0.75} = 52 \text{ tons/sq ft.}$$

3–17. Actual Settlements. In order to evaluate actual settlements under footings, it is necessary to determine by tests the relationship between void and stress for the particular soil which is affected. With this information available it is possible to predict with some confidence the settlement under a footing or building.

Soil occurring in nature is made up of solids and voids, as shown schematically in Fig. 3–17. Assume that the volume of solids in this sample is 1 cu ft and the volume of voids is e_0. The ratio of volume of voids to the volume of solids is called the *void ratio*.

Fig. 3–18 shows a compressible soil stratum of thickness H. An increase

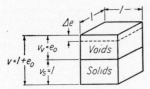

FIG. 3–17. Volumetric change.

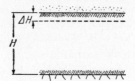

FIG. 3–18. Compression of soil stratum.

of vertical stress in this layer will reduce the volume of voids and the total decrease in thickness is ΔH. A comparison to Fig. 3–16 indicates that

$$\frac{\Delta H}{H} = \frac{\Delta e}{1 + e_0} ; \quad \Delta H = \frac{H\,\Delta e}{1 + e_0}. \tag{3-22}$$

A relationship between the stress and the void ratio in any given soil can be determined by testing a sample of it in the consolidometer shown in Fig. 3–19. The sample is enclosed in a cylindrical brass mold (sample ring)

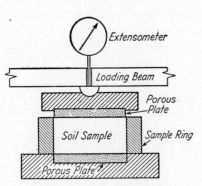

FIG. 3–19. Consolidometer.

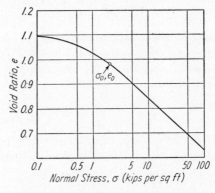

FIG. 3–20. Stress–void ratio curve.

between two porous stones through which water has free access to and from both surfaces of the specimen. A compressive stress, σ, is produced in the sample through a piston. The amount of compression is measured on a dial extensometer. The pressure is allowed to remain until the compression virtually stops, and then a larger pressure is produced. This procedure is repeated for the range of stress to which the soil is likely to be subjected under the structure.

The results from the consolidation test are next presented in the form of a stress–void ratio curve similar to the one shown in Fig. 3–20, which has been plotted with the logarithm of stress as the abscissa and the void ratio as ordinate. It is seen that the curve forms a straight line through the largest part of its range. The equation of the straight-line portion of the curve is

$$\Delta e = C_c \log_{10} \frac{\sigma_0 + \Delta\sigma}{\sigma_0} \qquad (3\text{-}23)$$

where Δe is the decrease in void ratio due to an increase in the soil stress, $\Delta\sigma$, with the initial stress, σ_0. The coefficient C_c is called the compression index and is a measure of the slope of the straight-line part of the curve. It is also an indication of the relative compressibility of the soil. The larger the compression index, the more compressible is the soil.

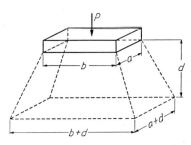

FIG. 3–21. Distribution of vertical pressure.

In order to evaluate settlements, it is necessary to determine the vertical stresses acting on each compressible soil stratum. The Boussinesq formula, Eq. (1–49), can be used, but will result in much numerical work. An approximate method may be used to find the average increase in stress at any depth, d, below the ground surface by assuming that the surface load spreads out uniformly over a larger area which may be arrived at by drawing lines from the edges of the footing with slopes 2:1 (2 vertical and 1 horizontal). Thus, according to Fig. 3–21, at a depth d the load P will produce an average stress of

$$\sigma = \frac{P}{(a + d)(b + d)} \qquad (3\text{-}24)$$

If the areas from two or more such pyramids overlap, the total of all the loads is assumed to be uniformly distributed over the area defined by the limits of the outermost pyramids.

3–18. Numerical Example. A square footing 6 ft × 6 ft is shown in Fig. 3–22. The pressure exerted by this footing to its surface contact area is 5000 psf. It is desired to evaluate the settlement of this footing due to the presence of the soft clay stratum which has a stress–void ratio curve shown in Fig. 3–20. The unit weight of the clay is 105 lb/cu ft and that of the overlying sand layer is 110 lb/cu ft. There is no water table.

The average stress in the clay stratum, σ_0, due to the weight of the overlying soil, is:

Sand: 8 × 110 . . . . 880 psf
Clay: 3 × 105 . . . . 315 psf
1195 psf.

The average stress in the clay stratum due to the footing pressure is, according to Eq. (3–24) and Fig. 3–21,

$$\sigma = 36 \times 5000 \div (6 + 11)^2 = 623 \text{ psf.}$$

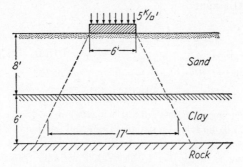

Fig. 3–22. Settlement of footing.

The compression index of the stress–void ratio curve in Fig. 3–19 is

$$C_c = \frac{0.98 - 0.63}{\log 100 - \log 2} = 0.20,$$

and the total compression of the clay stratum, according to Eqs. (3–22) and (3–23), is

$$\Delta H = H \frac{C_c \log_{10} \left(\frac{\sigma_0 + \Delta\sigma}{\sigma_0}\right)}{1 + e_0} = 6 \frac{0.2 \log_{10} \left(\frac{1195 + 623}{1195}\right)}{1 + 0.98},$$

$$\Delta H = 0.11 \text{ ft} = 1.32 \text{ in.}$$

Fig. 3–23 shows a number of footings, similar to the one in Fig. 3–22, spaced 14 ft on centers in both directions, and resting on soil strata also identical with those of the preceding example. It is desired to find the settlement due to the compression of the clay stratum.

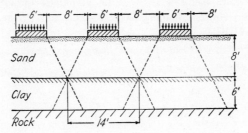

Fig. 3–23. Combined settlement of footings.

Because the pyramids, indicating the distribution of the loads, intersect at the top of the clay stratum the average vertical stress in this layer will be

$$\sigma = 180{,}000 \div 14^2 = 918 \text{ psf,}$$

and the total settlement

$$\Delta H = 6 \frac{0.2 \log_{10}\left(\dfrac{1195 + 918}{1195}\right)}{1 + 0.98} = 0.15 \text{ ft} = 1.8 \text{ in.}$$

PROBLEMS

3–1. A wall footing having a width of 8 ft is located in a cohesive soil having a unit weight of 105 lb/cu ft and an angle of internal friction of 14°. The distance from the top of the soil to the underside of the footing is 1 ft. The capacity of the footing is, according to Terzaghi's formula (safety factor of one), 36,250 lb/lin ft. Find unit cohesion. (*Ans.*: 564 psf.)

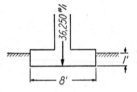

PROB. 3–1

3–2. Find the size of a square footing supporting a total load of 100 kips and resting on a compact sand-gravel mixture 4 ft below the top surface of this layer. Use Boston Building Code. (*Ans.*: 3 ft.)

3–3. It is desired to design a square footing supporting 163 kips with a settlement of $\frac{3}{8}$ in. Two tests are made with contact areas of 12 in. square and 18 in. square. The loads which produce $\frac{3}{8}$-in. settlements are, respectively, 11,200 lb and 19,200 lb. Use Housel's method for finding the side of the square footing. (*Ans.*: 6 ft.)

3–4. Find the required width for a wall footing placed 5 ft below the top surface in a cohesionless sand. Angle of internal friction is 24°, soil weight is 95 lb/cu ft, safety factor is 1. Use: (a) Rankine's formula; (b) Terzaghi's formula; (c) Boston Building Code, Class 9 soil. (*Ans.*: (a) 9.3 ft.; (b) 6.6 ft; (c) 11.1 ft.)

CHAPTER 4

FOOTINGS

4–1. Introduction. Footings may be defined as foundation units which transmit loads to the supporting soil. A single footing generally supports a column (usually in a building) while a combined footing carries two or more columns.

The objects of footing design are: first, to determine correctly the area in contact with the underlying soil, and second, to proportion the shape of the footing considering, say, thickness and amount of reinforcement.

Footings may be designed with a certain factor of safety against failure of the supporting soil; such failures will always be shear failures and the methods for such a design were discussed in Chap. 3. If the foundation for a building consists of a number of individual footings, then the criterion which forms the basis on which the proportionate size of the footings must rest is that of equal settlements; this phase of the design has also received attention in a previous chapter. In the following the factors which influence the strength of the footing itself will be discussed.

4–2. Review of Reinforced Concrete. As reinforced concrete is by far the most widely used material for footings, a short résumé of its most important aspects will be given below. The nomenclature is as follows:

$A_1, A_2, \ldots$ = cross-sectional areas of steel bars,

$\quad A_s$ = total cross-sectional area of reinforcement,

$\quad b$ = width of section,

$\quad C$ = total compression,

$\quad d$ = distance from extreme compressive fiber to steel reinforcement,

$\quad dx$ = infinitesimal distance,

$\quad E_c$ = modulus of elasticity for concrete,

$\quad E_s$ = modulus of elasticity for steel,

$\quad kd$ = distance from extreme compressive fiber to neutral axis,

$\quad jd$ = distance between resultants of the tensile and compressive forces on the section,

$\quad f_c$ = maximum compressive concrete stress,

$\quad f_s$ = tension stress in steel reinforcement,

$\quad n$ = $E_s \div E_c$,

$o_1, o_2, \ldots$ = perimeter of steel bars,

$\quad M$ = bending moment,

T = tension in steel reinforcement,
u = bond stress,
V = total shear on section,
v = shearing stress,
$p = A_s \div bd$.

In Fig. 4–1(a) are shown the forces which act on a reinforced concrete member subjected to the action of a bending moment M. If this bending

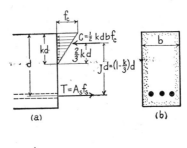

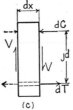

FIG. 4–1.   Review of reinforced concrete.

moment is referred to the centroid of the steel reinforcement, it can be equated to the moment of the internal compression stresses. Thus the maximum compressive stress in the concrete is found to be

$$f_c = \frac{M}{\frac{1}{2}kjbd^2} \cdot \qquad (4\text{--}1)$$

If, likewise, the external moment M is referred to the center of compression it can be equated to the moment of the total tension in the reinforcement, and the tensile stress in the steel bars is found to be

$$f_s = \frac{M}{A_s jd} \cdot \qquad (4\text{--}2)$$

The quantities k and j can be expressed in terms of the stresses f_c and f_s. Thus, by indicating the proportionality of shortening of extreme top fibers and elongation of steel reinforcement,

$$\frac{f_c \div E_c}{f_s \div E_s} = \frac{kd}{d - kd} \; ; \quad k = \frac{1}{1 + \dfrac{f_s}{nf_c}} \cdot \tag{4-3}$$

From the equality of total tension to total compression,

$$\tfrac{1}{2}kbdf_c = A_s f_s,$$

the ratio $f_s \div f_c$ can be eliminated by Eq. (4-3) and k expressed solely by the steel ratio p and modular ratio n; thus

$$k = \sqrt{2pn + (pn)^2} - pn. \tag{4-4}$$

If there is no reinforcement above the neutral axis, it is seen that

$$j = 1 - \frac{k}{3} \cdot \tag{4-5}$$

In Fig. 4-1(c) is shown a portion of a reinforced concrete beam lying between two sections an infinite distance dx apart. If, then, a horizontal section is passed through this portion anywhere between reinforcement and neutral axis, it is seen that the total shear on this section must equal the increment dT in the steel reinforcement. Thus,

$$vb \; dx = dT; \quad v = \frac{1}{b} \frac{dT}{dx}, \tag{4-6}$$

but

$$T = A_s f_s = \frac{M}{jd} \; ; \quad \text{so} \quad \frac{dT}{dx} = \frac{1}{jd} \frac{dM}{dx}$$

If the bending moment is expressed in terms of the shear,

$$V = \frac{dM}{dx} = jd \frac{dT}{dx}, \tag{4-7}$$

then Eq. (4-6) becomes

$$v = \frac{V}{bjd} \cdot \tag{4-8}$$

The bond stresses $(u_1, u_2, u_3, \ldots)$ which occur along surfaces of contact between steel and concrete, Fig. 4-1(c), must equal the increment in tension in the reinforcement. Thus,

$$dT = (u_1 o_1 + u_2 o_2 + u_3 o_3 + \cdots)dx, \tag{4-9}$$

where o_1, o_2, o_3 indicate bar perimeters. If different sizes of steel rods are used in the same section, the equality of strains gives

$$\frac{u_1 o_1}{A_1} = \frac{u_2 o_2}{A_2} = \frac{u_3 o_3}{A_3} \cdot \tag{4-10}$$

From Eqs. (4–7), (4–9), and (4–10)

$$\frac{V}{jd} = u_1 o_1 + u_1 o_1 \frac{A_2}{A_1} + u_1 o_1 \frac{A_3}{A_1} \qquad (4\text{–}11)$$

$$u_1 = \frac{V}{jdo_1} \times \frac{A_1}{A_s},$$

$$u_2 = \frac{V}{jdo_2} \times \frac{A_2}{A_s},$$

$$u_3 = \frac{V}{jdo_3} \times \frac{A_3}{A_s}. \qquad (4\text{–}12)$$

It is seen that reinforcing bars of different sizes in the same section will develop different bond stresses. Thus, for a section reinforced with three round bars of diam $\frac{3}{4}$ in., $\frac{7}{8}$ in., and 1 in., respectively, if other quantities are

$$V = 10 \text{ kips}, \quad d = 20 \text{ in., and } j = \tfrac{7}{8},$$

the formulas in Eq. (4–12) give

$$\tfrac{3}{4}\text{-in.}^{\phi} \text{ bar:} \quad u_1 = 59 \text{ psi.}$$

$$\tfrac{7}{8}\text{-in.}^{\phi} \text{ bar:} \quad u_2 = 68 \text{ psi.}$$

$$1\text{-in.}^{\phi} \text{ bar:} \quad u_3 = 78 \text{ psi.}$$

4–3. Single Footings. Fig. 4–2(a) shows a continuous footing supporting a wall. If the wall and footing are of monolithic concrete, the bending moment governing the depth and amounts of reinforcing steel should be taken at the face of the wall. If a brick wall is supported on a concrete footing, it is customary* to figure the bending moment half-way between the middle and the edge of wall.

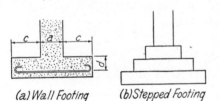

(a) Wall Footing   (b) Stepped Footing

Fig. 4–2

Fig. 4–2(b) shows a stepped footing in which the widening from the column base to the soil contact area is gradual by steps. If the base is widened out abruptly it is called a spread footing. Fig. 4–3 shows a number of such footings.

In the case of a sloping top surface and underlying uniform soil conditions, it is not uncommon to carry continuous footings (usually for walls)

*Building Regulations for Reinforced Concrete (American Concrete Institute, 1951).

Courtesy of Hagstrom Construction Company

FIG. 4-3. Spread footings.

gradually down to lower levels. Footings of this type (see Fig. 4–4) are also called *stepped* footings.

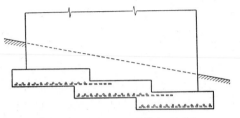

FIG. 4–4. Stepped wall footing.

A square footing, as the one shown in Fig. 4–5, is subjected to upward uniform pressure on its bottom and downward uniform pressure in the column shaft. The difference between the resultants of the two pressures will equal the weight of the footing.

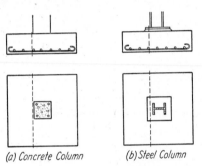

(a) Concrete Column   (b) Steel Column

FIG. 4–5. Reinforced concrete footings.

Footings may fail in bending, shear, or bond. In the case of bending, the stresses on the most highly stressed section should be investigated. The following rules for selecting the critical section have been recommended by the American Concrete Institute and have been adopted by a majority of building codes. The critical section should be taken:

(a) At the face of the column, pedestal, or wall, for footings supporting a concrete column, pedestal, or wall [Fig. 4–5(a)].
(b) Halfway between the middle and the edge of the wall for footings under masonry walls.
(c) Halfway between the face of the column and the edge of the metallic base plate for footings under steel columns [Fig. 4–5(b)].

The entire width of the footing can be assumed to resist the compression due to bending. In one-way footings, where main reinforcing is placed only in one direction, enough reinforcement must be provided to resist the full bending moment. Single square footings are usually constructed with reinforcement in two perpendicular directions and are therefore called *two-way* footings. The American Concrete Institute recommends that in two-way footings, the total tensile reinforcement at any section shall provide a moment of resistance equal to only 85 per cent of the bending moment computed on a critical section extending completely across the footing. It should be noted that the bending moment will seldom govern the depth and amount of reinforcement of two-way footing. Shear and bond requirements are usually the deciding factors.

Footings should be designed to resist effectively the diagonal tension caused by shearing forces. The critical section for shear to be used as a measure of diagonal tension is obtained by passing a series of vertical planes through the footing, each of which is parallel to a corresponding face of the column and located a distance from the face equal to the effective depth, d, as shown in Fig. 4–6. Each face of the critical section is assumed to resist an external shear equal to one-fourth of the upward pressure outside the complete section. The critical section for bond is assumed to be the same as for bending (Fig. 4–5). According to the specifications of the American Concrete Institute the total tensile reinforcement shall provide a bond resistance at least equal to 85 per cent of the external shear at the section. In the case of a one-way footing no reduction is allowed in the bond resistance.

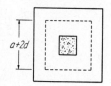

Fig. 4–6. Critical section in shear.

4–4. Numerical Example. Let it be desired to design a square footing to carry a load of 361 kips delivered by a concrete column 16 in. × 16 in. Soil bearing pressure can be assumed to be 6 kips per sq ft. Allowable stresses in concrete and steel are $f_c = 1125$ psi; $f_s = 20,000$ psi; $v = 75$ psi; and $u = 200$ psi (deformed bars without end hooks).

If the weight of the footing is estimated at 19,000 lb, the contact area should be not less than $380 \div 6 = 63.3$ ft. The footing should be 8 ft square. In computing bending and shearing stresses in the footing, only the column load should be considered:

$$p = 361,000 \div 64 = 5640 \text{ psf.}$$

The depth of the footing is usually governed by the requirement of resistance to shear. Referring to Fig. 4–6 and Eq. (4–8), it is seen that

$$75 = \frac{5640\left[64 - \dfrac{(16 + 2d)^2}{144}\right]}{4(16 + 2d) \times 0.866 \times d},$$

$$d^2 + 9.85d - 519.1 = 0; \quad d = 18.4 \text{ in.}$$

If the distance from the top to a plane where the two layers of steel rods make contact is made $18\frac{1}{2}$ in. it is seen that the amount of reinforcing steel can be determined from the bond requirement. According to Eq. (4–11) the spacing, x, of 1-in. round bars must be such that

$$200 = \frac{0.85 \times 5640 \times 3.33}{0.866 \times 18.5 \times \dfrac{12}{x} \times 3.14} \qquad x = 7.56 \text{ in.}$$

The spacing can be made $7\frac{1}{2}$ in. in each direction. It is interesting to check this design for bending stresses. According to Eq. (4–1) the maximum compressive stress is

$$f_c = \frac{5640 \times \frac{1}{2} \times 3.33^2 \times 12}{\frac{1}{2}0.403 \times 0.866 \times 12 \times 18.5^2} = 524 \text{ psi,}$$

and according to Eq. (4–2) the tensile stress in the reinforcing

$$f_s = \frac{0.85 \times 5640 \times \frac{1}{2} \times 3.33^2 \times 12}{0.866 \times 18.5 \times \dfrac{12}{7.5} \times 0.79} = 15{,}850 \text{ psi.}$$

The final design of the footing is shown in Fig. 4–7.

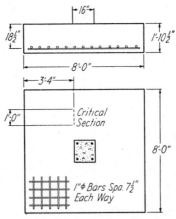

FIG. 4–7. Numerical example, single footing.

4–5. Rectangular Footings. Single footings are most economical in materials if the contact area is square. If a rectangular shape is unavoidable, definite rules are in existence for the design. The following numerical example follows the specifications of the American Concrete Institute.

Assume the column load and the soil bearing capacity are the same as in the preceding example ($P = 361$ kips; $p = 6000$ psf). The allowable stresses in steel and concrete are also the same as were used for the design of Fig. 4–7 namely: $f_s = 20{,}000$; $f_c = 1125$; $v = 75$; and $u = 200$, all expressed in pounds per square inch.

If 20 kips is assumed as the weight of the footing the contact area should be slightly less than 64 sq ft. If one dimension must not exceed 7 ft, 3 in., the other dimension must be 9 ft ($9.00 \times 7.25 = 65.2$ sq ft). The concrete column is square with a side of 16 in. The net upward pressure is

$$p = 361{,}000 \div 65.2 = 5540 \text{ psf.}$$

One face of the critical section in shear is shown in Fig. 4–8. It is considered as resisting an external shear equal to the load on an area

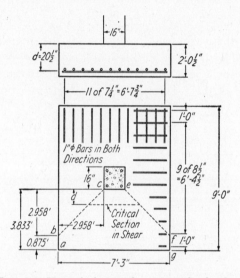

Fig. 4–8. Numerical example, rectangular footing.

bounded by the said face, two diagonal lines drawn from the column corners and making 45° angles with the principal axes of the footing, and that portion of the corresponding edge or edges of the footing intercepted between the two diagonals.

The area of *abcefg* in Fig. 4–8 is 19.0336 sq ft. Application of Eq. (4–9) gives

$$\frac{\left[19.0336 - \dfrac{d(16 + d)}{144}\right]5540}{(16 + 2d) \times 0.866 \times d} = 75,$$

$$d = 20.5 \text{ in.}$$

The maximum bond stresses will occur at sections passed in front of column faces. The shears on these sections can be reduced by 15 per cent. If 1-in. round bars are used, their spacing x can be found by application of Eq. (4–12). Thus, in the long direction,

$$200 = \frac{0.85 \times 5540 \times 3.833}{0.866 \times 20.5 \times \dfrac{12}{x} \times 3.14} \ ; \quad x = 7.4 \text{ in. or } 7\tfrac{1}{4} \text{ in.}$$

This reinforcement that runs in the long direction shall be distributed uniformly across the full width of the footing. In the case of the reinforcement in the short direction, a closer spacing should be used near the column center. First the total number of reinforcing bars, n, is found:

$$\frac{0.85 \times 5540 \times 2.958 \times 9}{0.866 \times 20.5 \times n \times 3.14} = 200,$$

$$n = 11.2, \text{ or } 12 \text{ bars.}$$

A portion of these bars shall be uniformly distributed across a band width B, centered with respect to the centerline of the column and having a width equal to the length of the short side of the footing. According to the specifications of the American Concrete Institute, the portion of the reinforcement to be placed in the center band shall be computed from the formula

$$\frac{\text{Reinforcement in band width, } B}{\text{Total reinforcement in short direction}} = \frac{2}{S+1}, \qquad (4\text{–}13)$$

where S = ratio of the long side to the short side of the footing. Substituting in this formula gives

$$\frac{1}{9 \div 7.25 + 1} = 0.893.$$

This ratio should be multiplied by the theoretical number of bars required in the short direction, thus: $0.893 \times 11.2 = 10$. Ten bars should be placed with close spacing and the remaining two outside the band of width $B = 7.25$ ft, as shown in Fig. 4–8.

It remains to check the compression and tension stresses caused by bending. These will be highest due to bending in the long direction. Maximum compression stress in the top of the footing in front of face ce (Fig. 4–8) will be

$$f_c = \frac{5540 \times \tfrac{1}{2} \times 3.833^2 \times 12}{\tfrac{1}{2} \times 0.866 \times 0.403 \times 12 \times 20.5^2} = 555 \text{ psi.}$$

In the case of the tensile stresses in the reinforcement the bending moment can be reduced by 15 per cent; thus,

$$f_s = \frac{0.85 \times 5540 \times \tfrac{1}{2}3.833^2 \times 12}{0.866 \times 20.5 \times \dfrac{12}{7.25} \times 0.785} = 18{,}000 \text{ psi.}$$

Both stresses are well below the allowable limits.

4–6. Combined Rectangular Footings. A combined footing is one which supports two columns. Combined footings are necessary to avoid encroaching upon property adjacent to the building site. It follows that combined footings ordinarily include either one or two exterior columns.

Two factors, which govern the design of combined footings, are:

(1) The area should be big enough to produce the safe allowable soil pressure.

(2) The shape should be such that a uniform net soil pressure is given.

Fig. 4–9 shows three types of combined footings in current use; for all three types the property line is shown as a dash and dot. If the distance between the faces of the exterior columns and the edge of the footing is limited to a few feet, it may be possible to combine two exterior columns, usually having equal loads. In this case, as shown in Fig. 4–9(a), the footing will be symmetrical in both directions about the centroid of the two loads. If the columns can be located at the fifth points from the ends, bending moments under the columns and at center of footings will be equal and the depth a minimum.

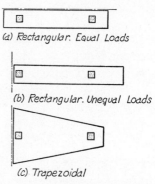

(a) Rectangular. Equal Loads

(b) Rectangular. Unequal Loads

(c) Trapezoidal

Fig. 4–9. Combined footings.

If the space available beyond the outside faces of the exterior columns is further limited, then it will be necessary to combine an exterior column with an interior column. Ordinarily the latter transmits the larger load and, as the centroid must coincide with the center, the rectangular footing will be shaped as shown in Fig. 4–9(b).

If the exterior column transmits a heavier load than the interior column, then the centroid of the two will lie closer to the former and a combination footing of the two columns must be shaped as a trapezoid as shown in Fig. 4–9(c).

As an example of a combined rectangular footing, let it be desired to design a combined footing to carry the loads of 600 kips and 1200 kips from an exterior and interior column, respectively. The distance between the column centers is 29 ft. The allowable soil pressure is 6 kips/sq ft, and the footing cannot extend more than 2 ft, 6 in. beyond the centerline of the exterior column.

If the weight of the footing is estimated at 230 kips, the total required area of the footing should be

$$(600 + 1200 + 230) \div 6 = 338 \text{ ft}^2.$$

The resultant of the two column loads lies a distance of 19 ft, 4 in. from the center of the exterior column. Thus, total length of the footing is

$$2(2.5 + 19.33) = 43.66 \text{ ft.}$$

The width of the footing is found by dividing the required area by this length. Thus,

$$338 \div 43.66 = 7.75 \text{ ft.}$$

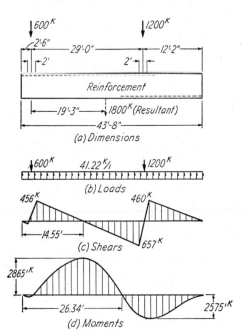

FIG. 4–10. Rectangular footing.

Net soil pressure that will produce bending and shearing stresses in this footing is found by dividing the footing area into the sum of the two column loads, thus,

$$1800 \div 338 = 5.33 \text{ kips/sq ft.}$$

Combined footings are usually designed as inverted beams and the allowable unit stresses are those in use for the superstructure. If an effective depth of 50 in. is used, the maximum compressive stress will be

$$f_c = \frac{2{,}865{,}000 \times 12}{\frac{1}{2} \times 0.403 \times 0.866 \times 93 \times 50^2} = 847 \text{ psi,}$$

and the number, n, of 1-in. round bars to be placed near the top will be

$$n = \frac{2{,}865{,}000 \times 12}{0.866 \times 50 \times 20{,}000 \times 0.785} = 50.$$

Reinforcing steel bars must also be placed in the bottom of the portion of the footing which projects beyond the interior column. The number, n_1, of 1-in. round steel bars must equal

$$n_1 = \frac{2,575,000 \times 12}{0.866 \times 50 \times 20,000 \times 0.785} = 46.$$

The portions of the footing immediately under the two columns will distribute the column loads in the transverse direction. Reinforcing bars should be placed in the bottom to take care of tensile stresses from this transmission. In the case of the exterior column the width of the transverse beam can be assumed to be 5 ft, and the load intensity equal to $600 \div 7.75 = 77.42$ kips/lin ft. The maximum bending moment will occur at the face of the column; thus,

$$M = \tfrac{1}{8} \times 77.42(7.75 - 2)^2 = 320 \text{ ft-kips.}$$

Six 1-in. round bars will be sufficient for this bending moment, the stress being

$$f_s = \frac{320,000 \times 12}{0.866 \times 50 \times 6 \times 0.785} = 18,825 \text{ psi.}$$

The interior column load is twice the exterior one; therefore the number of transverse 1-in. round bars under this column must be twice the number under the exterior column. Vertical stirrups are needed adjacent to the columns to take care of excess shear. Typical details are shown in Fig. 4–11.

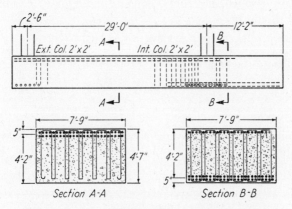

FIG. 4–11. Rectangular footing, structural details.

4–7. Combined Trapezoidal Footings. When the exterior column transmits the heaviest load, a rectangular footing is not possible. In order to make the centroid coincide with the resultant of the two forces, a trapezoidal footing may be used.

A numerical example is illustrated in Fig. 4–12, where a combined footing is designed to support two columns 20 ft on centers and transmitting loads of 300 kips and 450 kips. The columns are of square sections of 22 in. and 28 in., respectively. The soil pressure is 6 kips/sq ft and the

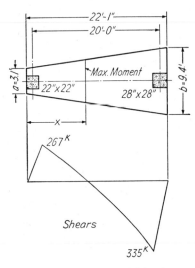

FIG. 4–12. Trapezoidal footing.

footing will be proportioned so that it does not extend beyond the column faces. If it is assumed that the weight of the footing is 75 kips, the total footing area should be

$$(75 + 300 + 450) \div 6 = 137.5 \text{ sq ft.}$$

If a and b denote the lengths of the two parallel sides, then

$$\tfrac{1}{2}(a + b)22.08 = 137.5, \tag{4–14}$$

$$a + b = 12.5.$$

The resultant of the two column loads lies 12 ft from the center of the smaller column; therefore, the distance from the centroid of the trapezoid to the small side must be

$$\frac{22.1}{3} \times \frac{a + 2b}{a + b} = 12.92 \text{ ft.} \tag{4–15}$$

From Eqs. (4–14) and (4–15) are found:

$$a = 3.1 \text{ ft}, \quad b = 9.4 \text{ ft.}$$

The shear and bond requirements will usually govern the thickness and reinforcement of a trapezoidal footing. Thus, if the maximum shearing stress must not exceed 110 psi, it is seen from Fig. 4–12 that the depth should be determined from the equations which express this intensity at the inside faces of the two columns, or

$$\frac{335,000}{8.7 \times 12 \times \frac{7}{8} \times d} = 110, \tag{4–16}$$

$$\frac{267,000}{3.6 \times 12 \times \frac{7}{8} \times d} = 110, \tag{4–17}$$

8.7 and 3.6 being the width of the foundation in feet at these locations.

Eq. (4–17) gives the larger value for the depth, namely $d = 66.5$ in. In order to check the bending stresses it is necessary to locate the section which has the maximum bending moment per linear foot. The unit pressure which produces bending and shearing stresses in the footing is

$$(300 + 450) \div 137.5 = 5.455 \text{ kips/sq ft,}$$

and according to Fig. 4–12 the bending moment per linear foot at a distance x from the short side is

$$M_x = \frac{300(x - 0.92) - 5.455\left(3.1\,\frac{x^2}{2} + 0.143\,\frac{x^3}{3}\right)}{3.1 + 0.285x}. \tag{4–18}$$

The maximum value of this moment is found by placing the first derivative of Eq. (4–18) equal to zero and solving for x. Thus,

$$\frac{dM_x}{dx} = 0; \quad x^3 + 32.6x^2 + 354x - 6816 = 0.$$

By trial this equation is found to be satisfied by $x = 9.3$ ft, which gives a maximum moment of 273 ft-kips/linear foot when substituted in Eq. (4–18). The corresponding maximum bending stress is

$$f_c = \frac{273,000 \times 12}{\frac{1}{2} \times \frac{3}{8} \times \frac{7}{8} \times 12 \times 66.5^2} = 357 \text{ psi.}$$

The reinforcement needed to resist the maximum bending moment must have a cross-sectional area of

$$A_s = \frac{273,000 \times 12}{20,000 \times 0.875 \times 66.5} = 2.81 \text{ sq in.}$$

As this critical section has a width of 5.8 ft, the total amount of steel reinforcement to resist bending should have a cross-sectional area of not less than

$$5.8 \times 2.81 = 16.3 \text{ sq in.}$$

This requirement can be satisfied by eighteen 1-in. square bars. The bond stress limit will often necessitate an increase in the number of bars at the ends of a trapezoidal footing. If an allowable bond stress of 80 psi (common for 2000 psi concrete, no special anchorage) is assumed, it is seen from Fig. 4–12 that the total circumference of bars at the ends should be

$$80 = \frac{335,000}{0.875 \times 66.5 \; \Sigma o}, \quad \Sigma o = 72;$$

$$80 = \frac{267,000}{0.875 \times 66.5 \; \Sigma o}, \quad \Sigma o = 60,$$

or eighteen 1-in. square bars and fifteen 1-in. square bars at the wide and narrow ends, respectively. The longitudinal reinforcement should be placed in the top of the footing.

Transverse reinforcement should be provided in both top and bottom of the footing. In this example, 1-in. round bars spaced 12 in. will be sufficient for the footing. Vertical stirrups should be placed near the ends to take care of the excess shear.

4–8. Raft Foundations. A raft foundation is a continuous footing which supports an entire structure. (A mat foundation is another name for large footings of this type.) It is used generally on soils of very low bearing power where single footings would be so large that very little space would be left between them.

If the columns, resting on a raft foundation, carry equal loads, then the load on each column is transferred to that part of the site in its immediate neighborhood and to no other part of the raft; and the bending moments will be similar to those occurring in single footings. When there is a considerable difference between column loads, the excess load must be transferred from heavily loaded areas to lightly loaded areas in order to maintain the same pressure intensity under the various portions of the raft. The raft must be strong enough for this transmission.

An example of the design of a simple raft is shown in Fig. 4–13. A center column, carrying a load of 350 kips, and two outside columns, each carrying 257 kips, are supported on a soil with an allowable soil pressure of 2 kips/sq ft. A footing 54 ft long and 8 ft wide will develop a uniform pressure of this magnitude, and this pressure is assumed to exist under the raft. While such a pressure distribution satisfies statics, it is not, of course, the actual pressure that will depend on the deflection of the raft. In order to make certain that this distribution will eventually be reached, the footing must be strong enough to resist stresses resulting from it. Shears and moments are therefore plotted from the assumed distribution, and depth and reinforcement determined from these. The raft is shaped as an inverted T; the thickness and the reinforcement in the slab portion can be determined from the cantilever moment. The transverse reinforcement should, of course, be placed in the bottom of the slab, and the longitudinal reinforcement should be placed in the top of the footing between columns, and in the bottom under these and in the overhangs as indicated by the moment diagram. Excess shearing stresses should be provided for by stirrups.

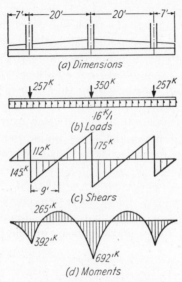

(a) Dimensions

(b) Loads

(c) Shears

(d) Moments

FIG. 4-13. Raft foundation.

The ultimate in raft construction is reached when the entire foundation for a building consists of one solid slab of reinforced concrete, usually called a *mat* foundation. The mat is designed as an inverted slab system spanning between columns and walls and carrying the building weight as a load uniformly distributed over the soil.

Having adopted a mat type of foundation, the engineer will usually develop a design which will offer a minimum general settlement with a maximum uniformity of settlement throughout the building. As nearly as possible, the design is based on uniform distribution of the weight of the building over its entire area, which will not produce an ultimate settlement exceeding a certain amount.

Thus, the usual foundation mat is designed as an inverted slab system sustaining an upward uniform pressure, because such a design permits a limited amount of variation in column loading, distributes the building weight over the local soft spots in the bearing strata, and provides generally a certain amount of continuity in the foundation structure. It cannot, however, without objectionable settlements, care for large variations in column loads or span over large areas of soft ground; and, particularly, it cannot prevent a certain amount of *dishing* or sagging toward the center of the mat area, which is characteristic of such a foundation on a compressible soil. In order to prevent this dishing an arrangement of intersecting crosswalls or Vierendeel trusses (trusses without diagonals) may be utilized.*

There are three types of mat foundation: (1) plain slab, (2) flat slab, and (3) slab-and-girder.

The plain-slab mat consists of a thick slab of concrete of uniform thickness, reinforced with bars both ways at top and bottom. The column capitals may project above or below the top of the slab or they may be omitted and the slab strengthened by additional reinforcement around the column bases. Slab thicknesses up to 5 ft have been used for plain-slab mat foundations.†

The flat-slab mat consists of a concrete slab over the whole area surmounted by truncated pyramidal bases under the columns. Flat-slab construction is suitable for cases having evenly spaced columns which are evenly loaded. They have been used extensively for underground reservoirs, for which they are particularly well adapted.

The slab-and-girder type of construction offers probably the most reliable mat foundation and is frequently used. In designing the stiffening girders, it will often be found that the shears present more difficulties than the bending moments.

4–9. Example of Mat Foundation. A really satisfactory method for the design of mat foundations has yet to be developed. In the following will be presented an approximate method of procedure which has been used for designs in Great Britain.‡

Consider the plan presented in Fig. 4–14, which shows a mat foundation for a small building. The mat is stiffened by girders, indicated by *G1*, *G2*, *G3*, and *G4*, built monolithic with and above the bottom slab. Sometimes the beams are placed underneath the slab, but a more practical arrangement is the one shown. The column loads are indicated and it will be assumed that these loads, exclusive of the weight of the mat foundation, must be distributed over an area large enough to reduce the uniform pressure to 1000 psf. As the sum of all the column loads equals 3020 kips, it follows that the projection of the slab beyond the centerlines of the

---

*See G. W. Glick, "Foundations of the New Telephone Building, Albany, N. Y.," *Proceedings*, International Conference on Soil Mechanics and Foundation Engineering (1936), Vol. 1, p. 278.

†See G. W. Glick, "Rigid Rectangular Frame Foundation for Albany Telephone Building," *Engineering News-Record* (November 27, 1930).

‡See C. E. Reynolds, *Practical Examples of Reinforced Concrete Design* (London, 1938), p. 184.

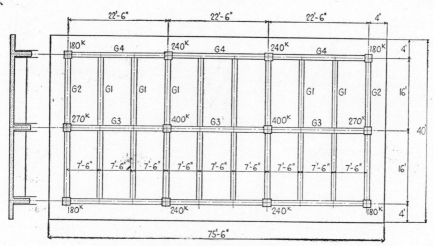

Fig. 4–14. Mat foundation.

outside columns can be found thus:

$$(67.5 + 2x)(32 + 2x) = 3020; \quad x = 4.$$

The slab thickness can be determined by limiting the stress due to bending to the allowable amount. If this stress cannot exceed 1000 psi and noting that the maximum bending moment in the slab occurs at the base of the cantilever section, the effective depth can be found thus:

$$\frac{1000 \times 4 \times 2 \times 12}{\frac{1}{2} \times \frac{3}{8} \times \frac{7}{8} \times 12d^2} = 1000; \quad d = 7 \text{ in.}$$

Assuming a protective cover of 3 in. for the steel reinforcing, it is seen that the slab thickness should be $10\frac{1}{2}$ in. under the marginal girders $G2$ and $G4$. If the bending moment in the slab lying between the columns is taken as

$$\tfrac{1}{10}1000 \times 7.5^2 = 5625 \text{ ft-lb,}$$

the slab thickness can be reduced somewhat for the interior part of the slab. The reinforcement, which for the cantilever portion should be placed in the bottom and in the interior portion in both top and bottom, can be determined in the usual manner.

The shear and moment diagrams will now be developed for the stiffening girders on the assumption that the net soil pressure everywhere is 1000 psf. The uniformly distributed loads on the girders $G1$ and $G2$ in Fig. 4–14 are, respectively,

$$1000 \times 7.5 = 7500 \text{ lb/ft,}$$

$$1000 \times (\tfrac{1}{2}7.5 + 4) = 7750 \text{ lb/ft.}$$

These loads are indicated in Fig. 4–15. If X_1 and X_2 denote the center reactions of the two girders, then these must be proportional to the loads

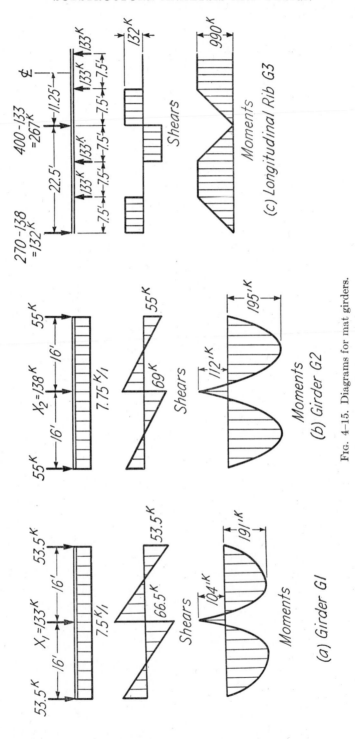

Fig. 4-15. Diagrams for mat girders.

on the respective members. Thus,

$$X_1 \div X_2 = 7500 \div 7750.$$

Furthermore, the sum of all the center reactions must equal the sum of the loads on the four center columns. Thus,

$$8X_1 + 2X_2 = 2 \times 270 + 2 \times 400.$$

Solving the last two equations gives

$$X_1 = 133 \text{ kips}; \quad X_2 = 138 \text{ kips}.$$

With the reactions known, the shear and moment diagrams can be plotted for girders $G1$ and $G2$ as shown in Fig. 4–15.

$$R = \tfrac{1}{2}(32 \times 7.5 - 133) = 53.5.$$

The two longitudinal ribs $G3$ and $G4$ can next be analyzed, as all forces on them are known. Fig. 4–15(c) shows shear and moment diagrams for one-half of the center rib, $G3$. This girder must, in accordance with the assumptions, carry only concentrated loads from the interior girder $G1$ and $G2$. In addition to the concentrated loads, the outside longitudinal ribs, $G4$, will carry a uniformly distributed load from the adjacent canti-lever portion of the slab.

4–10. Raft for Water Tower. In order to minimize the effects of any unequal settlement that may occur when a tank is filled for the first time, it may be to advantage to construct the foundation as a continuous circular raft instead of using isolated single footings. A similar form of footing is met with in chimney construction. Because of the presence of a comparatively large wind moment, this raft structure will not at all times exert approximately the same pressure on its surface of contact; a considerable variation may occur between opposite edges.

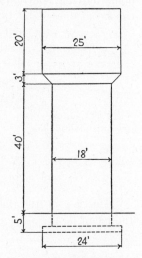

FIG. 4–16. Water tower.

As an example, consider the foundation for the water tower shown in Fig. 4–16. The capacity of the tank is assumed to be 70,000 gal and the pressure under the raft must not exceed 4000 psf. Additional assumptions are:

Weight of empty tower	535 kips
Weight of foundation	80 kips
Weight of 70,000 gal	585 kips
Total weight	1200 kips
Wind moment at foundation level	1600 ft-kips

The total maximum pressure can be expressed as the sum of the uniform pressure due to the direct load and the linearly varying pressure caused by moment. If this total pressure must not exceed 4 kips/sq ft, then

$$\frac{1200}{\frac{\pi}{4}D^2} + \frac{1600}{\frac{\pi}{32}D^3} = 4,$$

$$D^3 - 382D - 4074 = 0, \quad D = 23.6, \text{say } 24 \text{ ft.}$$

The thickness of the circular footing will depend upon the bending stresses caused by the net pressure. This net upward pressure is found by excluding the weight of the raft from the total pressure. Thus,

$$\frac{1120}{452} \pm \frac{1600}{1357} = 3.66 \text{ and } 1.30 \text{ kips/sq ft.}$$

If the raft is assumed simply supported along the periphery of the hollow circular shaft on which the tank is supported, then bending moments can be evaluated by taking the moments in a simply supported circular plate and subtracting the moments due to the loads on the overhanging portions. From Fig. 4–17 it is seen that the average load intensity is 2480 psf. The maximum bending moment in a simply supported circular plate occurs at the center and is equal to*

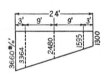

FIG. 4–17. Net pressures with full tank.

$$M = \frac{3 + \mu}{16\pi} W, \tag{4–19}$$

where μ = Poisson's ratio, usually 0.15 for concrete,
 W = total load.

If in Eq. (4–19) the total load on the inside circular area is based on the mean net pressure in Fig. 4–17, then the unrestrained moment is

$$\frac{3.15}{16} 2480 \times 9^2 = 39{,}550 \text{ ft-lb.}$$

This moment will be reduced by the load acting on the overhanging ends. On opposite points of a diameter lying in the plane of the overturning moment, these pressures would be

$$\tfrac{1}{2}(3660 + 3364) \times 3 \times \tfrac{3}{2} = 15{,}800 \text{ ft-lb,}$$

$$\tfrac{1}{2}(1595 + 1300) \times 3 \times \tfrac{3}{2} = 6520 \text{ ft-lb.}$$

---

*Stephen Timoshenko, *Theory of Plates and Shells* (New York, 1940), p. 60.

The mean of these two moments should be subtracted from the unrestrained moment in order to obtain the restrained moment, thus,

$$39,550 - \tfrac{1}{2}(15,800 + 6520) = 28,390 \text{ ft-lb.}$$

Assuming a concrete working stress of 1350 psi, the effective depth of the slab can be found by Eq. (4–1), thus,

$$d = \sqrt{\frac{28,390 \times 12}{\tfrac{1}{2} \times 403 \times 0.866 \times 1350 \times 12}} = 11.25 \text{ in.}$$

In order to allow a protective cover of concrete of $2\tfrac{1}{2}$ in. and two layers of reinforcing bars, it is seen that the slab thickness should be at least 15 in. The interior of the slab should have reinforcement in the top in two perpendicular directions and decreasing from the center toward the circumference. In the cantilever portion the reinforcement should be placed in the bottom in radial directions and have sufficient anchorage beyond the supporting shaft.

It must, of course, be realized that the preceding method of analysis is approximate as it superimposes upon the results of the elastic plate theory some assumptions relative to beam action. It should also be realized that in the designs of tower foundations, other loading conditions are often critical. In so far as wind is concerned the condition of empty tower plus full wind should be investigated. This is the combination which often places compression over only a portion of the footing and, in many instances, determines the size of the footing.

4–11. Grillage Footings. A typical grillage footing is shown in Fig. 4–18. It consists of two or more tiers of I-beams. Each tier is placed at right angles to the one below it, and the load is carried to the soil through beam action. The individual beams of each tier are held together by diaphragms, consisting of a system of bolts and pipe separations. The diaphragms or separators should be placed near each end of the beams and at intermediate positions not over 5 ft apart.

Grillage beams should not be painted and the whole system should be completely encased in concrete. The bottom beams should have at least 6 in. of concrete underneath and preferably 9 in. The

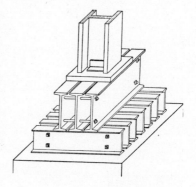

FIG. 4–18. Steel grillage footing.

clear space between the ends of the beam flanges should not be less than 2 in. nor more than three-quarters of the flange width. The assembled grillage is usually blocked up in position and leveled before the concrete is poured around it.

During the latter part of last century the steel grillage footing was extensively used, but the rapid development of reinforced concrete during the past forty years has made the steel grillage footing all but obsolete. They are still used for underpinning work and there is in existence a very large number of these footings.

In the design of grillage footings it is assumed that (a) the concrete filling carries no stress and acts merely as a protection against corrosion, (b) each tier acts independently of the other tiers, (c) the pressure from the footing is uniformly distributed over the bed, and (d) the pressure of one tier of beams is uniformly distributed on the tier below.

4–12. Numerical Example. Let it be desired to design a grillage footing for a column load of 824 kips. The column rests on a 36 in. × 36 in. steel slab, which transfers the load to the upper tier beams. The allowable soil pressure is 5.5 kips/sq ft. Allowable working stresses for the structural steel are 16,000 and 10,000 lb/in. in bending and shear, respectively.

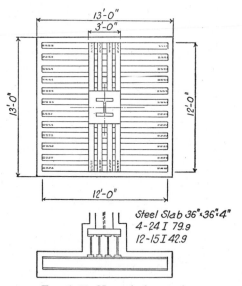

Fig. 4–19. Numerical example.

Fig. 4–19 shows the general arrangement. Necessary computations are listed in the following:

Column load . . . . 824 kips
Estimated weight of footing . . . . 76 kips
Total . . . . 900 kips

Required bearing area 900 ÷ 5.5 = 164. Footing 13 ft × 13 ft = 169 sq ft with four beams in upper tier and twelve beams in lower tier; net pressure/lin ft of beams will be:

$$\text{Upper tier: } 824 \div (\ 4 \times 12) = 17.1.$$

$$\text{Lower tier: } 824 \div (12 \times 12) = 5.7.$$

Maximum bending moment for the upper tier will be

$$17.1 \times 6 \times (3 - 0.75) = 231 \text{ ft-kips.}$$

The maximum bending stress is found by dividing the bending moment by the section modulus. Thus,

$$231{,}000 \times 12 \div 174 = 15{,}930 \text{ psi.}$$

The bending moments in the lower tier beams will be one-third of those in the upper tier. Hence, the maximum bending stress will be

$$\frac{231{,}000 \times 12}{3 \times 59} = 15{,}660 \text{ psi.}$$

Shearing and buckling stresses should be checked in the usual manner and will be found to be below permissible values.

4–13. Underpinning. The installation of new foundations under an existing structure is called *underpinning*. The operation usually requires two distinct steps—namely, the temporary support of the structure during the installation of the new substructure and the construction of the new foundation.

Underpinning may be necessary when excavation for new construction, such as subways and lowering of street elevations, is to be carried below the level of existing foundations. It may also be necessary on account of faulty design of the original substructure or changing soil conditions.[*]

Temporary support of the structure prior to underpinning may be effected by the use of *shores, needles,* or both. Shores are heavy timbers that are placed against the walls or sides of the structure and act as inclined struts (see Fig. 4–20). The proper shoring of a structure requires a good deal of judgment and experience, so that the shores exert as small a horizontal thrust as possible and so that no damage is caused to the structure. It is good practice to place the heads of the shores opposite a floor in order to reduce the lateral push on the wall. Proper transfer of load from the structure to the shores requires considerable attention; suitable niches must be cut in the wall, and the space between the heads and the masonry must be grouted to insure uniform bearing.

---

[*]For a complete discussion of this subject see E. A. Prentis and L. White, *Underpinning* (New York, 1931).

Temporary support of the structure may be carried out by the use of needle beams as shown in Fig. 4–21. Holes are cut through the wall just above the ground level, through which timber beams or steel girders are inserted (hence the name "needles"). These beams are supported on each side of the wall and are brought into contact with the superstructure by means of wedges and cement grouting.

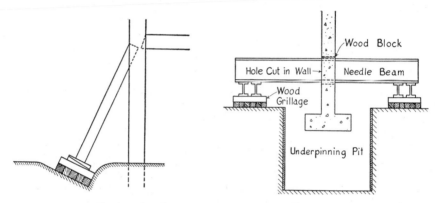

FIG. 4–20. Shoring of wall.　　FIG. 4–21. Simple needling operation.

The footings carrying the needles and the shores should be given careful attention; they should be adequate, otherwise settlement will occur when the load is transferred to them.

After the temporary supports have been placed under the structure, the new foundation can be installed. Usually pits are excavated under the old foundation down to the desired level and new footings are constructed, or piles are driven either on both sides of the wall or in the pit directly under it. If headroom is lacking, the piles can be made of short sections of steel pipes, to be cleaned out and filled with concrete once the desired level has been reached.

It is of great importance that the space between the existing and the additional substructures is filled completely to carry the load of the superstructure. The underpinning should be put to work by bringing the load to it. If this is not done, the load will eventually be carried to the underpinning by settlement of the structure itself.

So-called *pretest underpinning* has been successfully used by organizations specializing in strengthening and rebuilding substructures. By this method sectional steel cylinders are jacked down beneath the foundations of a structure to a satisfactory bearing material, after which they are cleaned out and filled with concrete. Each cylinder is then tested to an overload, usually about 50 per cent in excess of the permanent load. While the full test pressure is maintained on the jacks, a short steel column is placed on top of the cylinder, and the load of the footing is permanently transferred to the underpinning cylinder by means of steel wedges (see Fig. 4–22).

Courtesy of Spencer, White, and Prentis, Inc.

FIG. 4–22. Pretest underpinning.

PROBLEMS

4–1. This single spread footing is reinforced with sixteen 1 in. square bars in each direction and supports a square column. It is known that the maximum bond stress, u, is 114 psi. Find the load in the column and average pressure under the footing. (*Ans.*: 431 kips and 7 ksf.)

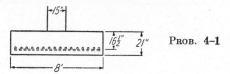

PROB. 4–1

4–2. This reinforced concrete rectangular footing is 28 ft long, 6 ft wide, and 4 ft thick. The total soil pressure underneath (including the weight of the footing) is 6550 psf. Find column loads. (*Ans.*: 400 and 600 kips.)

PROB. 4–2   PROB. 4–3

4–3. This reinforced concrete trapezoidal footing is 3 ft thick. The total soil pressure (including the weight of the footing) is 5000 psf. Find the column loads A and B. (*Ans.*: $A = 391$ kips.)

4–4. What is the ratio between the lengths of the parallel sides of a trapezoidal footing supporting two columns 22 ft on centers and carrying equal loads? The distances from the parallel sides to the column centers should be 3 ft and 5 ft. (*Ans.*: 1.5.)

4–5. Design a rectangular footing to support two columns having loads of 400 kips and 500 kips, respectively, and being 18 ft on centers. The weight of the footing is 100 kips and the allowable bearing value is 4 ksf. The footing must extend only 1 ft beyond the center of the smaller column. (*Ans.*: 22 ft long, 11 ft, 4 in. wide.)

4–6. Find the maximum bending moment in the rectangular footing in Prob. 4–5. (*Ans.*: 1550 ft-kips.)

4–7. Using same data as in Prob. 4–5, additional information is that the footing can extend only 1 ft beyond the centerlines of each column. Find the lengths of the parallel sides of the trapedoizal footing. (*Ans.*: 8 ft, 9 in., and 16 ft, 3 in.)

DRIVING "BATTER PILES"

CHAPTER 5

PILES OF STEEL, TIMBER, AND CONCRETE

5-1. Introduction. Piles are structural units by means of which loads are transmitted to lower levels. The principal use of piles occurs in the foundations of bridges, buildings, and other structures, where they may effect economy of construction by eliminating the necessity of deep expensive foundations of other types.

The all-important consideration in the design of a pile foundation is the capacity of the soil to carry the load brought to it by a single pile, or a group of piles. It is essential, therefore, to have detailed knowledge of the soil at the site, from the ground surface to a depth well below the points of possible piles.

Piles may be classified as *friction piles* or *end-bearing piles*, according to the manner in which they transfer their loads into the underlying soil. A friction pile develops bearing capacity, either partly or wholly, by *skin friction;* the load is transferred to the adjacent soil by friction along the embedded length of the pile. An end-bearing pile transfers practically all of its load by point bearing to the firm soil stratum upon which it rests.

In addition to vertical foundation-bearing piles, there are other types, such as batter piles, which make an angle with the vertical and are designed to give lateral stability or to resist upward forces.

There are numerous and complex combinations of soil materials and arrangements existing in nature. The designer of pile foundations must, therefore, depend to an unusual degree on experience and judgment. Complete information on soil conditions and experience in interpreting this information are absolutely essential factors in the correct design of pile foundations.* Final design of any important structure should not be made without loading or driving tests.

Piles are generally brought down to their final positions by a succession of blows delivered to the tops by a pile hammer, which, for heavy construction, is usually a double-acting steam hammer. A pile driver equipped with a steam hammer and leads is shown in Fig. 5-1. The leads consist of upright parallel members for guiding the pile and the hammer.

When piles are driven into fine-grained sand, the top surface may subside (sometimes as much as a foot). This indicates that the vibrating action of the hammer has resulted in a large reduction of voids. Such action involves a considerable increase in the bearing power and frictional

---

*See Arthur Casagrande, "The Structure of Clay and Its Importance in Foundation Engineering," *Journal of Boston Society of Civil Engineers* (April, 1932).

Courtesy of Spencer, White, and Prentis, Inc.

FIG. 5-1. Pile driver.

resistance of the sand, and the bearing capacity of a soil may actually be raised in this manner. On the other hand, it is not uncommon that driving piles into soft clay causes the surface to rise and that the driving of one pile will cause adjacent piles, already driven, to rise. This indicates that there has been no compaction of the soil and no increase in bearing capacity and frictional resistance.

If it is desired to compact uniformly a soil in a given area, pile driving should start at the center and proceed outward to the perimeter. If the order of procedure were reversed, the driving would become more difficult as the area without piles became smaller; and, to secure uniform penetration, the outer piles would be forced to rise some.

Piles may be driven by the aid of water jets. This, briefly, consists in displacing the material in contact with the lower portion of the pile by discharging water under pressure. As the water comes up around the pile carrying with it some of the material, it also diminishes the frictional resistance of the pile by forming a lubricating film on it.

While the water jet may be used to advantage in any soil except hard-pan and rock, the best results are obtained in sand and gravel. Jet pipes may be embedded in concrete piles, or they may be attached to the outside of the pile in such a way that they can easily be withdrawn. It is advisable to use two jets placed on opposite sides of the pile, since this will enable the pile to be placed more correctly. The size of the pipes ranges from $1\frac{1}{2}$ to $2\frac{1}{2}$ in. and the size of the nozzle from no contraction to $\frac{1}{2}$ in. The maximum water pressure to be provided varies from 100 to 225 psi and the volume discharged from 50 to 200 gpm. In the use of jetting, care must be exercised not to loosen adjoining piles already driven.

5–2. Pile Spacing. In the case of an end-bearing pile driven through poor soil to contact with hard material, it can be assumed that all, or nearly all, of the pile's support will be in end-bearing on such hard material. Such piles can be spaced as closely as it is practicable to drive them, which is generally $3 \times D$, where D is the diameter of the pile section's inscribed circle. The capacity of such a group is generally assumed to equal the capacity of one pile multiplied by the number of piles.

The support provided by the soil for a single isolated friction pile, as determined by test loading, is usually greater than that of each of the piles of a group of piles, simultaneously loaded. This is because most of the soil which assists in supporting a single pile (due to radial distribution of the load through vertical shear) will also be required to assist in the support of other piles driven nearby.

The tendency of a pile foundation to settle due to group action is dependent upon the compressibility and the shear capacity of the soil around the piles and below their points. This tendency to settle is great in case of frictional support in poor soil and it is dependent upon the spacing, length of penetration, and loading of the piles and upon the size and pattern of the cluster. The greater the overlapping of distributed loads in the center of a cluster (as in a case of a cluster of large area with round or square pattern and great total load), the greater will be the additional settlement of the piles near the center (due to the greater vertical pressure below their points and due to the greater distance from such piles to the periphery of the vertical shear planes immediately outside of the outer rows of piles). In the case of a square or rectangular cluster, in contrast with a round cluster, the corner piles will tend to settle more than the others in the outer rows because of the greater magnitude of the shear at the intersection of adjacent shear planes.

The usual spacing of friction piles is too close, a tendency which is undoubtedly due to a desire to keep the sizes of the footings as small as possible and also to the lack of definite recommendations in building specifications.

The following requirement is listed in the specifications of the Ohio State Highway Department:*

Except in the case of short penetration through poor soil to rock, the pile spacing shall be not less than 3 ft and preferably not less than 3 ft, 6 in. In the case of a large area, preference shall be given to a still greater spacing with correspondingly greater load per pile and greater penetration, which for the same area of cluster will result in deeper outer vertical planes and a lesser unit shear, will cause greater horizontal distribution, and will cause the piles to reach less compressible soil. Battered piles in the outer and intermediate rows, using a greater rate of batter for the outermost rows, will move the critical vertical shear planes appreciably outward, thus considerably lengthening the periphery of the shear planes with consequent lesser unit shear and increasing the total bearing area beneath the points. Besides, in the case of a cluster of rather large square or round area, piles should be omitted in the center, and the vertical piles immediately around the center space should be driven to a capacity about 75 per cent greater. Those at the corners (in case of square area) should be driven to a capacity about 50 per cent greater than the computed design load. In the case of a long and narrow footing with two rows of piles, it will ordinarily be necessary to observe only the rule calling for wide spacing with a relatively great load per pile and relatively great length of penetration.

In order to avoid the paradox of having piles strong enough to support the superstructure but embedded in a soil, the volume of which is not sufficient to support the piles, the Boston Building Code requires that the pressure intensity on a plane through the bottoms of the piles be checked. Thus:†

The allowable pile loading shall be limited by the provision that the vertical pressures in the bearing materials at or below the points of the piles, produced by the loads on all piles in a foundation, shall not exceed the allowable bearing values of such materials. Piles or pile groups shall be assumed to transfer their loads to the bearing materials by spreading the load uniformly at an angle of 60° with the horizontal, starting at a polygon circumscribing the piles at the top of the satisfactory bearing stratum in which they are embedded, but the area considered as supporting the load shall not extend beyond the intersection of the 60° planes of adjacent piles or pile groups.

It is interesting to note that the preceding requirement allows no distribution through unsatisfactory soils (such as those excluded from the

*Specifications for Design of Highway Structures, State of Ohio (1946), Sec. 104.
†Boston Building Code, Sec. 2909(b).

materials listed in Table 3–1). The assumed distribution at an angle of 60° with the horizontal is, of course, not correct, but is probably a reasonably safe assumption to use as a basis of calculations.

Much more definite is the so-called Converse-Labarre formula for reducing the supporting value of a group of friction piles. This formula, which has been adopted by a number of building codes,* gives an efficiency factor for friction piles in terms of the spacing and size of cluster. It should be observed that lengths of the piles or distances embedded in friction strata do not appear in the formula. According to this formula, the supporting value of piles, depending solely on friction when driven, shall be determined by multiplying the bearing value of a single pile by an efficiency factor F; thus,

$$F = 1 - \theta \frac{(n-1)m + (m-1)n}{90mn}, \qquad (5\text{–}1)$$

where n = number of piles per row,
m = number of rows,
θ = arc tan (d/s), in degrees,
d = diameter of pile,
s = spacing of pile centers.

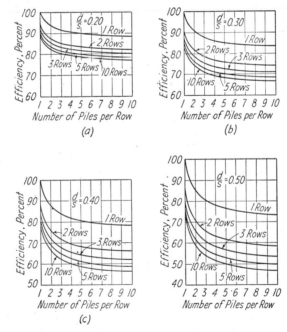

FIG. 5–2. Efficiency of friction pile groups.

*Pacific Coast Building Officials; American Association of State Highway Officials; City of New Orleans.

In the accompanying diagrams,* Fig. 5–2, solutions have been plotted for several values of d/s selected as being representative of the magnitude of range commonly encountered in practice.

As a numerical example let it be desired to find the capacity of a pile cluster consisting of sixteen piles arranged in four rows of four. The spacing in both directions is three times the pile dimension. A pile load test indicates that the safe capacity of one pile is 20 tons.

According to Eq. (5–1), the eficiency factor is

$$F = 1 - \frac{3 \times 4 + 3 \times 4}{90 \times 4 \times 4} \text{ arc tan } \frac{1}{3} = 1 - \frac{18.43}{60} = 0.692,$$

and the total capacity according to this method is

$$20 \times 16 \times 0.692 = 221 \text{ tons.}$$

The efficiency factor, F, can also be found by interpolating between the values found by the diagrams in Fig. 5–2(b) and (c). As these diagrams correspond to $d/s = 0.30$ and 0.40, respectively, the efficiency factor for $s = 3d$ is found by interpolation; thus,

$$F = 0.641 + \tfrac{2}{3}(0.723 - 0.641) = 0.695.$$

5–3. Timber Piles. Wood piles or timber piles are tree trunks with the branches cut off, driven with the small end down. The end may be cut off square, it may be pointed, or it may be provided with a metal shoe.

Pile specifications† usually call for a uniform taper, the pile to be so straight that a line drawn through the center of the butt (the large end) and the tip (the small end) will not fall outside the pile. With a minimum tip size of 5 in., the butt may range up to 20 in. or even more in diameter, depending on desired length (see Table 5–1).

Timber piles are generally used for comparatively low loads; thus, the Ohio State Highway Department states that 16-in. timber piles should not be required to support more than 27 tons, while the reaction on a 10-in. timber must not exceed 17 tons.

Where wood piles are constantly submerged or cut off below the ground-water level, they apparently have an indefinite life. If, however, they are exposed to alternate wetting and drying, they slowly decay unless they are impregnated with creosote or some other germicide. The decay of wood is the result of the action of certain low forms of plant life called *fungi*. Substances in wood form the food of the fungi, and as these substances are consumed, the wood is disintegrated. The species of fungi

*See I. B. Rau, "Curves Give Efficiencies of Friction Pile Groups," *Civil Engineering* (July, 1954), p. 61.

†See "Specification for Wood Piles," American Railway Engineering Association (1953), Sec. 7-1-37.

TABLE 5–1

DIAMETERS OF THREE CLASSES OF PILES*

CLASS A AND CLASS B PILES (These differ in size only)						CLASS C PILEa (These differ from Classes A and B in size and quality)			
CLASS A			CLASS B						
Diameter 3' from Butt Inches		Minimum Diameter of Tip Inches	Diameter 3' from Butt Inches		Minimum Diameter of Tip Inches	Diameter 3' from Butt Inches		Minimum Diameter of Tip Inches	Length in Feet
Minimum	Maximum		Minimum	Maximum		Minimum	Maximum		
DOUGLAS FIR AND SOUTHERN PINE PILESb									
14	18	10	12	20	8	12	20	8	Under 40
14	18	9	12	20	7	12	20	6	40 to 50, incl.
14	18	8	13	20	7	12	20	6	51 to 70, incl.
14	20	7	13	20	6	12	20	6	71 to 90, incl.
14	20	6	13	20	5	12	20	5	Over 90
BLACK OAK, CHESTNUT, CYPRESS, PIN OAK, POST OR BURR OAK, RED OAK, WHITE OAK OR WILLOW OAK PILES									
14	18	10	12	18	8	12	20	8	Under 30
14	18	9	13	20	8	12	20	8	30 to 40, incl.
14	18	8	13	20	7	12	20	6	Over 40
CEDAR PILES									
14	22	10	12	22	8	12	22	8	Under 30
14	22	9	13	22	8	12	22	8	30 to 40, incl.
14	22	8	13	22	7	12	22	7	Over 40

*From ASTM Standard specification.

aIn Class C piles, a minimum diameter (at cut-off) of 10 in. may be specified for lengths of 20 ft and under.

bWhere larch, lodgepole, or Norway pine, spruce, or tamarack piles are specified, their dimension shall correspond to the requirements shown for Douglas fir and Southern pine.

that cause decay require food, air, the right amount of moisture, and a favorable temperature. Timber that is continuously below water level does not decay. Poisoning the food supply by impregnating the timber with a suitable preservative is the easiest and surest method of preventing decay.

In waterfront structures timber may also be damaged by insects (termites and wharf borers), and marine borers. Timber can be protected against decay and attack of insects by proper pressure treatment with suitable toxic agents. Coal-tar creosote and zinc chloride are most generally used. Creosote can be used for piles completely buried in the ground and also for piles exposed to the weather or immersed in water. Timber treated with zinc chloride may be painted.

The American Society of Civil Engineers in a pamphlet entitled *Timber Piles and Construction Timbers* has listed information pertaining to wood piles.* The following paragraphs are taken from this manual:

Timber piles in place are usually difficult and expensive to renew. Obviously they should be selected with care and with reference to the service expected of them. A uniform specification will tend to result in a more standardized product and a cheaper one. For convenience in specifying piles for structures of varying requirements, piles have been divided into three classes:

Class A piles are to be used for heavily loaded structures, for those having piles with considerable unsupported length, or those which, for other reasons, require the strongest grade of piles;

Class B piles have the same requirements for quality as Class A but are of smaller diameter; and,

Class C piles may be used as foundation piles where the cut-off will be permanently under water level and treatment is not required for protection against marine borers. This class of piles may also be used for cofferdams, falsework, and other temporary structures.

The piles shall have the limiting dimensions listed in Table 5-1. These dimensions are minimum or maximum as stated, but a tolerance of $\frac{1}{2}$ in. in a given diam will be allowed in not more than 25 per cent of the pieces of that diam.

Piles shall taper uniformly from the point of butt measurement to the tip. Piles shall be free from short or reversed bends, and from crooks greater than one-half the diam of the pile at the middle of the bend. A line drawn from the center of the butt to the center of the tip shall lie within the body of the pile.

All knots and limbs shall be trimmed or cut smoothly, flush with the surface of the pile. Ends must be cut square with the axis of the pile. Class A and Class B piles shall be peeled smooth, clean, and free from inner bark. Class C piles need not be peeled, but they shall be free from any defects which may impair their strength as piles, such as decay, splits, twist of grain exceeding one-half of the circumference in any 20 ft of length.

Untreated foundation piles, unless continuously wet or otherwise protected, are subject to attack by decay, termites, and, in certain localities, by wharf borers. Unless it is certain that their heads will remain below ground water during the life of the structure, they should receive preservative treatment. In general, structures in salt water should be considered subject to attack by marine borers. Even where there is no previous record of destructive attack, the widespread attack in New England, first noted in 1933, shows that changing conditions may bring attack. Since the water conditions which govern attack are unknown, a prediction as to the future is uncertain and conservative practice normally justifies treatment.

When treatment to protect against borers is unnecessary, as in fresh water,

---

Manual of Engineering Practice, American Society of Civil Engineers, No. 17.

it is still a long-time economy measure unless the piles are very long. If this be the case, untreated piles may be cut off at water level and treated timber used above water to prevent decay.

The most commonly used pile timbers are the cedars, cypress, Douglas fir, the oaks, pines, and spruces. If conditions justify the use of untreated piles, any wood with sufficient strength may be used. If the piles are to be treated, Douglas fir, the red oak group, and southern pine are the most satisfactory. The white oak group does not furnish a satisfactory pile timber for treatment.

For protection against marine borers, decay, or termite attack, no impregnating material has proved equal to high-grade, coal-tar creosote. The best results are obtained from a treatment which secures the maximum penetration by the preservative.

It is just as necessary, for good results, that the timber be properly prepared for the treatment and that the treating be correctly done as it is that the creosote be of the best quality. If at all possible, timber should be ordered sufficiently early to permit air-seasoning before treatment.

Timber piles have occasionally been driven butt end down, to prevent uplift which would otherwise act against the taper of the pile. An important use of timber piles is as fenders and bumpers in front of piers and wharves, for which their elasticity and easy replacement make them especially suitable.

5-4. Steel Piles. During the period from about 1880 to 1905 a number of bridges were built throughout the Middle West on supports consisting of steel bearing piles in the form of rolled and fabricated sections. Most of the bridges were used for river crossings where heavy floods and ice floes occur yearly; the piles, therefore, were subjected both above and below ground to the action of moisture. In only a few of these bridges were the piles encased in concrete or protected in any way, except by coats of red lead paints. Examinations of a great number of these piles show that the decrease in section due to corrosion has not been more than 1 per cent in twenty years.* Even smaller reductions may be expected in copper steel which, if specified, should contain not less than 0.2 per cent of copper.

Steel piles have greater capacity per pile. This may be utilized to greatest advantage in locations where the piling can be driven into hard ground material such as hardpan and shale or to firm bearing on solid rock. In such cases extremely high bearing capacities can be developed. But also in soft soil, steel piling may be used to advantage, where a long length of penetration is necessary to reach a low-lying stratum or to develop, by friction, required bearing capacities.

Less space is required for storage and shipping of steel piling. Also,

---

*See J. G. Mason and A. L. Ogle, "Steel Pile Foundations in Nebraska," *Civil Engineering* (September, 1932), p. 553.

on account of the facility of splicing rolled steel shapes on the job, there is practically no limit to the length that can be used. Steel piling can withstand very rough handling. While wood piles may split and concrete piles crack, the stresses in rolled steel piles are generally quite small.

The principal advantage of steel piles, however, lies in their ability to withstand the punishment of the long-continued and hard driving necessary to obtain the required penetration. They have the fortunate characteristic of showing any distress due to driving at the extreme top. In a short period of hard, fast driving, the top will bend and finally wrinkle. This damage usually occurs within the top 6 to 12 in., leaving the remainder in perfect condition. The damaged end can be cut off with a torch, and the driving can be resumed with but little loss of time.

One of the disadvantages of using steel piles is the material's susceptibility to corrosion. While steel piles are not subject to attack and destruction by borers, insects, or other organisms (such as limnoria, teredos and termites), they are, under certain circumstances, susceptible to corrosion. Experience indicates that corrosion is not a serious problem when the piles are completely below ground-water level, but it must be guarded against where sea water is present, where ground water has a high salinity content, or where the piles are subject to alternate wetting

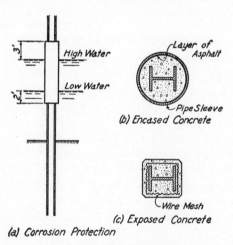

(a) Corrosion Protection

(b) Encased Concrete

(c) Exposed Concrete

FIG. 5-3. Pile protection.

or drying. Fig. 5-3 shows concrete protection of a steel pile extending through air, water, and saturated ground. Experience indicates the desirability of protecting steel bearing piles from a point below low water up to some distance above high water. The distance the protection extends above high water is dependent on the degree of exposure of the structure due to wave action. Along rivers and protected sites, 2 to 3 ft above high waterline is sufficient. Along exposed beaches or on the shores of any large bodies of water, the protection may have to be carried up to considerable height in order to get above prevalent height of waves during rough weather.

It is advisable that a heavy coating of tar or asphalt be applied hot to the steel pile before driving. After the piles are driven, steel cylinders with their inside surfaces coated can be placed around the piles and the space about the pile filled with concrete. Fig. 5–3(c) shows this type of protection as well-exposed concrete reinforced with wire mesh.

In some instances, steel bearing piles have received 2 to 3 in. of gunite concrete while on the ground at the job site. If properly cured and reinforced with wire mesh, subsequent driving of the piles will not injure the gunite protection. It is advisable, however, to coat the exterior of the gunite concrete with a heavy coating of tar or asphalt.

The surface corrosion of steel is proportionate to the amount of moist atmosphere and dissolved or free oxygen coming in contact with it. The rate of corrosion slows up considerably as soon as the steel takes on a film of products of corrosion. The products of corrosion will permeate the ground adjacent to the pile, generally for several inches, and form a dense and impervious encasement around the steel. Expecially where piles are driven in sand, conditions are particularly favorable to the formation of an impervious coating of ferro-silicate, as soon as the steel corrodes slightly, that will form an encasement which is effective in preventing further corrosion. Thus, it is seen that in subgrade structures, where fresh oxygen cannot be brought to the steel either by penetration of air or by subsurface water currents, no special protection of the steel is necessary. On the other hand, in structures such as pile bents, which extend continuously from below a stream or sea bottom, some form of protection is desirable in the region of maximum corrosion, which is usually between the low and high water marks. As shown in Fig. 5–3 the encasement should begin at a point about 2 ft below low water and extend up to a point above high water, where maintenance such as painting can be applied to the rest of the pile.

Steel bearing piles should generally not be spaced closer center to center than two and one-half times their nominal size and preferably not closer than three times their nominal size.

The points of the piles should be left square and blunt without any pointing. Square-ended piles penetrate readily in a straight line without any tendency to cant. They are not deflected when they strike obstructions. Where piles are driven to solid rock, the square ends may be increased in cross-sectional area by welding or riveting on suitable angles and plates. This method is shown in Fig. 5–4. It is general practice to build the ends of the piles so that the pressure between the steel and the rock ranges from 3000 to 6000 psi. Furthermore, welds or rivets are usually proportioned to develop stresses of 10,000 psi on added steel areas.

The bearing capacity of steel piles can be increased by the use of various types of attachments to compress the earth more effectively or to develop

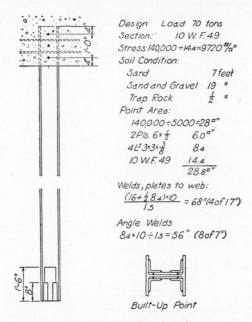

Design   Load 70 tons
Section: 10 W. F. 49
Stress:140,000÷14.4=9720#/□"
Soil Condition:
    Sand   7 feet
    Sand and Gravel   19 "
    Trap Rock $\frac{1}{2}$ "
Point Area:
    140,000÷5000=28□"
    2Pls. 6×$\frac{1}{2}$ 6.0□"
    4L^s 3×3×$\frac{3}{8}$ 8.4
    10 W.F. 49   14.4
                          28.8□"

Welds, plates to web:
$$\frac{(16+\frac{1}{2}8.4)\times10}{1.5} = 68"(4of17")$$

Angle Welds
    8.4×10÷1.5=56" (8of7")

Built-Up Point

Fig. 5-4. Steel bearing pile.

direct bearing on the underlying soil. A very effective type of attachment is the so-called *lagging* which is shown in Fig. 5–5. It consists of short pieces of rolled steel shape that are welded to the main section. In this way the bearing capacities of steel piles can be considerably increased; for the case shown in Fig. 5–5, an increase of at least one-third can ordinarily be expected.

It is important to provide adequate connections between the steel piles and the piers and footings. Where piles extend considerable distances up into concrete piers, no special treatment is required since the bond between the concrete and the steel is more than enough to develop the pile capacities. If the pile extends only a few feet into the pier, some means for transferring the load from concrete to steel should be provided. This can be done by tying concrete to the steel by means of reinforcing rods inserted through holes in the web and flanges of the steel piles, as shown in Fig. 5–4. The holes should be burned in the field after driving has been completed. If the pile terminates but a few inches above the bottom of the footing, a cap is required (see Fig. 5–5).

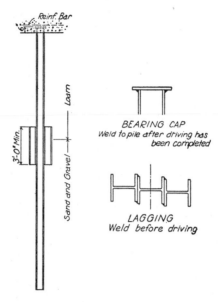

FIG. 5–5. Steel bearing pile.

5–5. Selection of Steel Piling. Because of the high structural strength of steel piling and its ability to withstand the hard driving that is necessary to develop high bearing value, careful investigation of the ultimate bearing capacity for each particular location is warranted. Actual loading tests should be made for piles of a proposed structure to determine or check the design load.

Most of the earlier installations of steel bearing piles consisted of sections of 8-in. depth and flange width, but larger sections are now frequently used on account of their greater lateral strength. The larger sections can be used with economy in many cases. The bearing capacity for a given penetration can generally be assumed to vary approximately as the square of the nominal size.

Even though complete information regarding the type of soil is available, reasonable prediction of safe bearing values can be made only from driving records and load tests. For preliminary and tentative designs, however, Table 5–2 can be used, subject to final determination of actual length of piles by test.

In order to illustrate the use of Table 5–2, let it be desired to determine a structural steel shape which will safely support a load of 30 tons in a hard clay that offers between high and medium resistance to driving.

The dash line indicated in Fig. 5–6 should be used for the net perimeter of a steel pile. Thus, a section designated as $8WF31$ has a net perimeter equal to $4 \times 8 = 32$ in. $= 2.67$ ft. The sustaining value can, according to Table 5–2, be assumed to be 500 lb/sq ft. The minimum penetration should therefore be

$$\frac{60,000}{500 \times 2.67} = 45 \text{ ft.}$$

TABLE 5–2

FRICTIONAL RESISTANCE FOR STEEL PILES*

Soil Condition	Piles Driven to†	Sustaining Value (Lb/Sq Ft)
Sand and gravel................	Practical refusal	1000
Gravel.........................	Practical refusal	950
Sand	Practical refusal	700
Hard, sandy clay...............	High resistance	600
Hard clay	Medium resistance	400
Medium clay	Low resistance	250

*Compiled from data given in *Steel Bearing Piles*, Publication of Carnegie Steel Co. (Pittsburgh, 1935) p. 46.
†Definition of Driving Terms:
    Refusal.....................0.00 to 0.10⎫
    Practical refusal..............0.10 to 0.25⎪ in. per blow, using
    High resistance...............0.25 to 0.50⎬ hammer delivering approximately
    Medium resistance............0.60 to 1.00⎪ 15,000 ft-lb per blow.
    Low resistance...............1.25 to 1.75⎭

Steel piles can generally be set into position and driven by means of simple leads suspended from the boom of the hoisting equipment. Where test piles indicate fairly uniform driving conditions and where the length of the pile is determined by penetration desired rather than direct bearing on rock, the most economical results are obtained by ordering the piles in the lengths required from the rolling mill. When piles are to be driven to a certain resistance, their individual lengths may vary considerably if there are great differences in the underlying soil. Under these conditions, one of the most economical methods is to drive for the first pile a section longer than that which is known to be required; this section may be one piece or several pieces spliced together. The surplus length at the top is then cut off by burning after the necessary

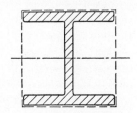

FIG. 5–6. Net perimeter for steel pile.

penetration has been obtained. This length is welded on to a long section, used for the second pile, and driven with the short portion downward; again, any surplus length at the top may be cut off. By this method every linear foot of section is used and the splices are staggered at random throughout the pile group. Furthermore, there is no interruption in the driving, because long lengths of piling can be made up ahead of the driving. When this method is used, the piles are generally furnished in uniform lengths of 65 ft or less. The splicing arrangement permits their adaptation to a wide range of penetrations. Lengths exceeding 120 ft have been driven by this method.

5–6. Precast Concrete Piles. Precast piles of reinforced concrete are extensively used for foundation work. They may be round, square, or octagonal in section; they may be of uniform cross section or they may be tapered; and they may be made with or without metal shoes. But, in all cases, they are reinforced by longitudinal steel bars and lateral reinforcement in the form of hoops and spirals.

Concrete piles can be used for any location where piles are required. The location of the ground-water table need not be considered when concrete piles are used, because there is no deterioration at the waterline if the concrete is properly made. Concrete piles are fireproof. This is of importance where trestles for roads and railways consist of concrete piles extending above the groundline; grass fires and forest fires will not usually cause any structural damage.

Reinforced concrete piles in waterfront structures are called upon to meet very unfavorable exposure conditions when they extend from the harbor bottom into water and air. Such piles are subject to destructive action caused by rusting of the reinforcement and spalling of the concrete. It is particularly serious when the structures are located in tidal waters where destructive action is accelerated by alternate wetting and drying of the concrete due to the rise and fall of the tide—especially if combined with alternate freezing and thawing. Experience has shown that the quality of the aggregates, the composition of the cement, the protective cover over the reinforcement, and the workmanship in mixing and placing the concrete are controlling factors in attaining the desired permanence of the piles.

Fig. 5–7 shows cross sections of square and octagonal piles and a typical side view. A jet pipe is shown which can discharge water just above the tapered bottom part. This arrangement avoids clogged-up jets, which often result from pipes discharging under the bottom point.

Concrete piles are generally built with a tapered bottom part as shown in Fig. 5–7. The taper will not materially change the capacity of an end-bearing pile; it will, however, facilitate the placing and driving and will greatly reduce the tendency of the pile to move during driving.

Fairly large percentages of steel should be used for longitudinal reinforcement—from $1\frac{1}{2}$ to 4 per cent. The splices for the reinforcement should be either welded or lap splices. The lateral reinforcement should be hoops, spaced 6 in. except at the top where closer spacing should be used to prevent damage by the hammer blows.

For bearing piles that are to be completely buried in the ground, the

amount of concrete cover is not of major importance. If, however, piles
are to be exposed above the ground, as in trestles and docks, adequate
cover for the reinforcing bars is essential. For ordinary outdoor exposures,

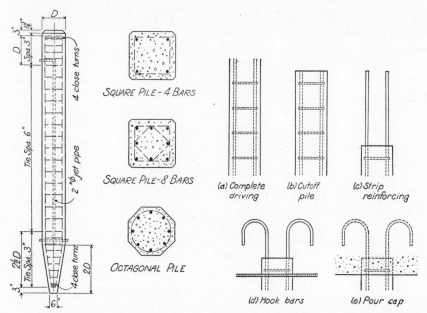

FIG. 5–7. Reinforced concrete piles.   FIG. 5–8. Connecting concrete piles to pier.

a cover outside of all bars and ties of $1\frac{1}{2}$ in. of concrete should be provided.
For severe exposures, as in sea water or where there are many cycles of
freezing and thawing, a clear cover of 3 in. should be used.

Rigid connections can readily be made between concrete piles and
concrete caps, as indicated in Fig. 5–8. After driving has been completed,
the pile should be cut off at such a height that the subsequently exposed
reinforcement will have sufficient lengths for hooking into the cap. The
concrete is then stripped off, generally by pneumatic tools, leaving the
reinforcing rods to be bent and the cap to be poured below (usually about
6 in.) the top of the pile.

Concrete piles can be made with cross sections varying from 12 in.
× 12 in. to 24 in. × 24 in. and with a bearing capacity ranging from 30
tons to 150 tons.

The frictional resistance of reinforced concrete piles depends upon the
material with which they are in contact, and reliable values can be established only by tests for each individual case; as a rule, it is approximately
double that of a steel pile. For preliminary designs, twice the values of
those listed in Table 5–2 can be used for precast piles.

5-7. Handling Stresses. Piles of reinforced concrete are generally manufactured and stored in horizontal positions. Economy and efficiency usually necessitate early removal of the piles to the storage yard. It is not unusual that the piles are moved while the concrete is only a few days old and has attained only a fraction of its designed strength. Handling and transportation stresses are therefore of importance in precast concrete piles.

Fig. 5–9 shows different arrangements for lifting and moving a concrete pile. The maximum bending moments are given in terms of the pile

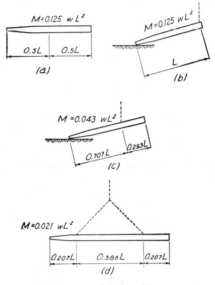

Fig. 5–9. Pile handling.

length L, and weight of pile per linear foot w. The fifth-point support, shown in Fig. 5–9(d), is probably the most common arrangement, as this will produce equal positive and negative bending moments. In order to insure fifth-point support, pipe sleeves may be placed in the concrete at these points or they may be located properly by painted stripes.

When pipe sleeves are used, the support is generally made by eye bolts that make contacts with the underside of the pile through nuts and washers. In this case the top and bottom sides of the cross section will remain horizontal and the two corner bars will be stressed in tension. If, on the other hand, the pile is lifted up by means of slings, it will generally turn in such a manner that one diagonal of the square concrete section becomes horizontal. In this position the bending moment to be resisted by the section will act in a plane through the vertical diagonal. Compressive stresses thus set up will reach a maximum at the apex, as shown in Fig. 5–10; it should be noted that in this position the stresses in the concrete and in the steel become much greater than in the position of horizontal and vertical sides of the square.

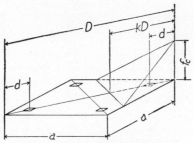

FIG. 5–10. Diagonal bending.

If the usual assumptions of reinforced concrete analysis are made, equations for maximum tensile and compressive stresses can be derived.* These assumptions, which were discussed in Chap. 4, are proportionality between stress and strain and disregard of tensile stresses in concrete.

Referring again to Fig. 5–10, the position of the neutral axis can be determined by the following equation:

$$k^3 + \tfrac{3}{8}p(4n - 1)k - \tfrac{3}{4}pn = 0. \tag{5-2}$$

The maximum compression stress in the concrete will equal

$$f_c = \frac{M}{D^3} \times \frac{6k}{k^3(1 - k) + \dfrac{3}{2}pn\left(\dfrac{1}{2} - \dfrac{d}{D}\right)^2}. \tag{5-3}$$

Maximum tension will occur in the bar most distant from the neutral axis and will equal

$$f_s = nf_c\left(\frac{1 - k}{k} - \frac{d}{kD}\right). \tag{5-4}$$

The following symbols (see Fig. 5–10) have been used:

D = length of diagonal,
d = distance from corner to reinforcing bar,
f_c = maximum compressive stress in concrete,
f_s = maximum tensile stress in reinforcing bar,
k = distance from apex of compression area to neutral axis over length of diagonal,
M = bending moment,
n = ratio of moduli of elasticity,
p = steel area divided by total concrete area.

*See "Diagonal Bending of Square Concrete Sections," *Civil Engineering* (August, 1938), p. 549.

Fig. 5–11 gives the relationship between k and p for values of n equal to 10, 12, and 15.

As a numerical example consider a square concrete pile, 15 in. $\times$ 15 in. $\times$ 60 ft long reinforced with four 1-in. square bars, the distances from the centers of these bars to the outside being 3 in. It is desired to find the maximum compressive and tensile stresses, if this pile is lifted by placing slings around it at the fifth points. Assume $n = 15$.

Using $p = 4 \div 225 = 0.0178$, Fig. 5–11 gives $k = 0.374$. The value of pn is $15 \times 0.0178 = 0.267$. The maximum bending moment is

$$\frac{15 \times 15}{144} \, 150 \times 12 \times 6 = 16{,}850 \text{ ft-lb.}$$

With k and pn known and $d \div D = 0.2$, f_c can be computed by Eq. (5–3); thus,

$$f_c = \frac{16{,}850 \times 12}{21.2^3} \, 32.7 = 693 \text{ psi.}$$

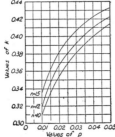

The maximum steel stress is

$$f_s = 693 \times 15 \times \left(\frac{0.626}{0.374} - \frac{0.200}{0.374} \right) = 11{,}850 \text{ psi.}$$

In handling and transporting steel piles, precautions must be taken to prevent local kinking of flanges or other permanent deformation. Timber piles are comparatively easy to handle and ship; they can withstand the bending stresses caused by lifting relatively better than can steel or concrete piles.

5–8. Pile Driving. Piles are, with few exceptions, brought down to their final positions by driving, sometimes supplemented by jetting.

A pile driver (see Fig. 5–1) is a construction tool equipped with a hammer and a hoisting gear for handling the pile and for lifting the hammer. Its characteristic feature is the leads, which are upright parallel members supporting the sheaves used to hoist the hammer and guide the pile.

A drop hammer is essentially a solid metal casting that is allowed to fall on top of the pile by gravity. The weight of a drop hammer varies with the weight of the pile and with the type of hoisting engine. It may vary from 500 lb for posts and small piles to 5000 lb for heavy construction.

A steam hammer rests during the driving on top of the pile. It consists of two essential parts: (1) the stationary part of which the steam cylinder is a part; and (2) the moving part, called the ram, consisting of piston, piston rod, and striking head. There are two types of steam hammers: (1) single-acting, in which the ram is raised by steam pressure and allowed

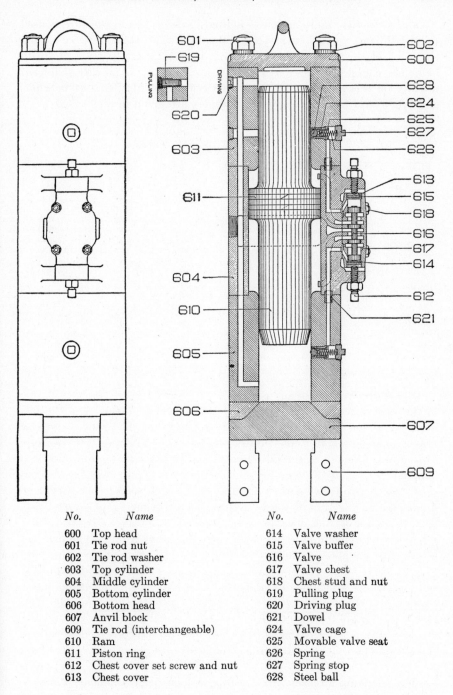

No.	Name	No.	Name
600	Top head	614	Valve washer
601	Tie rod nut	615	Valve buffer
602	Tie rod washer	616	Valve
603	Top cylinder	617	Valve chest
604	Middle cylinder	618	Chest stud and nut
605	Bottom cylinder	619	Pulling plug
606	Bottom head	620	Driving plug
607	Anvil block	621	Dowel
609	Tie rod (interchangeable)	624	Valve cage
610	Ram	625	Movable valve seat
611	Piston ring	626	Spring
612	Chest cover set screw and nut	627	Spring stop
613	Chest cover	628	Steel ball

Fig. 5–12. Double-acting pile hammer. (Courtesy of McKiernan-Terry Corporation.)

to fall by gravity; and (2) double-acting, in which steam pressure is used to raise the ram and also to accelerate the downward stroke, thus increasing the force of the blow (see Fig. 5–12). The stationary portion of steam hammers encases an anvil block, and the hammer blows are delivered directly on this block, which rests on the head of the pile. Dimensions and other data for various steam hammers are given in Table 5–3.

TABLE 5–3

DATA FOR TYPICAL STEAM HAMMERS

Type	Weight of Hammer (Lb)	Weight of Ram (Lb)	Length of Stroke (In.)	Strokes per Min.	Energy per Blow (Ft-Lb)
Single Acting	1,400	550	21	80	825
	3,700	1,800	24	80	3,600
	6,700	3,000	29	70	7,260
	9,600	5,000	36	60	15,000
	16,500	7,500	39	50	24,375
	19,000	9,300	39	50	30,200
Double Acting	1,500	200	7	300	1,000
	2,900	400	8¾	275	2,500
	5,000	800	9½	225	4,150
	7,000	1,600	17	145	8,750
	10,850	3,000	19	105	13,100
	14,000	5,000	19	95	19,150
	28,000	10,000	24	90	55,000

A pile driven by a steam hammer is kept continuously in motion, due to the rapid succession of blows, and the vibration imparted to the pile loosens the soil around it and facilitates driving. The quick blows of these hammers tend to convert the effect of the blows into a steady pressure causing less damage to the pile than that caused by the action of a drop hammer.

Where it is inconvenient from lack of space, or some other reason, to use a pile-driving frame, double-acting steam hammers can be used suspended from a derrick or crane.

Steam hammers may be used to assist in pulling a pile. The hammer is lashed to the pile, in a reverted position, and the ram strikes an upward blow while, at the same time, the pile is subjected to an upward pull by suitable rigging which may be supported independently of the pile hammer. This is of particular importance in the use of sheet piling for cofferdams and other temporary structures. If the full extent of economy in the use of sheet piles is to be obtained, it is necessary to have an economical and efficient method of extracting them for future use.

5–9. Driving Stresses. In selecting pile-driving equipment, it is often economical to chose a large hammer which, by transmitting a considerable amount of energy, will reduce the time required for driving. Too large a hammer, however, may injure the piles and, for reinforced concrete piles especially, driving stresses should be looked into.

For concrete piles, steam hammers should generally develop an energy per blow at each full stroke of the piston of not less than 3500 ft-lb/cu yd of concrete in the pile being driven, while the total energy of the hammer should not be less than 6000 ft-lb/blow.

An extensive investigation of the stresses in reinforced concrete piles during driving was conducted at the British Building Research Station at Garston, England.* Tests made in connection with this investigation showed that the most important stresses in causing failure during driving occurred at the head or foot of the pile. It was recommended that the longitudinal reinforcement be stopped about 1 in. from the top surface of the pile and not hooked. While the total percentage of longitudinal reinforcement did not materially affect the ultimate driving resistance of a pile, it was found that the amount of lateral reinforcement did influence it profoundly, particularly at the head and toe. For piles subjected to hard driving it was recommended that, for a length of two and one-half times the external diameter of the pile, the volume of lateral reinforcement should not be less than 1 per cent of the gross volume of the corresponding length of pile. The diameter of the ties should conform with the usual practice for reinforced concrete and be not less than $\frac{3}{16}$ in. or one-fourth the diameter of the main bars, whichever is greater. An examination of Fig. 5–7, which represents usual American practice, will show agreement with these specifications. It was also observed at the above-mentioned tests that the performance of piles reinforced with heavy spirals ($2\frac{1}{4}$ per cent) was definitely good.

Various protective devices are used to prevent excessive stresses in piles while being driven. Timber piles are protected against splitting at the butt by chamfering the edges of the pile head, or by placing a steel band around the head. The point of the timber pile is sometimes protected by a steel shoe. Heads of concrete piles are protected during driving by cushions of rope or by wooden blocks. Steel piles need less protection during driving than do other types. Some form of pile cap, preferably shaped to the steel section being driven, should be used to insure an axial blow.

The formula for driving stresses in reinforced concrete piles developed in the following paragraphs has been used by the Bureau of Yards and Docks of the United States Navy.† It is based on the assumptions that

---

*See *Technical Paper No. 20*, Department of Scientific and Industrial Research (London, 1938).

†See *Standards of Design for Concrete*, U. S. Navy (November 15, 1929), No. 3Yb, 9-03d.

the pile is supported entirely at the bottom, that it is driven to refusal, and that no energy is lost by deformation of the hammer. The following notation is used:

A = cross-sectional area of pile, sq in.,
E = modulus of elasticity of concrete, psi,
h = drop of hammer, in.,
l = length of pile, in.,
N = energy of steam hammer, in.-lb,
n = modular ratio,
p = ratio of longitudinal reinforcement,
f = stress in pile, psi,
W = weight of ram, lb,
w = weight of pile, lb.

Assuming a drop hammer and equating external work to dynamic strain energy gives

$$Wh = fA(1 + pn)\frac{fl}{E}. \qquad (5\text{--}5)$$

The weight of a concrete pile is

$$w = 0.0868\ Al; \qquad (5\text{--}6)$$

hence,

$$Wh = f\frac{f}{E}(1 + pn)\frac{w}{0.0868},$$

$$f = \sqrt{\frac{W}{w}E\frac{h}{1 + pn}0.0868}. \qquad (5\text{--}7)$$

In the case of a steam hammer, where N represents the total energy per blow,

$$f = \sqrt{\frac{0.0868NE}{w(1 + pn)}} \qquad (5\text{--}8)$$

It is important to realize the limitations of the preceding expression. In addition to the assumptions already listed, no allowance has been made for the driving cap which is used to cushion the blow. Most steam hammers are designed so that the hammer blow strikes on an anvil block rather than on the pile directly. This will lessen the impact of the blow; but, in the case of concrete piles, further cushioning is effected by the use of a specially designed cap containing packing of such material as felt, coiled hemp rope, sack cloth, wallboard, or rubber. A relatively high value can, therefore, be allowed for the stress f, as determined by Eq. (5–8)—usually one-half of the compressive strength of the concrete.

As a numerical example let it be desired to find the heaviest possible hammer which can be used for driving a concrete pile 16 in. $\times$ 16 in. $\times$ 60 ft and reinforced with four $1\frac{1}{4}$-in. square bars. The concrete has a modulus of elasticity of 3,000,000 psi and a 28-day ultimate strength of 4000 psi; the modular ratio n can be assumed to be equal to 10.

If the allowable impact stress is assumed to be equal to one-half of the control cylinder strength, then the hammer energy N can be found from Eq. (5–8); thus,

$$2000 = \sqrt{\frac{N \times 3 \times 10^6 \times 0.0868}{16,000 \times (1 + 0.25)}},$$

$$N = 307,700 \text{ in.-lb} = 25,600 \text{ ft-lb}.$$

5–10. Pile-Driving Formulas. The bearing power of a pile depends not only on the strength of the pile but also, and primarily, on the support which is given to the pile by the surrounding earth. While the strength of the pile itself can be computed with considerable accuracy, the supporting power of the soil is rather difficult to estimate. There are two methods for evaluating the bearing power of a pile as controlled by the surrounding earth. The most common method consists of calculating the bearing power of the pile from the energy required to drive it. The other method consists of subjecting the pile to the action of a test load and observing its behavior.

A pile is driven into the ground by a succession of blows from a falling weight. The penetration per blow can be used as a measure of the load-carrying capacity of a single pile, as determined by a pile-driving formula. Although these formulas may be somewhat inaccurate under certain conditions and have often been criticized, they are, nevertheless, very widely used and afford a simple method of estimating the approximate bearing capacity of each pile.

A so-called *complete* pile-driving formula can be established by equating the total energy delivered by the hammer to the pile to the sum of five terms representing the useful work and losses, namely:

(1) The useful work, which is expressed as the product of the total resistance of the soil and the penetration per hammer blow (force times distance),
(2) The loss of energy due to impact,
(3) The loss due to elastic compression of the driving cap,
(4) The loss due to elastic compression of the pile,
(5) The loss due to elastic compression of the soil.

All other dynamic pile-driving formulas, as far as known, may be derived from this complete equation by making various simplifications and omissions.

In the discussion of pile-driving formulas, the following notation will be use:

A = cross-sectional area of pile, sq in.,
E = modulus of elasticity, psi,
F = hammer energy per blow, ft-lb,
H = height of fall of ram, ft,
l = length of pile, in.,
P = safe bearing value of pile, lb,
R = total resistance of soil, lb,
S = pile penetration per blow, ft,
s = pile penetration per blow, in.,
W = weight of falling ram, lb,
w = weight of pile, lb.

If a drop hammer is used, the available energy is $W \times H$ and the work required to drive the pile is $R \times S$. If the four additional terms in the pile-driving formula are expressed by a single quantity, then this quantity can be assumed to be proportional to the capacity, P, of the pile. For convenience it may be represented by $2PC$ where C is a constant. Equating external work to internal work gives

$$W \times H = R \times S + 2PC \tag{5-9}$$

Substituting $s = 12S$ and $P = R \div 6$ (a factor of safety of 6) gives

$$P = \frac{2WH}{s + C}, \tag{5-10}$$

which is generally called the *Engineering-News* formula (proposed in the year 1888). To the constant, C, is assigned an empirical value, which is 1.0 when a drop hammer is used; thus,

$$P = \frac{2WH}{s + 1.0}. \tag{5-11}$$

For steam hammers the value of C is taken as 0.1. Thus, for a single-acting steam hammer,

$$P = \frac{2WH}{s + 0.1}. \tag{5-12}$$

For double-acting steam hammers the formula is also applicable if the total energy (the sum of the steam pressure and the energy from the fall of the ram) is used; thus,

$$P = \frac{2F}{s + 0.1}. \tag{5-13}$$

The energy, F, is listed for various speeds (strokes per minute) in Table 5–3. These data are usually determined by the manufacturers with the use of indicator diagrams and high-speed moving picture apparatus which determine the velocity of the ram at the point of impact.

The *Engineering-News* formula may be expected to give fairly reliable results in sandy and otherwise pervious soil, but it often gives results too low for clay soils. Results for small penetrations are, as a rule, somewhat erratic.

For driving heavy piles with light hammers the *Engineering-News* formula is unsatisfactory and is sometimes modified to include the ratio of pile weight to ram weight. The modified formula is

$$P = \frac{2F}{s + 0.1 \frac{w}{W}}.$$ (5-14)

It is seen that the modified *Engineering-News* formula will require smaller final penetrations for heavy piles driven by light hammers. Other formulas in use increase the energy of the hammer and at the same time multiply by a coefficient, smaller than unity and depending on weights of pile and striking portion of hammer. Thus the Minnesota State Highway Department recommends the following formulas:

1. All types of piles driven with gravity hammers,

$$P = \frac{3WH}{s + 1.0} \times \frac{W + 0.1w}{W + w}.$$ (5-15)

2. Timber, concrete, and shell-type piles driven with steam hammers,

$$P = \frac{3.5F}{s + 0.1} \times \frac{W + 0.1w}{W + w}.$$ (5-16)

3. Steel piling (structural sections) driven with steam hammers,

$$P = \frac{3.5F}{s + 0.1} \times \frac{W + 0.2w}{W + w}.$$ (5-17)

Numerous attempts have been made to derive dynamic pile-driving formulas which will serve to correlate static bearing capacity of a pile with its behavior during driving. Two of these will be discussed in the following paragraphs.

If the pile is assumed to be inelastic, it and the ram will have a common velocity v_1 after impact and the momentum of the pile and the ram will equal the momentum of the falling hammer (having a velocity of v_2 before striking).

$$Wv_2 = (W + w)v_1$$

$$v_1 = \frac{W}{W + w} v_2 = \frac{W}{W + w} \sqrt{2gH}.$$

The deceleration, a, of the pile is found thus,

$$a = \frac{v_1{}^2}{2s} = \frac{gH}{s}\left(\frac{W}{W+w}\right)^2.$$

The total resistance of the soil is equal to mass times deceleration

$$R = \frac{W+w}{g}\,a = \frac{W+w}{g}\times\frac{gH}{s}\left(\frac{W}{W+w}\right)^2 = \frac{H}{s}\times\frac{W^2}{W+w},$$

$$Rs = WH\,\frac{W}{W+w}. \qquad\qquad (5\text{--}18)$$

If the loss of energy in compressing the pile is taken into account Eq. (5–18) becomes (l = length of pile; A = cross-sectional area)

$$Rs + \frac{R^2 l}{2AE} = WH\,\frac{W}{W+w}. \qquad\qquad (5\text{--}19)$$

Solving gives

$$R = \frac{AE}{l}\left(-s + \sqrt{s^2 + \frac{2W^2 H}{W+w}\times\frac{l}{AE}}\right). \qquad\qquad (5\text{--}20)$$

This formula is called Redtenbacker's formula and is used extensively in Europe, usually with a safety factor of 3.*

Pile-driving formulas are often solved for the penetration s. A negative value for the penetration from these formulas is an indication that a heavier hammer must be used.

5–11. Numerical Examples. As a first example let it be desired to find the final penetration per blow for creosoted Southern Pine piles having a butt diameter of 15 in. and a tip diameter of 11 in. and carrying loads of 16 tons. An examination of the soil leads to a preliminary estimate of pile length of 50 ft. Assume a single-acting steam hammer with a ram weighing 1800 lb and falling 2 ft. Use the Modified *Engineering-News* formula.

Assuming a unit weight 55 lb/cu ft for creosoted wood and an average diameter of 13 in., the weight of one pile is

$$w = \frac{133}{144}\times 50\times 55 = 2540\text{ lb,}$$

and the penetration is found from Eq. (5–15); thus,

$$32{,}000 = \frac{2\times 1800\times 2}{s + 0.1\dfrac{2540}{1800}},$$

$$s = 0.08\text{ in.}$$

---

*See Karl Terzaghi, "The Science of Foundation," *Trans. A.S.C.E.* (1929), Vol. 93, p. 207.

For a second numerical example let it be assumed that concrete piles 15 in. × 15 in. × 40 ft and reinforced with eight $\frac{7}{8}$-in. round steel rods are to carry loads of 40 tons each. A double-acting steam hammer having a ram weighing 5000 lb and delivering an energy of 19,150 ft-lb per blow will be used. Find the final penetration per blow at the end of driving.

According to *Engineering-News* formula

$$80,000 = \frac{2 \times 19,150}{s + 0.1};$$

$$s = 0.38 \text{ in.}$$

The weight of one pile is

$$w = \frac{225}{144} 150 \times 40 = 9400 \text{ lb.,}$$

and according to the modified formula, Eq. (5–15),

$$80,000 = \frac{2 \times 19,150}{s + 0.1 \dfrac{9400}{5000}};$$

$$s = 0.29 \text{ in.}$$

Next let it be desired to check the load on this pile for the penetration of 0.29 in., using Redtenbacker's formula with a safety factor of 3. The modulus of elasticity for the concrete is 3,000,000 psi and the transformed cross-sectional area of the pile is

$$A = 225 + (10 - 1)4.82 = 268 \text{ sq in.}$$

According to Eq. (5–20)

$$P = \frac{268 \times 3000}{3 \times 480}\left(-0.29 + \sqrt{0.084 + \frac{2 \times 5 \times 19.15 \times 12}{5 + 9.4} \times \frac{480}{268 \times 3000}}\right).$$

$$P = 75 \text{ kips.}$$

If the same problem is solved by the Minnesota State Highway formula, Eq. (5–16) it is seen that

$$80,000 = \frac{3.5 \times 19,150}{s + 0.1} \times \frac{5000 + 940}{5000 + 9400},$$

$$s = 0.25 \text{ in.}$$

5–12. Cast-in-Place Piles. Concrete piles, made by filling holes which have been formed in the ground by fresh concrete, are frequently used. There are certain advantages to molding in the ground with or without steel tubes as part of the piles; reinforcement is usually not required and extensions and cutoffs are readily made.

The tubes, or molds, are made of thin steel sheets if the tubes are to be left permanently in the ground as part of the pile; but heavier material is used if the tubes serve only as forms and are gradually withdrawn as the concrete is poured into the hole. This type of pile has been used in recent years for some very important work, and there are many situations where it has decided advantages. Most types of cast-in-place piles are protected by patent rights or at least are made by organizations specializing in one form of pile or another; they usually fall into three distinct categories: (1) the shell type, (2) the shell-less type, and (3) open-end steel pipes.

The shell type (or cased piles) consists of a steel casing with a steel interior core, called the *mandrel*, which is driven into the ground to the desired penetration in the same manner as a steel or concrete pile. The mandrel, which is collapsible, is then removed and the casing is filled with concrete. The casing is usually assembled from sections, which can be

Courtesy of Raymond Concrete Pile Co.

FIG. 5–13. Construction of cast-in-place piles.

seen in Fig. 5–13, as can a group of concrete-filled shells ready for the footing. These piles are usually tapered, having a minimum diameter of 8 in. at the point and 14 in. at the head. The usual load for this size pile is 30 tons. Cast-in-place piles of the shell type have been used for lengths of slightly more than 100 ft. The shells are usually spirally reinforced, but another variation has a fluted tapered shell with a strong closed point and may be driven without a mandrel.

The shell-less type, or uncased, pile is constructed by driving down a straight pipe with a mandrel, which can be withdrawn upon completion of the driving. Concrete is placed in the hole and compressed with the mandrel as the shell is pulled up. It follows that this type can be used only in firm soil where there is no risk of the adjacent earth mixing with the concrete during placing.

Fig. 5–14. Driving steel pipe piles with restricted headroom.

Pipe piles are constructed by driving a heavy steel pipe and removing the earth from its interior, usually by air or water jets, after bedrock or the desired penetration has been reached. After excavation of the interior has been completed, the pipe is filled with concrete. Open-end pipe piles are made of steel tubing from 10 to 20 in. outside diameter and from $\frac{5}{16}$ to $\frac{5}{8}$ in. thick; they have been driven to depths as great as 155 ft and have carried loads as high as 150 tons.

Pipe piles can be readily spliced by welding or by means of internal sleeves. This makes possible driving without leads under restricted clearance as shown in Fig. 5–14. Placing of concrete into the pile after driving precludes damage to the concrete core due to driving.

5–13. Allowable Loads on Cast-in-Place Piles.

Most building specifications require that the concrete used in cast-in-place piles must have a minimum strength of 2500 psi and the placing shall be continuous from tip to cut-off elevation, and shall be carried on in such a manner as to avoid segregation.

Pile-driving formulas can be used for estimating allowable loads on cast-in-place by substituting for the weight of the pile either the weight of the mandrel in the case of the shell type of pile or the weight of the empty pipe for a steel pipe pile (either open end or closed end). The Municipal Code of Chicago recommends the *Engineering-News* formula [Eqs. (5–12) and (5–13)] for piles and mandrels whose weight is equal to or less than the weight of the striking parts. For piles or mandrels whose weight is greater than the weight of the striking parts the following formula is recommended:

$$P = \frac{2F}{s + 0.1}\left(1 - \frac{M}{10W}\right), \tag{5-21}$$

where M is the weight of the mandrel.

As a first numerical example, let it be desired to find the allowable load on a cast-in-place pile driven with hammer delivering an energy of 19,150 ft-lb per blow if the final penetration is $\frac{1}{2}$ in. The mandrel weighs 12 kips and the striking parts of the hammer 5 kips. Substituting in Eq. (5–21) gives

$$P = \frac{38,300}{0.5 + 0.1}\left(1 - \frac{12,000}{50,000}\right) = 48,500 \text{ lb.}$$

As a second numerical example, it is desired to find the final penetration per blow for an open-end pipe pile consisting of a steel shell to be filled with concrete after the earth has been removed from its interior. The steel pipe has an outside diameter of 16 in., a thickness of $\frac{3}{4}$ in., and a length of 40 ft. The pile must be capable of supporting 30 tons and the driving will be done with a double-acting steam hammer having a ram weighing 3000 lb and delivering 12,000 ft-lb of energy per blow.   The Modified *Engineering-News* formula will be used.

The cross-sectional area of the steel pipe is $A = 36$ sq in., and its total weight, $w = 4900$ lb.   Substituting in Eq. (5–14) gives

$$60,000 = \frac{2 \times 12,000}{s + 0.1 \dfrac{4900}{3000}},$$

and solving for s gives

$$s = 0.24.$$

The average final penetration should be $\frac{1}{4}$ in.

5–14. Discussion of Pile Formulas.   Pile-driving formulas represent attempts to correlate the dynamic resistance of earth to rapid penetrations with the static resistance of the pile.   It is generally recognized that these formulas can be nothing more than empirical formulas, applicable to limited conditions in each case.   They serve as "yardsticks" to obtain reasonably safe and uniform results over an entire project.

Pile-driving formulas are applicable to cohesionless materials, such as sand and gravel, but are not to be relied upon where the pile is to rest in a cohesive soil such as clay.   The formulas should not be used where the pile is driven through soft material to a hard stratum, for in that case it will act as a column and should be designed as such.

The value of the penetration to be used in the formulas is generally taken as an average of the last five or ten blows.

The most widely used of the dynamic formulas is, without doubt, the *Engineering-News* formula.   This is an energy equation, simplified to the point where it is true only within certain limits, and for a long time it has been the standard empirical formula, at least in the United States, for determining when a pile has been driven to a sufficient resistance.   Many engineers have questioned its validity; but, as an easily applicable rule-of-thumb, it and its associated formulas, such as the Modified *Engineering-News* formula, are indispensable in pile-driving operations.

Because of the uncertainty involved in the relationship between the dynamic driving resistance and the subsequent static carrying capacity of a pile, formulas have been developed for determining the bearing capacity of a pile on the basis of static considerations.   An empirical static formula for the bearing capacity of a pile is represented by

$$P = pA + fS, \tag{5–22}$$

where P = ultimate bearing capacity of pile,
$\quad\ \ p$ = ultimate bearing capacity of soil below the pile point,
$\quad\ \ A$ = area of pile point,
$\quad\ \ f$ = ultimate value of skin friction between pile and soil,
$\quad\ \ S$ = embedded surface of pile.

In order to use the static formula, it is necessary to have complete information about the physical properties of the surrounding soil. The determination of these properties is usually difficult, because the pile must be either driven or jetted into the ground.

The following discussion is an attempt to rationalize the use of the static formula, which is similar to one proposed by United States Navy.* For friction piles in clay the second term in Eq. (5–22) can be assumed to be equal to

$$P_f = \pi DLc, \qquad (5\text{–}23)$$

where D is the diameter (or side) of the cross-section, L the length of embedment, and c the unit cohesion. It is assumed that the unit frictional resistance equals the cohesion. For a pile driven into a cohesionless material the same term can be assumed to equal

$$P_f = \pi DLp_v \tan \phi, \qquad (5\text{–}24)$$

where ϕ is the angle of internal friction and p_v is the average vertical load on the soil around the embedded length L (see Fig. 5–15). The latter can be assumed to be

$$p_v = \tfrac{1}{2}wL + p_0, \qquad (5\text{–}25)$$

where p_0 represents the weights of the over-burden. If the material providing friction has some cohesiveness, in addition to an angle of friction, the cohesion can be converted to frictional resistance; thus,

$$\tan x = \tan \phi + \frac{c}{p_v},$$

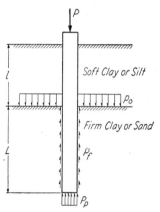

Fig. 5–15. Theoretical bearing capacity of pile.

which can be substituted for $\tan \phi$ in Eq. (5–24).

The first term of Eq. (5–22) is due to point bearing, which can be taken as

$$P_p = Ap, \qquad (5\text{–}26)$$

where p is given by Eq. (3–6). The third term in this expression can be disregarded. Therefore,

$$p = w(l + L) \tan^4 \left(45° + \frac{\phi}{2}\right) + \frac{2c}{\tan (45° - \tfrac{1}{2}\phi) \sin^2 (45° - \tfrac{1}{2}\phi)}. \qquad (5\text{–}27)$$

---

*See "Soil Mechanics and Earth Structures," Technical Publication of Bureau of Yards and Docks, U. S. Navy (October, 1953), p. 96.

As a numerical example let it be assumed that friction piles are driven into clay having a unit cohesion equal to 1000 psf. Other data are as follows: $w = 100$ lb/cu ft; $l = 10$ ft; $L = 20$ ft; $D = 15$ in. It is desired to find the bearing capacity with a factor of safety of 3. Substituting in Eq. (5–27) gives

$$p = 100 \times 30 + 2000 \div \left(\frac{\sqrt{2}}{2}\right)^2 = 7000 \text{ psf,}$$

and in Eqs. (5–23) and (5–26),

$$P = P_p + P_f = \tfrac{1}{3}(\tfrac{1}{4}\pi 1.25^2 \times 7 + \pi \times 1.25 \times 20) = 29 \text{ kips.}$$

As a second numerical example let it be assumed that the same pile is driven through a cohesionless material having an angle of internal friction $\phi = 30°$. With the same factor of safety of 3, find the safe load. From Eq. (5–27) it is found that

$$p = 30 \times 100 \times \tan^4 60° = 27,000 \text{ psf,}$$

and from Eq. (5–25),

$$p_v = \tfrac{1}{2}20 \times 100 + 10 \times 100 = 2000 \text{ psf.}$$

Substituting in Eqs. (5–23) and (5–26),

$$P = P_p + P_f = \tfrac{1}{3}(\tfrac{1}{4}\pi 1.25^2 \times 27 + \pi 1.25 \times 2 \times 20 \times \tan 30°)$$

$$= 41 \text{ kips.}$$

5–15. Test Piles. A test pile is one on which a loading test is made in order to determine its load carrying capacity and settlement rate under various loads. Pile-loading tests furnish more dependable information than pile-driving formulas. If a test can be made on a group of piles, the data become very reliable; this, however, necessitates extremely large loads and most pile-loading tests are made with single piles.

Fig. 5–16(a) shows a loading platform which can be built on top of the test pile. The concrete cap cast on top of the pile provides bearing for the timber beams which support crossbeams and plank flooring. Jacks or wedges may be placed at the outer ends to prevent the platform from tipping during loading. The test pile should be supported laterally to prevent sway. Another arrangement is shown in Fig. 5–16(b), where anchor piles are driven on each side of the pile to be tested, and the load is applied to the test pile by means of a hydraulic jack reacting against a beam attached to the anchor piles. In this arrangement, the anchor piles should be at least 5 ft from the test pile. The load should be applied in increments, and settlement readings should be made for each load increment. The amount of settlement that may be acceptable under a given test load depends on several factors, such as the type of structure to be supported and the nature of the design load which may be steady

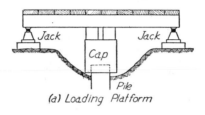

(a) Loading Platform

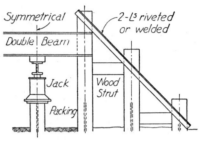

(b) Hydraulic Jack Loading

FIG. 5–16. Pile-loading tests.

or intermittent.   The Boston Building Code* contains the following requirements relative to pile-loading tests:

(1)   A pile to be tested shall be loaded to at least twice the proposed working load, the load being applied in increments of not over 10,000 lb.   At least 4 hr shall elapse between the addition of successive increments.   Measurements of the settlement accurate to $\frac{1}{32}$ in. shall be taken and recorded immediately before and after each increment of load is added.   In determining the settlement, proper deduction shall be made for elastic compression of the pile under the test load.

(2)   The allowable pile load shall not exceed one-half of that causing a total settlement of $\frac{1}{2}$ in. which remains constant for 48 hr, but the load on the bearing materials at the level of the points or upon any lower stratum shall not exceed the allowable bearing values.

5–16.   Plans and Specifications.   It is always economical to make a thorough preliminary subsurface survey before preparing foundation plans and specifications.†   Too often structures are meticulously designed above ground, only to be placed on foundations that have been designed with incomplete and inaccurate information.   Foundations resting on

---

*Boston Building Code, Sec. 2917.

†See K. V. Taylor, C. T. Morris and J. P. Burkey, "The Predetermination of Piling Requirements for Bridge Foundations," Bulletin No. 90 (Engineering Experiment Station, Ohio State University, 1931).

piles that do not penetrate to a solid stratum are particularly susceptible to settlement, and it is difficult and frequently impossible to predict the amount. Reliable core borings should always be made in sufficient number to disclose the nature of the subsoils beneath the entire site. When it is discovered that the stratum, upon which the pile points are to rest, is perhaps insufficient to carry the loads to be placed on it, thorough analysis and loading tests should be made. A rough estimate of the pressure at any level below the pile points can be made by spreading the total load uniformly at an angle of 60° with the horizontal, starting at a polygon circumscribing the piles at the top of the satisfactory bearing stratum in which they are embedded. The average pressure at the bottom level of the piles may then be taken as the total load divided by this area.

No matter how convenient a single and standardized type of pile construction may appear, it is nevertheless desirable that both design and methods of construction be sufficiently flexible to permit changes to be made during the period of construction. To anticipate in the design the exact subsoil conditions that will be encountered is, of course, desirable and it is actually accomplished on most projects. In a number of cases, however, before construction is started little is definitely known about conditions below the surface.

A typical plan of reinforced concrete piles is shown in Fig. 5–17. Sepa-

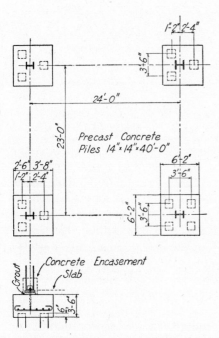

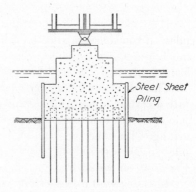

FIG. 5–17. Typical pile foundation.   FIG. 5–18. Pile-supported bridge pier.

rate footings transmit the column loads to the piles. In case of earth-quakeproof construction it may be desirable to tie together the footings by reinforced concrete struts. In general where unconnected footings are used, each group should consist of not less than three piles. The group should be so arranged that its centroid coincides with the centerline of the supported column. The piles should project into the footings from 6 to 12 in., and in addition, the longitudinal reinforcement should extend from 24 to 36 in. In case of a steel superstructure, it is customary to stop the footing about 1 in. below the bottom of the steel masonry plate and grout underneath after the correct elevation has been obtained.

Fig. 5–18 shows a bridge pier supported on piles and surrounded by water. To prevent scouring of the ground under and adjacent to the pier, it is often advisable to construct an enclosure of steel sheet piling. This enclosure may also serve as formwork during underwater pouring of the concrete for the pier.

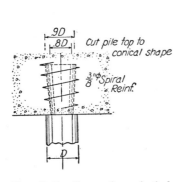

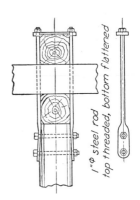

FIG. 5–19. Connection of timber pile to concrete cap.

FIG. 5–20. Connection of timber pile to timber deck.

It is not possible to determine in advance the exact lengths of bearing piles. From borings and test piles a rough estimate can be made which must be supplemented by an allowance to cover possible variations of soil conditions.

The connection of timber pile to the superstructure will usually necessitate a certain amount of work after completion of driving. If the timber pile connects to a concrete superstructure, the attachment should be so arranged that the concrete will not shrink away from the pile; and if the pile can be stressed in tension, that tensile stresses can be transmitted. Fig. 5–19 shows such a connection.

In the case of a timber pile connecting to a timber superstructure, the attachment may be built by the use of steel straps as suggested in Fig. 5–20.

PROBLEMS

5-1. Concrete piles 15 in. × 15 in. × 50 ft, 0 in. are driven by a double-acting steam hammer of capacity 10,000 ft-lb per blow. What should be the percentage of reinforcement if the stresses due to driving must not exceed 1500 psi? $E = 3,000,000$ psi. (*Ans.*: 1.87 per cent.)

5-2. What is the maximum compressive stress developed in a 14 in. × 14 in. × 50 ft, 0 in. concrete pile due to driving to refusal with a drop hammer having a ram of 5000 lb and a fall of 3 ft? The pile is reinforced with 4 1-in. square bars. $E = 2,500,000$ psi. (*Ans.*: 1755 psi.)

5-3. Find the maximum size double-acting steam hammer that can be used for driving 18 in. × 18 in. × 55 ft, 0 in. reinforced concrete piles having eight 1-in. round bars. $E = 3,000,000$ psi, and allowable driving stress is 2500 psi. (*Ans.*: 44,500 ft-lb.)

5-4. Given a concrete pile 15 in. × 15 in. × 44 ft, 0 in. long. Modulus of elasticity for concrete is 3,000,000 psi. The pile is reinforced with eight longitudinal bars. Find the size of this bar if it is known that the largest single-acting steam hammer (see Table 5-1) will produce a driving stress equal to 2600 psi. (*Ans.*: 1 in. square.)

5-5. Using the same pile as in Prob. 5-4, find the load which it can support if driving with the largest single-acting steam hammer (see Table 5-1) is stopped when the penetration per blow is $\frac{1}{2}$ in. Use (a) *Engineering-News* formula; (b) Modified *Engineering-News* formula; (c) Minnesota State Highway formula. (*Ans.*: 101 kips, 98 kips, 93 kips.)

5-6. Using the same pile as in Prob. 5-4, find the maximum bending moment in the pile if it is lifted by placing slings around it at points 6 ft and 9 ft from each end.

5-7. A pile group consists of 30 piles (5 rows, 6 columns) equally spaced in both directions and having diameters of 12 in. The capacity load of the entire group is 688 kips. The piles are driven by a double-acting steam hammer (total weight 10,850 lb; see Table 5-1) until the final penetration is $\frac{3}{4}$ in. Find pile spacing. Use *Engineering-News* formula and assume the piles to be friction piles (Pacific Coast Building Officials Code). (*Ans.*: 4 ft.)

PROB. 5-7   PROB. 5-8

5-8. A pile group is made up of an unknown number of piles, spaced 4 ft in both directions. There are six piles in each row. The piles are driven by a double-acting steam hammer, delivering 15,400 ft-lb/blow, until the final penetration is 0.9 in. The entire group should have a capacity of 822 kips. Find the total number of piles. Use *Engineering-News* formula and assume the piles to be friction piles (Pacific Coast Building Officials Code). (*Ans.*: 36.)

PILE GROUPS SUPPORT COLUMN FOOTINGS IN MULTI-STORY BUILDING

CHAPTER 6

PILE GROUPS

6–1. Introduction. Piles used in foundations always make up groups through which are transmitted, to the desired sublevel, the known forces from the superstructure. The division of the known force among the individual piles of the group is the object of study in this chapter.

A pile group generally consists of a large number of piles, often several hundred. It would seem, therefore, that the problems pertaining to analysis of pile groups must, statically, be highly indeterminate and consequently very complex. A closer examination, however, reveals many redeeming features which tend to simplify the problems. First, piles in the same group are always of the same cross-sectional make-up and they can, without appreciable error, be assumed to be of the same effective length. Secondly, it is always economical to restrict the number of directions to two (opposite batters) or, at the very most, three (vertical and opposite batters). Thus a pile group may be broken up into a few subgroups consisting of identical units.

The end conditions of the piles can be assumed to be either hinged or fixed. Piles of wood or steel extending only short distances into a concrete superstructure, as is generally the case, should be assumed as connecting to this through frictionless hinges, while reinforced concrete piles with their main reinforcement extended and hooked into a concrete cap should be considered as fixed at their tops. A bearing pile which penetrates only a short distance into a hard and compact soil can be considered as transferring its load through a bottom hinge, while a pile extending a considerable distance into any uniform soil may be assumed as fixed at some point above its actual bottom. Thus, according to the specifications of the Bureau of Yards and Docks, United States Navy, a concrete pile driven in firm material may be considered fixed 5 ft below the groundline and in soft material 10 ft below the groundline.

6–2. Maxwell's Theorem. Analyses of pile groups can be simplified by making use of the fact that the distortions of the piles are generally of considerable magnitude, while those occurring in the large and rigid mass of concrete which constitutes the superstructure are negligible. The superstructure, in other words, can be considered infinitely rigid as compared to the piles. In the following, use will be made of Maxwell's theorem of reciprocity.*

---

*See L. E. Grinter, *Theory of Modern Steel Structures* (New York, 1937), Vol. 2, p. 41.

In Fig. 6–1(a), let a body be subjected to the action of a force, P, acting at point 2. The deflection of point 1, in the direction of the dotted

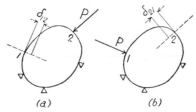

(a)   (b)

FIG. 6–1. Maxwell's theorem.

line, is indicated by δ_{12}. In Fig. 6–1(b) the force P has been moved to point 1, acting in the direction along which the first deflection was measured. If the deflection of point 2, due to the force at 1, is called δ_{21}, then Maxwell's theorem states that

$$\delta_{12} = \delta_{21}, \qquad\qquad (6\text{–}1)$$

or that the displacement along one path caused by a load along some other path is equal to the displacement along the second path due to the same load along the first path.

6–3. Method of Center of Rotation. If the piles can be assumed hinged at their tops and bottoms and arranged in parallel planes, the pressures can be determined graphically as shown in the following. This method is based on Maxwell's theorem of reciprocity and was first proposed by H. M. Westergaard.*

If the superstructure is assumed to be infinitely rigid compared to the piles, then its change of position resulting from application of load can be regarded as a rotation with respect to some point, which may be called the *center of rotation*.

Suppose now that the center of rotation, designated r in Fig. 6–2, is known. The notation to be used is as follows:

θ = angle of rotation, measured in radians,

e = shortening of pile,

E = modulus of elasticity,

A = cross-sectional area of pile,

P = total pressure on any pile,

p = distance from centerline of pile to center of rotation; p shall be considered positive if a shortening of the pile will increase the angle of rotation, otherwise negative,

l = length of pile, measured from the assumed hinge at the top to the theoretical point of support (at which a hinge is assumed) near the lower end.

*See *Journal of Western Society of Engineers* (December 1917), Vol. 22, No. 10, p. 704.

In Fig. 6–2, *1–2* is the original position of a pile and *2–3* the displacement of the top end due to the rotation of the pile head through the angle θ about the center of rotation, r; *2–4* is the shortening, e, of the pile. Point *5* is the projection of the center of rotation on the centerline of the pile. If point *5* is considered as attached to the pier, it moves to position *6*.

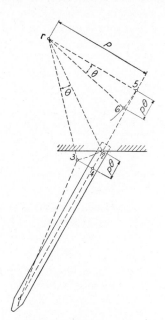

FIG. 6–2. Pile reaction.

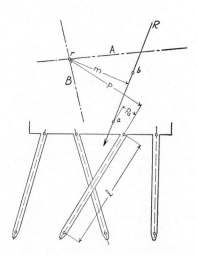

FIG. 6–3. Center of rotation for pile group.

As the displacements are treated as infinitesimal quantities we may write: Distance *6–3* = *6–4*; hence, *2–4* = *5–6*, or the shortening of the pile is

$$e = p\theta. \tag{6-2}$$

By applying Hooke's law to the pile shown in Fig. 6–2, it is seen that

$$P = \frac{eEA}{l} = \frac{p\theta EA}{l} = \frac{p}{l}\,\theta EA. \tag{6-3}$$

In other words, the pile pressures are proportional to the quantities $p \div l$.

Fig. 6–3 shows a pile group connected by hinges to a concrete pier and subjected to the action of a force R. Let r indicate the center of rotation corresponding to the force R; that is, if lines of different directions are drawn through r, then deflections of this point will be zero in all directions. It follows that, if the force R is removed and the structure instead subjected to the action of a force A through the former center of rotation r, the new center of rotation a will lie somewhere on the former force R.

This is the case as a consequence of Maxwell's theorem of reciprocity, which states that

$$\delta_{ra} = \delta_{ar}. \tag{6-4}$$

Thus, it is seen that forces going through the point r have centers of rotation lying on the line R. From this it follows that the center of rotation for a given force can be found by selecting on the given force two arbitrary points and determining the two forces whose centers of rotation these points would be. The point of intersection of these two imaginary forces is the center of rotation of the original given force. If three points are chosen on the original force, it will be found that the three corresponding imaginary forces will, barring inaccuracies in the graphical constructions or algebraic computations, all intersect in the same point.

The determination of the center of rotation is thus the first step in the treatment of any particular case of loading. Let R in Fig. 6–3 be the resultant force transmitted through the pier to the group of piles; r is the corresponding center of rotation, which is to be determined. Now, assume temporarily that the pier rotates through a certain angle about the point a, chosen anywhere on the resultant force R. This rotation would produce certain deformations in the piles. The corresponding pressures could be found by Eq. (6–3), but, as the product θEA occurs as a common factor in all the pile pressures, only proportional values ($p_a \div l$) need be assigned to the individual piles, where p_a denotes the distances from the temporary center of rotation a to the individual piles and l denotes their lengths. The resultant A of these imaginary pile pressures can then be determined either algebraically or graphically.

This procedure is then repeated for another point b on the original force R, and another imaginary resultant B is found. The actual center of rotation r is the point of intersection of A and B.

There remains now to determine the actual pressures in the piles. With the actual center of rotation r known, proportional values are readily found by dividing for each pile its perpendicular distance from r by its theoretical length. The factor θEA in Eq. (6–3) may then be found by expressing static equilibrium between these pile pressures and the resultant R. Referring to Fig. 6–3, it is seen that, if moments are taken about r, then

$$\sum \frac{p}{l} \theta EA \times p = Rm; \quad \theta EA = \frac{Rm}{\sum \dfrac{p^2}{l}}. \tag{6-5}$$

6–4. Illustrative Example. In Fig. 6–4 is shown an eccentrically loaded pile group. For the sake of simplicity it will be assumed that the four piles, designated A, B, C, and D, are all of the same length; the pres-

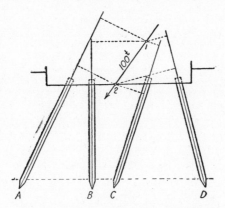

FIG. 6–4. Eccentrically loaded pile group.

sures will then be proportional to the distances from the center of rotation. It is desired to find the total pressures transmitted by the piles due to the action of a force of 100 tons, as indicated. The analysis will be made by graphical constructions.

In order to find the actual center of rotation corresponding to the given force, two arbitrary points, *1* and *2*, are selected on this force; and perpendicular distances are measured from these points to the centerlines of the piles, as indicated in Fig. 6–4. Then, in succession, are found the two forces R_1 and R_2 (see Fig. 6–5) which would result if first point *1* and subsequently point *2* were assumed to be centers of rotation; their point of intersection is the actual center of rotation, and relative values of the pile pressures will be proportional to the distances from this center to their centerlines. Absolute values may then be obtained by multiplying these tentative pressures by a coefficient which will make their resultant equal to 100 tons.

The necessary graphical constructions, which include three force polygons and two funicular polygons are shown in Fig. 6–5. In drawing the force polygon corresponding to point *1*, the distances from this point to the lines *A*, *B*, *C*, and *D* are used for pile forces and the resultant located with reference to the structure by means of a funicular (or equilibrium) polygon.

After the actual center of rotation has been located, the pile pressures can be determined graphically. These pressures will be proportional to the distances *a*, *b*, *c*, and *d*. If, with these magnitudes, force polygon *3* is drawn, the resultant of the pressures will be parallel to the given force but not equal to it in magnitude. A graphical multiplication may be performed, as shown in Fig. 6–5, which will increase the pile pressures to their correct values.

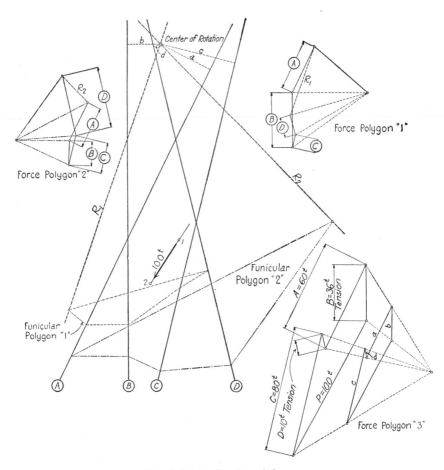

FIG. 6–5. Application of theory.

6–5. Method of Elastic Center. This method can be used to advantage in the case of a pile group consisting of hinged piles in only two directions.

The elastic center of a pile group does not coincide with the center of rotation corresponding to the given position of the load; it is the special position this rotational center would occupy if the force is infinitely far removed, in other words a couple. Consequently the elastic center is found as the intersection of two lines representing the resultants of the two subgroups, if all the piles are assumed to carry equal loads. The elastic center, then, is a fixed point which can be found without any reference to the forces acting on the structure.

The construction of the elastic center as the intersection of the centerlines of the two subgroups follows from Maxwell's theorem of reciprocity. If a point is selected on the infinitely far removed force in the direction of one pile group, then all the piles in this group will have no pressures while those in the other group will have equal pressures; consequently, the resultant will be the centerline of the second group.

It also follows from Maxwell's theorem that, if a force goes through the elastic center, then the center of rotation is at infinity in a direction perpendicular to the force and the displacement of the structure is a parallel motion in the direction of the force. Thus, for a pile group consisting of two subgroups of parallel piles, hinged top and bottom, it is evident that an outside force through the elastic center will result in pile pressures which may be determined by resolving the force into components parallel with the direction of the piles in the two groups and by dividing the magnitudes of the components by the number of piles in the respective groups.

Pile loads due to a rotating moment M may be found as follows. The moment will cause a rotation θ about the elastic center. As a result, the reaction exerted by a pile due to the change of length will be, according to Eq. (6–3),

$$P_M = \frac{EA}{l}\, \theta r,$$

where r is the distance from the elastic center to the pile. The moment of all the pile reactions with respect to the elastic center must equal the rotating moment. Thus,

$$M = \sum \frac{EA}{l} r^2 \theta; \quad \theta = \frac{M}{\sum \dfrac{EA}{l} r^2}. \tag{6–6}$$

The load on an individual pile is then determined by

$$P_M = \frac{\dfrac{EA}{l} r}{\sum \dfrac{EA}{l} r^2}\, M. \tag{6–7}$$

If all the piles have the same length, the same cross-sectional area, and are made of the same material,

$$P_M = \frac{r}{\sum r^2}\, M. \tag{6–8}$$

Let the number of piles in Group A be n_A and in Group B, n_B; and let the component of the resultant in the direction of the A-piles be R_A and in the direction of the B-piles, R_B. The load on any pile may then be found from

$$P_A = \frac{R_A}{n_A} + \frac{r}{\sum r^2}\, M, \tag{6–9a}$$

$$P_B = \frac{R_B}{n_B} + \frac{r}{\sum r^2}\, M. \tag{6–9b}$$

The summation, Σr^2, should be extended over both the A piles and the B piles. Careful attention should be given to the signs of the pile pressures. A small translation in the direction of the resultant and a small rotation in the direction of the rotating moment should be assumed and the nature of the pressures, whether tension or compression, should be noted.

6–6. Numerical Example. Fig. 6–6 shows a cross section of a lock wall supported on steel bearing piles arranged in parallel rows, 2 ft, 6 in.

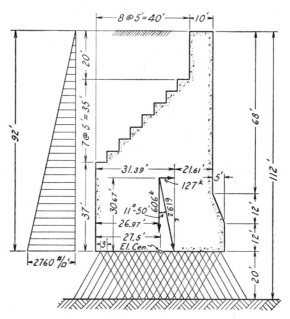

Fig. 6–6. Pile-supported lock wall.

apart, and alternately sloping towards the front and the rear. The piles can be assumed hinged at their tops and bottoms. The wall is subjected to the action of forces caused by the weight of the concrete (150 lb/cu ft), the weight of the earth fill directly above its stepped rear (85 lb/cu ft), and the lateral earth pressure acting on the vertical portions of its rear (this earth pressure is assumed to be equivalent to a liquid pressure of 30 lb/sq ft). The resultant of all of these forces is shown on Fig. 6–6.

If a section of the wall, 5 ft thick, is now considered, it is seen that the elastic center will be located at the midpoint of the bottom. Computations leading to maximum pile pressures in accordance with Eq. (6–9a) and (6–9b) are shown in an analysis of a pile-supported lock wall by the elastic center method. See Fig. 6–7; each row contains eighteen piles sloping alternately in the two directions (Group *A* and Group *B*). The

Fig. 6–7

angle of batter is 30°. The distance between rows is 2 ft, 6 in. Lateral earth pressure is equivalent to a liquid pressure of 30 lb/cu ft. Polar moment of inertia for two pile groups is:

$$4(1.3^2 + 3.9^2 + 6.5^2 + 9.1^2 + 11.7^2 + 14.3^2 + 16.9^2 + 19.5^2 + 22.1^2) = 6554.$$

Most highly stressed piles will resist forces equal to:

$$P_A = \left[\frac{223}{18} + \frac{619 \times 5.78 \times 22.1}{6554} \right] \times 5 = 122^k,$$

$$P_B = \left[\frac{477}{18} + \frac{619 \times 5.78 \times 22.1}{6554} \right] \times 5 = 193^k.$$

6–7. Restrained Piles.* Piles driven to a considerable distance into a compact soil can be assumed restrained at a certain depth. Piles, notably those of reinforced concrete, may also be built into the superstructure in such manner that fixity is developed at their tops. Under these conditions pile stresses will be due to axial load and bending, and can be computed by adding *dummy* piles perpendicular to each of the real piles, the location and length of the dummy piles to be such that the effect on the pier of an unrestrained real pile plus one or two unrestrained piles is the same as that of the restrained real pile. After the locations and lengths of the dummy piles have been determined, the procedure of load determination is exactly as if all piles were real and unrestrained. Thus, the dummy piles are but imaginary piles added for the purpose of facilitating the computations. The loads found on the dummy piles will represent the actual shears in the real piles.

Consider first the case of a pile restrained in the foundation material at some point of its axis and connected to the pier through a hinge. It is

*See C. P. Vetter, "Design of Pile Foundations," *Trans. A.S.C.E.* (1939), Vol. 104, p. 758.

shown in Fig. 6–8 that the total effect of the pile foundation on the pier is not changed by considering the real piles hinged at both ends, providing a hinged dummy pile is added perpendicular to each real pile, intersecting it at the base of the pier.

It is seen that the real pile transmits through its top direct load as well as shear. Therefore, a dummy pile of the same cross section as the real

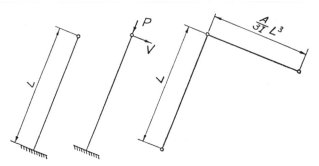

Fig. 6–8. Piles restrained at bottom.

pile, and offering the same lateral resistance as the fixed pile, must have a theoretical length l such that the deflection of the top of the fixed pile equals the shortening of the dummy pile, thus:

$$\frac{VL^3}{3EI} = \frac{Vl}{AE} \; ; \qquad l = L^3 \frac{A}{3I} \qquad (6\text{--}10)$$

where A and I represent the area and moment of inertia, respectively, of the real pile and L the distance from the base of the pier to the point where it is assumed restrained.

The stresses in the real pile, due to the restraint, are equal to those of a cantilever beam restrained at the bottom and transmitting a constant shear V, which is the direct load found in the dummy pile acting perpendicularly to the real pile at its top.

Consider next a pile restrained at the pier and not restrained in the foundation material. The real pile may be considered hinged at both ends if a dummy pile is added. The dummy pile should be normal to the real pile and should intersect it at the centroid of the lateral resistance in the ground, as shown in Fig. 6–9. Again the length of the dummy pile must be such that the lateral deflection of the cantilever beam restrained at the top equals the shortening of the dummy pile. Eq. (6–10) will, therefore, also apply to lengths of dummy piles compensating for restraints at tops of real piles.

Consider finally the case of a pile restrained both at the pier and in the foundation material. It will be shown in the following that the real pile

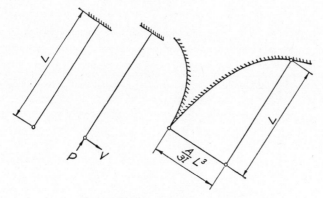

Fig. 6–9. Piles restrained at top.

can be considered hinged at both ends if two dummy piles are added to each real pile.

In Fig. 6–10 is shown a pier and one pile of a pile group. The pile is restrained at both ends and the center of rotation corresponding to the

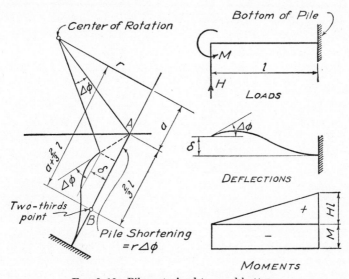

Fig. 6–10. Pile restrained top and bottom.

outside load is indicated. Assume a small rotation $\Delta\phi$ of the pier, and it is readily seen that the shortening of the pile will be $r\Delta\phi$ and that the lateral displacement of the top of the pile will be δ. Thus,

$$\frac{\delta}{r\Delta\phi} = \frac{a}{r} \; ; \qquad \delta = a\Delta\phi. \tag{6–11}$$

If now M and H denote the moment and shear, respectively, transmitted from the pier to the top of the pile, then the lateral and rotational displacement of the pile top can be found by the moment-area method, thus:

$$\delta = \frac{1}{EI} \left(\tfrac{1}{3} H l^3 - \tfrac{1}{2} M l^2 \right), \tag{6-12a}$$

$$\Delta\phi = \frac{1}{EI} \left(-\tfrac{1}{2} H l^2 + M l \right), \tag{6-12b}$$

$$H = \frac{6EI}{l^2} \left(\frac{2\delta}{l} + \Delta\phi \right) = \frac{12EI}{l^3} \Delta\phi \left(a + \frac{l}{2} \right), \tag{6-13a}$$

$$M = \frac{12EI}{l} \left(\frac{\delta}{2l} + \frac{\Delta\phi}{3} \right) = \frac{6EI}{l^2} \Delta\phi (a + \tfrac{2}{3} l). \tag{6-13b}$$

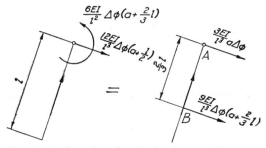

Fɪɢ. 6-11. Reactions for pile fixed top and bottom.

As shown in Fig. 6-11 the reaction of the pile upon the superstructure consists of direct load along the pile axis, a force perpendicular to the pile (shear), and a bending moment. The action of the bending and the shear is the same as that of two parallel forces, whose sum equals H and whose moment equals M. There is an infinite number of such divisions but the one which places the two forces at the top and the two-thirds point of the pile is of special interest. Referring again to Fig. 6-11, it is seen that the two forces at point A and point B will, as far as statics is concerned, satisfactorily substitute for moment and shear at A. Thus, the sum of the two forces is

$$\frac{3EI}{l^3} a\Delta\phi + \frac{9EI}{l^3} \Delta\phi(a + \tfrac{2}{3} l) = \frac{12EI}{l^3} \Delta\phi \left(a + \frac{l}{2} \right). \tag{6-14a}$$

The moment with respect to the top of the pile is

$$\frac{9EI}{l^3} \Delta\phi(a + \tfrac{2}{3} l) \times \tfrac{2}{3} l = \frac{6EI}{l^2} \Delta\phi(a + \tfrac{2}{3} l). \tag{6-14b}$$

From Fig. 6-10 it is seen that the component of the displacement of point A perpendicular to AB equals

$$a\Delta\phi. \tag{6-15}$$

If point B were rigidly connected to the pier, then its displacement normal to AB would equal

$$(a + \tfrac{2}{3}l)\Delta\phi. \tag{6-16}$$

The reason for substituting, in place of the moment and shear at the pile top, a force at the top supplemented by a force at the two-thirds point is now clear. From Fig. 6–11 it is seen that the expressions for these forces contain as factors the displacements of their respective points of application as given by Eq. (6–15) and (6–16). If dummy piles are placed at points A and B, then their lengths should be such that their compressive strains will be equal to the displacements of these points. Thus, for the dummy pile at A,

$$\frac{\left(\dfrac{3EI}{l^3}\,a\Delta\phi\right)l_1}{AE} = a\Delta\phi,$$

$$l_1 = \frac{A}{3I}\, l^3. \tag{6-17}$$

And for the dummy pile at B,

$$\frac{\dfrac{9EI}{l^3}\,(a + \tfrac{2}{3}l)\,\Delta\phi}{AE}\, l_2 = (a + \tfrac{2}{3}l)\,\Delta\phi,$$

$$l_2 = \frac{A}{9I}\, l^3. \tag{6-18}$$

6–8. Numerical Examples. Fig. 6–12(a) shows three reinforced concrete piles which have been built rigidly into the pier they support. They

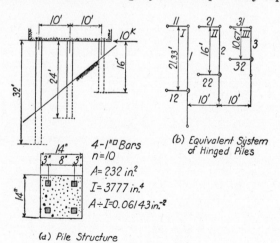

4-1″□ Bars
n = 10
A = 232 in.²
I = 3777 in.⁴
A ÷ I = 0.06143 in.⁻²

(b) Equivalent System of Hinged Piles

(a) Pile Structure

FIG. 6–12. Numerical example.

are also assumed fixed at certain points below the ground surfaces; the distances from the bottom of the pier to these assumed fixed planes are indicated. The structure is subjected to the action of a force of 10,000 lb acting along the bottom of the pier. It is desired to find moment shears and direct pressures in the three piles.

The equivalent pile system is shown in Fig. 6–12 (b); it consists of the three original piles now hinged top and bottom and supplemented by six dummy piles located at the tops and the two-thirds points. The lengths of these dummy piles depend on the structural make-up of the real piles. Fig. 6–12(a) gives computations for the ratio $A \div I$, where A and I represent area and moment of inertia of the transformed cross section of the pile. Table 6–1 lists lengths of real piles and dummy piles, the latter

TABLE 6–1

PILE LENGTHS

Real Piles		Dummy Piles			
1	32 ft	11	96633 ft	12	32227 ft
2	24 ft	21	40767 ft	22	13596 ft
3	16 ft	31	12079 ft	32	4028 ft

having been computed in accordance with Eqs. (6–17) and (6–18). It is interesting to note that the lengths of the dummy piles are much longer than the real piles (from 100 to 1000 times). This is always the case.

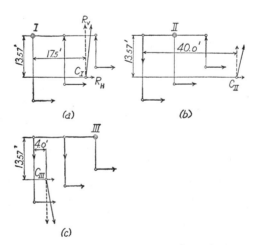

FIG. 6–13. Assumed centers of rotation.

Computations for locating the center of rotation are shown in Fig. 6–13. In succession it is assumed that points I, II, and III, all lying on the given force of 10,000 lb, are centers of rotation; and the corresponding resultants are determined. Table 6–2 lists pile pressures due to the three

TABLE 6–2

PILE PRESSURES IN FIG. 6–13

| | ASSUMED POINT OF ROTATION | | |
	I	II	III
1	0	−31.25	62.5
2	41.67	0	41.67
3	125.00	62.5	0
R_v	166.67	31.25	104.17
12	0.067	0.067	0.067
22	0.117	0.117	0.117
32	0.265	0.265	0.265
R_H	0.449	0.449	0.449

assumptions; for convenience, these may be taken simply as the distances from the three points to the respective piles divided by their lengths.

In Fig. 6–14 is shown the determination of the actual center of rotation C by intersection of the three resultants corresponding to the three

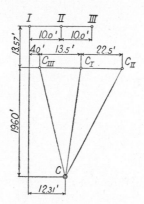

FIG. 6–14. Center of rotation, parallel piles.

temporarily assumed centers of rotations I, II, and III. Only two of these points need to be assumed; a third point, however, affords a check on the accuracy of the procedure.

With the center of rotation C located, the remainder of the analysis is a comparatively easy matter; the forces acting along the real and dummy piles are proportional to the distances from this point, and their absolute values are readily determined by the principles of statics. Thus in Table 6-3 are figured proportional values of dummy-pile pressures by

TABLE 6-3

DUMMY-PILE PRESSURES

Pile	$r/l*$	$r/l \div 0.9241$	Shear (Lb)
11	$1973.6 \div 96,333 = 0.0204$	0.0221	
12	$1952.2 \div 32,227 = 0.0606$	0.0656	
			877
21	$1973.6 \div 40,767 = 0.0484$	0.0524	
22	$1957.6 \div 13,596 = 0.1440$	0.1558	
			2082
31	$1973.6 \div 12,079 = 0.1634$	0.1768	
32	$1962.9 \div\ \ \ 4028 = 0.4873$	0.5273	
			7041
	0.9241	1.0000	10,000

* r = distance from Point C (Fig. 6-14), l = length (Table 6-1).

dividing their lengths (Table 6-1) into their distances from the center of rotation C; their actual values are found from the fact that their total

TABLE 6-4

REAL-PILE PRESSURES

Pile	Proportionate Values = r/l
1	$12.31 \div 32 = 0.3847$
2	$2.31 \div 24 = 0.0963$
3	$7.69 \div 16 = 0.4806$

Taking moments about Point I, Fig. 6-13(b),
$-0.0963X \times 10 + 4806X \times 20 - 656 \times 21.33 - 1558 \times 16 - 5273 \times 10.67 = 0; X = 11,000$ lb.
656 lb, 1558 lb, and 5273 lb are dummy pile pressures (see Table 6-3).

sum must equal 10,000 lb. Likewise proportional values of the pressures in the three real piles are listed in Table 6-4, and moments about any

TABLE 6-5

FINAL PILE LOADS

Pile	$11,000 \times r/l$ (Table 6-4)
1	4230 lb Comp.
2	1060 lb Comp.
3	5290 lb Tension

convenient point will yield the absolute values of these pressures. See Table 6-5.

It remains now to translate dummy-pile pressures into shears and moments in the original piles which were restrained at tops and bottoms. The sums of two dummy piles give the shears, as indicated in the last column of Table 6–3. The moment with respect to the pile top will give the moments at this point. Fig. 6–15 gives the final pressure.

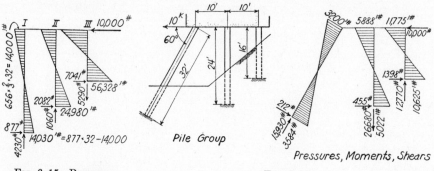

FIG. 6–15. Pressures, shears, and moments.

FIG. 6–16

In order to further illustrate the use of dummy piles, the analysis of the pile structure shown in Fig. 6–16 will be explained. This structure is similar to the one shown in Fig. 6–12 except that the front pile has been

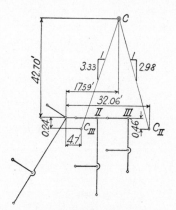

FIG. 6–17. Center of rotation, sloping front pile.

battered so as to make an angle of 60° with the horizontal. The analysis proceeds similarly to the preceding one. The three original piles are assumed hinged top and bottom and supplemented by three pairs of dummy piles—a pair for each of the original piles, perpendicular to their directions and placed at tops and two-thirds points. The equivalent system is shown in Fig. 6–17 which also indicates that the points *II* and *III* (both lying on external force of 10,000 lb) have been selected for auxiliary centers of rotation. These centers of rotation result in corresponding forces through points C_{II} and C_{III}, respectively; their point of intersection, C, is the center of rotation corresponding to the given force. The pile pressures will be proportional to their distances from C and application of the fundamental static requirements will yield actual pressures which, in turn, can be translated into shears and moments. Fig. 6–16 shows final shears, moments, and direct pressures.

It is interesting to compare diagrams of Fig. 6–15 and Fig. 6–16; such a comparison indicates the advantage of using battered piles. Thus the change of the front pile from a vertical to a sloping position will very materially reduce shears and moments but will also cause very great increases in the direct loads on the piles.

6–9. Parallel Piles. In the following will be presented a method of analysis applicable to groups that consist of vertical piles subjected to the action of horizontal loads. The centers of rotation for such cases lie always at very great distances from the group, as was found in Fig. 6–14. For this reason the motion of the pier will be very nearly a translation; all the pile tops will move equal amounts, and their elastic curve tangents will remain parallel to their original positions. This is illustrated in

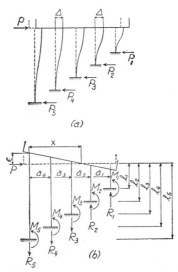

FIG. 6–18. Horizontal force acting
on vertical piles.

Fig. 6–18(a). Using the relationship between deflection and shear in structural members fixed top and bottom,

$$\Delta = \frac{P_1 l_1{}^3}{12EI} = \frac{P_2 l_2{}^3}{12EI} = \frac{P_3 l_3{}^3}{12EI} = \cdots ; \qquad (6\text{-}19)$$

$$\frac{P_1}{\dfrac{1}{l_1{}^3}} = \frac{P_2}{\dfrac{1}{l_2{}^3}} = \frac{P_3}{\dfrac{1}{l_3{}^3}} = \cdots , \qquad (6\text{-}20)$$

$$P_1 + P_2 + P_3 + \cdots = P, \qquad (6\text{-}21)$$

$$P_1 = P \frac{\dfrac{1}{l_1{}^3}}{\Sigma \dfrac{1}{l^3}} \ ; \quad P_2 = P \frac{\dfrac{1}{l_2{}^3}}{\Sigma \dfrac{1}{l^3}} \ ; \ \cdots \qquad (6\text{-}22)$$

In other words, the total shear in the piles will be distributed in accordance with the cubes of the reciprocal pile lengths.

The points of contraflexure will occur at midheights and will equal

$$M_1 = \tfrac{1}{2} P_1 l_1; \quad M_2 = \tfrac{1}{2} P_2 l_2; \ \cdots \qquad (6\text{-}23)$$

Although the principal movement of the pier is a horizontal translation, this will be accompanied by a very small rotation. This rotation will produce compression in some of the piles and tension in others, as indicated in Fig. 6–18 (b). Let ϵ denote the elongation of the front pile and x the distance from this member to the neutral axis. The sum of all the pile reactions must equal zero; thus,

$$R_1 + R_2 + R_3 + \cdots = 0. \qquad (6\text{-}24)$$

The pile reactions can be expressed in terms of Hooke's law thus:

$$R_1 = \frac{AE}{l_1} \epsilon \frac{a_1 - x}{x} \ ; \quad R_2 = \frac{AE}{l_2} \epsilon \frac{a_2 - x}{x} \ ; \cdots \qquad (6\text{-}25)$$

If Eq. (6–25) is substituted in Eq. (6–24), the product $AE\epsilon$ will cancel out and the distance, x, to the neutral axis can be found in terms of known quantities. Taking moments about any convenient point, for instance the top of the front pile, gives

$$\Sigma Ra + \Sigma Pl - \Sigma M = 0. \qquad (6\text{-}26)$$

With the position of the neutral axis known, Eq. (6–26) will yield a value of the product $AE\epsilon$ which, when substituted in Eq. (6–25), gives actual values of the direct loads in the piles.

See Fig. 6–19. The procedure outlined above is here applied to a previous numerical example, Fig. 6–12(a).

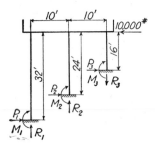

FIG. 6–19

$$(1 \div 16)^3 = 0.2441 \times 10^{-3}$$
$$(1 \div 24)^3 = 0.0724$$
$$(1 \div 32)^3 = 0.0305$$
$$\overline{\qquad 0.3470 \times 10^{-3}}$$

$$P_3 = \frac{0.2441}{0.3470} \times 10^4 = 7040 \text{ lb,}$$

$$P_2 = \frac{0.0724}{0.3470} \times 10^4 = 2080 \text{ lb,}$$

$$P_1 = \frac{0.0305}{0.3470} \times 10^4 = 880 \text{ lb.}$$

$$M_3 = 7040 \times 8 = 56,320; \qquad M_2 - 2080 \times 12 = 24,960;$$

$$M_1 = 880 \times 16 = 14,080.$$

$$\frac{AE}{32} \epsilon + \frac{AE}{24} \epsilon \frac{x - 10}{x} - \frac{AE}{16} \epsilon \frac{20 - x}{x} = 0, \qquad x = 12.3,$$

$$\frac{AE\epsilon}{32} 20 + \frac{AE\epsilon}{24} \frac{2.3}{12.3} 10 - 56,320 - 24,960 - 14,080 = 0,$$

$$AE\epsilon = 135,500.$$

$$R_1 = \frac{135,500}{32} = 4230,$$

$$R_2 = \frac{135,500}{24} \times \frac{2.3}{12.3} = 1085;$$

$$R_3 = \frac{135,500}{16} \times \frac{7.7}{12.3} = 5315.$$

It is of interest to compare these results to those previously found by a more exact method. The differences are quite insignificant.

6–10. Friction Piles. In the foregoing, piles that transfer their pressures through their bottom tips have been considered. If a pile is driven into a uniform and comparatively loose soil, it will transmit its load by frictional forces acting along its outside surface; its theoretical point of support will therefore be at some distance above the pile tip. If, as indicated in Fig. 6–20, it is assumed that the frictional resistance per linear

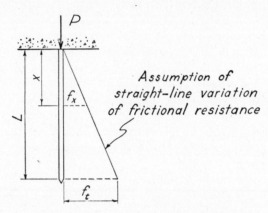

FIG. 6–20. Friction pile—equivalent bearing pile.

foot of pile increases rectilinearly from zero at the top of the pile to a maximum value at the tip, the elastic deformation of the pile, due to a load P applied axially at the top, is determined by

$$\Delta = \frac{1}{EA} \int_0^L (P - \tfrac{1}{2}f_x x)dx, \tag{6–27}$$

in which x is the distance measured from the base of the pier to some arbitrary depth along the pile, f_x is the frictional resistance per linear foot at that point, E is the elastic modulus of the pile material, and A is the cross-sectional area of the pile. Due to the assumed rectilinear variation,

$$f_x = \frac{x}{L} f_t, \tag{6–28}$$

in which f_t is the frictional resistance per linear foot at the tip of the pile. It is also seen that

$$\tfrac{1}{2}f_t L = P, \tag{6–29}$$

since the total resistance must equal the pile load. Hence

$$\Delta = \frac{1}{EA} \int_0^L \left(P - \frac{x^2}{L^2} P\right) dx = \frac{1}{EA} \times \tfrac{2}{3}L \times P. \tag{6–30}$$

The deformation of a friction pile is thus the same as that of a pile of two-thirds of its length driven to firm ground, and its effective length is two-thirds of the actual length.

It is apparent that, in the case of a pile hinged both at its connection to the pier and at the point where it transfers its load to the foundation, the lateral resistance of the ground to movements perpendicular to the pile axis has been disregarded. In this case, the exterior load on the pier is resisted solely by forces along the axes of the piles. On the other hand, there must be lateral resistance if the pile is entirely surrounded by earth. The resistance must depend on the magnitude of the lateral displacements, on the depth below the surface, and on the length of the pile.

In figuring the lengths of individual piles in a group of friction piles, fixed either at the top or at the lower end, or in both places, the effective lengths should not necessarily be those given by Eq. (6–30). If all the piles are reduced in the same proportion, the load distribution will remain the same. Until the results of further research on the subject are available, the location of the centroid of lateral forces can be fixed only by the judgment of the designer. A distance of from 5 to 10 ft along the pile axis to the point where a friction pile can be assumed fixed will usually be in accordance with the actual conditions.

If the pile group consists of piles in one direction alone, then stability can only be obtained by depending on the fixed ends at either top or bottom. If, on the other hand, the group is made up of piles in more than one direction, the bending stresses due to possible fixed-end conditions become comparatively less significant (compare Fig. 6–15 and Fig. 6–16) and the error, in assuming hinged end connections, unimportant.

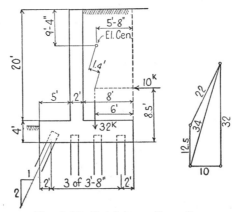

FIG. 6–21. Retaining wall on piles.

6–11. Practical Examples. Fig. 6–21 shows a reinforced concrete retaining wall supported on wood piles arranged in four rows; the front row consists of batter piles and the other three are made up of vertical piles. The total weight of the wall and the fill lying directly above the inside base is 32 kips, while the resultant of all lateral pressures on a vertical plane drawn through the edge is 10 kips. These forces are located as shown.

If the piles are assumed hinged at both ends, the elastic center can be located by intersecting the centerline of the batter pile with the centerline of the vertical group. The resultant of the two outside forces is constructed and dissolved into two components parallel to the pile directions.

If the front piles are spaced 3 ft on centers, the total compression in

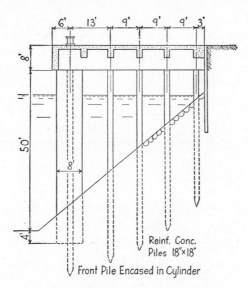

FIG. 6–22. Waterfront structure on piles.

one pile will be $3 \times 22 = 66$ kips $= 33$ tons. If the vertical piles are spaced 6 ft on centers, the front row of these piles will carry loads equal to

$$6\left[\frac{12.5}{3} + \frac{34 \times 1.4}{2 \times 3.67^2} \times 3.67\right] = 64 \text{ kips} = 32 \text{ tons.}$$

Fig. 6–22 shows a wharf structure supported on reinforced concrete piles. The front piles are encased in reinforced concrete cylinders filled with concrete, while the ground behind the wharf is confined behind a continuous line of sheet piling, bearing against the structure itself. It is desired to find the stresses set up in the piles and the cylinder due to the action of a lateral force of 25 kips acting along the underside of the heavy girder which connects the piles and carries the deck of the wharf.

The increase in section of the front pile will greatly increase the lateral strength of the structure and will relieve the rear piles. As the cylinder extends only a comparatively short distance below the ground, it is necessary to assume the front member hinged at its lower end.   If the cylinder is connected to the girder by steel dowels, it can be assumed fixed at its upper end.   The unencased piles will also be assumed fixed at their top ends and at a distance of 8 ft below the top of the ground surface. The structure may then be assumed to act as shown in Fig. 6–23.

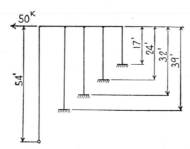

FIG. 6–23. Simplified structure.

The method developed for parallel piles may then be applied if it is remembered that displacement of the top of the hinged front member is

$$\frac{P_1 l_1^3}{3EI_1}, \tag{6–31}$$

while for the other piles, which are fixed at both ends, the deflections are

$$\frac{P_2 l_2^3}{12EI_2} = \frac{P_3 l_3^3}{12EI_3} = \frac{P_4 l_4^3}{12EI_4} = \frac{P_5 l_5^3}{12EI_5} \tag{6–32}$$

Equating (6–31) and (6–32) gives

$$\frac{P_1}{3I_1 \div l_1^3} = \frac{P_2}{12I_2 \div l_2^3} = \frac{P_3}{12I_3 \div l_3^3} = \frac{P_4}{12I_4 \div l_4^3} = \frac{P_5}{12I_5 \div l_5^3},$$

where $P_1 + P_2 + P_3 + P_4 + P_5 = 50$ kips.

Substituting,

$$I_1 = \frac{\pi}{4} \, 4^4 = 201,$$

$$I_2 = I_3 = I_4 = I_5 = \frac{1}{12} \, 1.5^4 = 0.42 \text{ ft}^4$$

and the values for l_1, l_2, l_3, and l_4, as shown on Fig. 6–23, give the following distribution of the lateral force of 50 kips:

$$
\begin{aligned}
P_1 &= 35,085 \text{ lb,} \\
P_2 &= 780 \text{ lb,} \\
P_3 &= 1410 \text{ lb,} \\
P_4 &= 3335 \text{ lb,} \\
P_5 &= 9390 \text{ lb.}
\end{aligned}
$$

The maximum bending moment in the cylinder will occur at its top and will equal

$$35{,}084 \times 54 = 1{,}894{,}590 \text{ ft-lb,}$$

giving a maximum bending stress of

$$(1{,}894{,}590 \times 12) \div \left(\frac{\pi}{4} 48^3\right) = 262 \text{ psi.}$$

Maximum bending stress in the unencased piles will occur at top and bottom of rear pile and will equal

$$\frac{9390 \times 8.5 \times 12}{\frac{1}{2} \times \frac{3}{8} \times \frac{7}{8} 18 \times 15^2} = 1420 \text{ psi.}$$

PROBLEMS

6–1. Find the forces in the three piles illustrated and assume hinged top and bottom. A force of 100 kips acts along the horizontal bottom plane of the superstructure. The piles have identical cross sections. (*Ans.*: 430 kips in center pile.)

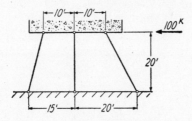

PROB. 6–1

6–2. In Prob. 6–1, change the horizontal dimension of 20 ft to 15 ft. Show that this new arrangement is unstable and cannot resist the horizontal force.

CONSTRUCTION OF DAM INSIDE CELLULAR COFFERDAM

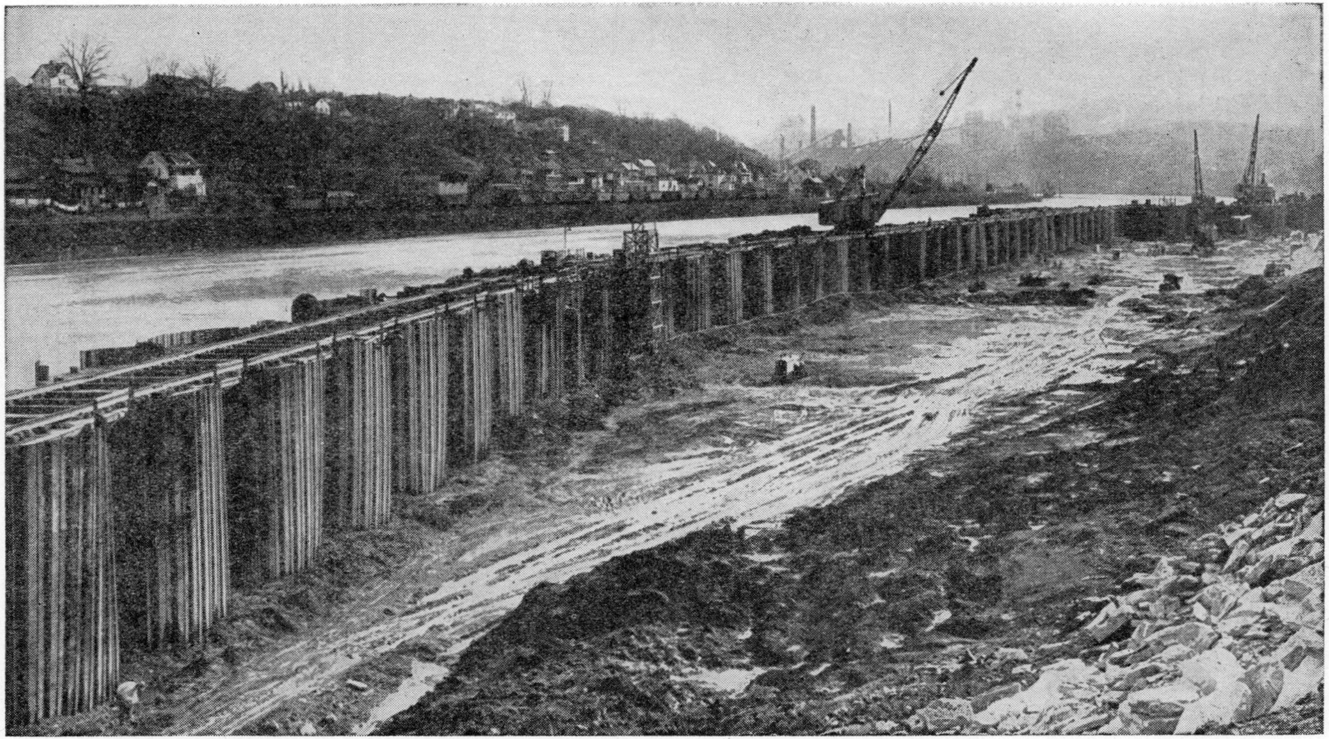

FIG. 7-1. Cellular cofferdam.

195

CHAPTER 7

CELLULAR COFFERDAMS

7-1. Introduction. A cofferdam is a temporary structure whose func tion is to exclude earth and water from an excavation in order that work may be done in the dry. As far as the exclusion of water is concerned, a cofferdam is usually meeting its requirements if it does not permit water to come in faster than it can be pumped out.

A cellular cofferdam consists of interconnected cells made up of interlocking steel sheet piling. The cells are filled with earth. Cellular cofferdams are used where the area to be excavated is of considerable extent. Inside a large enclosure it becomes impracticable to support the walls by cross-bracing—hence, the use of cellular cofferdams, which consist of self-stable units.

Fig. 7-1 shows a typical installation of a cellular cofferdam making possible the unwatering of a large area. Fig. 7-2 shows, in diagrammatic form, the use of cellular cofferdams for construction of a permanent concrete dam across a river. In order to allow uninterrupted flow of the water during the construction, the dam must be built in stages and adjacent areas unwatered successively as indicated in (a) and (b) of Fig. 7-2.

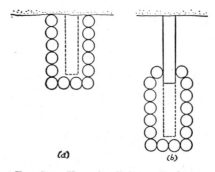

(a)   (b)

Fig. 7-2. Use of cellular cofferdams.

Although cellular cofferdams are usually feasible and economical for large enclosures, they have also been used for small areas, such as occupied by bridge piers, as shown in Fig. 7-3.

Fig. 7–3. Cellular cofferdam enclosing small area.

7-2. Types of Cellular Cofferdams. Two main types of these structures are in current use. One type, illustrated in Fig. 7-5, consists of a series of complete circles connected by shorter arcs. These connecting arcs are jointed to the full circles by means of fabricated T-pieces [Fig. 7-4(a)], and as these pieces usually are manufactured to make an angle

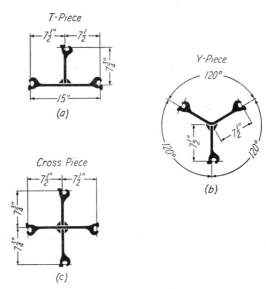

FIG. 7-4. Fabricated connections for cellular cofferdams.

of 90°, it is imperative that the two sets of circles form orthogonal curves. The distances and radii indicated in Fig. 7-5 give 90° intersections between circles. Also indicated in Fig. 7-5 is the average width, B, of a cellular cofferdam of the circular type.

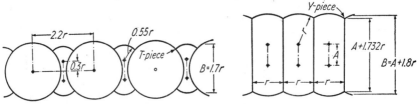

FIG. 7-5. Cellular cofferdam, circular type.   FIG. 7-6. Cellular cofferdam, diaphragm type.

Another type, illustrated in Fig. 7-6, consists of a series of arcs connected to straight diaphragm walls by means of fabricated Y-pieces. The legs of the Y-pieces [see Fig. 7-4(b)] form three angles of 120° each, thus making the chord equal to the radius of the arc and making the tensions in the arcs and crosswalls equal. Fig. 7-6 shows the usual arrangement of a diaphragm type cellular cofferdam. In order to combine a large width B with a small radius r (both required for a high dam) the centers for opposite arcs can be separated by a distance A. The average width B for a diaphragm type of dam is also given in Fig. 7–6.

If a diaphragm type of dam is used for a low height it will be found economical to combine a small width with a large radius as shown in Fig. 7–7. In this event it will be necessary to make the distance A negative.

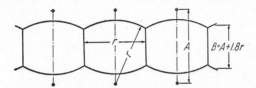

Fig. 7–7. Diaphragm type, Negative A.

The diaphragm type requires less sheet piling, but the circular type is advantageous in that each circle can be completely filled, and therefore made stable, immediately after the piles are driven. The diaphragm type must be filled in stages, keeping the height of the fill in adjoining cells as nearly as possible at the same height to avoid distortion of the diaphragm walls.

7–3. Computations. The complete elimination of bracing, which is the chief characteristic of cellular cofferdams, requires that each cell must be stable against: overturning, sliding, and tension in the interlocks.

Safety against overturning is secured when the resultant of all the forces acting on the cell falls within the middle third of the width. Stability against sliding is obtained when the ratio of the horizontal component of this force (the lateral pressure) to the vertical component (the weight of the cell) is less than one-half. Safety against tension in interlocks is obtained when the circumferential tension in the outside shells, as well as in the membranes, does not exceed the value specified by the steel manufacturing company.

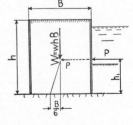

Fig. 7–8

Fig. 7–8 shows a cross section of a cellular cofferdam subjected to a lateral pressure, the resultant of which per unit width is the force P acting at a distance h_1 from the bottom. If the resultant of this force and the corresponding weight of the cofferdam is to fall at the middle third, then

$$\frac{B}{6} = \frac{Ph_1}{whB} \qquad B = \sqrt{\frac{6Ph_1}{wh}}. \tag{7–1}$$

The criterion for safety against sliding of the cofferdam is that the ratio of the horizontal component P to the vertical component W must be less than the coefficient of friction between the material which forms the fill of the cells of the cofferdam and the soil upon which it rests. There seems to be no record of any cofferdam ever failing by sliding, and a conservative value for the coefficient of friction is one-half. The width B can therefore be found from

$$\frac{P}{whB} = \frac{1}{2}; \qquad B = \frac{2P}{wh} \qquad (7\text{--}2)$$

The fill inside the compartments of the cofferdam will exert pressure against the outside walls, in which tension forces will be created. These forces must not exceed the allowable tension on the interlocks, which usually varies from 8000 to 12,000 lb/lin in. This requirement will limit the radius r and consequently the width B of the cofferdam, because the circumferential tension of a cylindrical shell is directly proportional to its radius. The relationship between tension t in the interlocks, radius r, and pressure p is

$$t = \tfrac{1}{12}pr. \qquad (7\text{--}3)$$

If p is expressed in lb/ft and r in feet, the tension t in the interlocks will be in lb/lin in. The pressure p is usually computed by

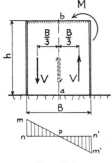

$$p = wh \tan^2\left(45° - \frac{\phi}{2}\right), \qquad (7\text{--}4)$$

where w is weight to fill and ϕ is its angle of internal friction.

In addition to failure by overturning, sliding, and rupture in tension of the interlocks near the base, as expressed by Eqs. (7–1), (7–2), and (7–3), a cellular cofferdam may fail from excessive shear on a vertical plane through its center, as will be demonstrated in the following.[*]

Fig. 7–9

In Fig. 7–9, the stresses produced by the moment M are represented by the two triangles mnp and $m'n'p$ under the section. If V is the total force represented by each triangle, then

$$M = V \times \frac{2}{3}B \quad \text{or} \quad V = \frac{3M}{2B}. \qquad (7\text{--}5)$$

The shear on the neutral plane ab must be equal to V, and the shearing resistance on this plane must be sufficient to prevent rupture. The shearing resistance on the neutral plane is equal to the normal pressure times the

[*]See Karl Terzaghi, "Stability and Stiffness of Cellular Cofferdams," *Trans. A.S.C.E.* (1945), p. 1083.

coefficient of internal friction, tan ϕ, of the fill. The normal pressure is due to the lateral earth pressure and its total value may be computed in the usual manner. Thus,

$$P_A = \tfrac{1}{2}wh^2 \tan^2\left(45° - \frac{\phi}{2}\right) \tag{7-6}$$

The total shearing resistance will be this value multiplied by the coefficient of internal friction. Thus,

$$\tfrac{1}{2}wh^2 \tan^2\left(45° - \frac{\phi}{2}\right)\tan \phi. \tag{7-7}$$

To this shearing resistance must be added the friction in the interlocks of the steel sheet piling, since no failure by shear can occur along plane ab without simultaneous slippage in the interlocks in this plane. The friction in the interlocks will depend on the circumferential tension. The total amount of tension on one interlock is

$$pr = \tfrac{1}{2}wh^2 \tan^2\left(45° - \frac{\phi}{2}\right)r. \tag{7-8}$$

The total resistance against slippage in the interlocks can be found by multiplying Eq. (7-8) by the coefficient of lock friction f as follows:

$$\tfrac{1}{2}wh^2 \tan^2\left(45° - \frac{\phi}{2}\right)rf, \tag{7-9}$$

which will apply to both the diaphragm and the circular types of cofferdams. It should be noted that the tension in the crosswalls of the diaphragm type of cofferdam is the same as in the curved portions.

In order to obtain a relationship expressing safety against rupture by vertical shear, the total shear as given by Eq. (7-5) is multiplied by the distance between two crosswalls and equated to the sum of shearing resistance of fill and lock resistance as given by Eq. (7-7) and 7-9). In case of the diaphragm type, the distance between crosswalls is equal to the radius r and the minimum value of width B will be

$$B = \frac{3M}{wh^2 \tan^2\left(45° - \frac{\phi}{2}\right)(\tan \phi + f)}. \tag{7-10}$$

For a circular type of cofferdam, which has two crosswalls on a length of $2.2r$ (see Fig. 7-5), this formula will be modified to

$$B = \frac{3M}{wh^2 \tan^2\left(45° - \frac{\phi}{2}\right)(\tan \phi + 0.9f)}. \tag{7-11}$$

7-4. Numerical Example. Let it be desired to design a cellular coffer-dam of the diaphragm type. No penetration of the sheet piling into the subsoil can be depended upon. Dimensions and properties of the fill are given in Fig. 7–10. Computations for pressures and overturning moments are listed in Fig. 7–11.

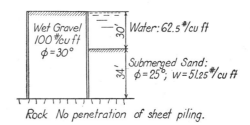

FIG. 7–10. Data for design of cofferdam.

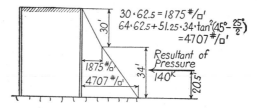

FIG. 7–11. Pressure on cofferdam.

The minimum width of the cofferdam must be such that safety is provided against overturning, sliding, and rupture by vertical shear. According to Eq. (7–1), safety against overturning requires that the width of the cofferdam must be at least

$$B = \sqrt{\frac{6 \times 2{,}870{,}000}{100 \times 64}} = 52 \text{ ft.}$$

According to Eq. (7–2), the minimum width needed for safety against sliding is

$$B = \frac{2 \times 140{,}000}{100 \times 64} = 44 \text{ ft.}$$

According to Eq. (7–10) safety against rupture by vertical shear will depend on the coefficient of lock friction f and the angle of internal friction ϕ of the fill inside the cofferdam. If it is assumed that $f = 0.3$ and $\phi = 30°$, then

$$B = \frac{3 \times 2{,}870{,}000}{100 \times 64^2 \times \tan^2 (45° - \tfrac{1}{2}30°)(\tan 30° + 0.3)} = 72 \text{ ft.}$$

The circumferential tension in curved portions, as well as in the crosswalls, is proportional to the radius r of the circular arcs. If it is assumed that tension on the interlocks must not exceed 6000 psi, the maximum value of the radius is determined from Eq. (7–3). Thus,

$$6000 = \tfrac{1}{12}100 \times 64 \times \tan^2 (45° - \tfrac{1}{2}30°)r,$$

$$r = 33.75 \text{ ft.}$$

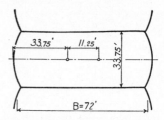

The final dimensions of the cofferdam are indicated in Fig. 7–12. According to Fig. 7–6 the distance between the two circle centers, A, was determined thus:

$$72 = A + 1.8 \times 33.75,$$

$$A = 11.25 \text{ ft.}$$

Fig. 7–12. Final dimensions of cofferdam.

It is important that the water be drained from the inside of the cofferdam. This can be done by covering the bottom of the cells with a filter layer of coarse gravel or broken stones, which should communicate through weep holes with the space occupied by enclosure of the dam, as shown in Fig. 7–13. Depending on the amount of percolation, weep holes may be spaced from 3 to 10 ft apart.

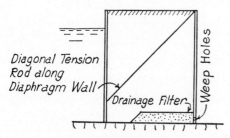

Fig. 7–13. Bottom filter.

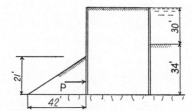

Fig. 7–14. Cellular cofferdam with inside beam.

The presence of an inside berm (an earth mass leaning against the cofferdam) will greatly increase the stability. A typical arrangement is shown in Fig. 7–14. Passive earth pressure from the berm will act in the opposite direction to the lateral forces tending to overturn the structure. The berm should preferably be built up during the unwatering and excavation of the fill inside the enclosure. Drainage filters can, of course, be incorporated in the berm.

In order to estimate the effects of the berm shown in Fig. 7–14, which is of rather modest dimensions, let it be assumed that it is to supplement the cellular cofferdam shown in Fig. 7–10 and that the soil employed for its construction has the characteristics of the gravel used for filling the compartments of the cofferdams. The force P, which represents the total passive earth pressure of the berm, can be computed as follows:

$$P = \frac{wh^2}{2}\left[\frac{\cos \phi}{1 - \sqrt{\sin \phi(\sin \phi - \cos \phi \tan \delta)}}\right]^2. \qquad (7\text{--}12)$$

Substituting the following values

$$w = 100, \quad h = 21, \quad \phi = 30°, \quad \tan \delta = \frac{21}{42},$$

gives $$P = 24{,}775 \text{ lb},$$

and $$M = 24{,}775 \times 7 = 173{,}400 \text{ ft-lb}.$$

The minimum width B of the cofferdam can be reduced in proportion to the revised bending moment. Thus,

$$\frac{2870 - 173}{2870}\, 72 = 67.5 \text{ ft.}$$

7–5. Approximate Rules. If acted upon by hydrostatic water pressure alone, the width of the cofferdam will be about 85 per cent of its height. Thus,

$$B = 0.85h. \qquad (7\text{--}13)$$

If the resultant of this hydrostatic pressure is P and if the lateral pressure is increased to P_1 (due to the presence of submerged soil), the width B_1 will be increased to

$$B_1 = \frac{P_1}{P}\, B. \qquad (7\text{--}14)$$

The crosswalls of cellular cofferdams can be reinforced by diagonal tension rods sloping from the unloaded side to the loaded side, as shown in Fig. 7–13. The stiffness and safety of the cofferdam will be materially increased by this reinforcement due to a higher coefficient of lock friction, and the width B can be correspondingly reduced. Similarly, lubrication of the locks may facilitate pulling the sheet piling, but it reduces the strength and stiffness of the cofferdam.

7–6. Cellular Cofferdams on Clay. If a cellular cofferdam is to be supported on a layer of clay it may be possible, contrary to rock foundations, to effect deep penetrations of the steel sheet piling into the underlying soil. Such cofferdams usually have somewhat greater stability than cofferdams on rock, as will be shown in the following discussion.

In the case of a cofferdam on rock the sheet piling will not have any appreciable penetration into the subsoil and a possibility exists for rupture by shear along the neutral plane, accompanied by slippage in the interlocks intersected by this neutral plane. Eqs. (7–10) and (7–11) expressed for the cofferdam on rock foundation the minimum width B, which will insure safety against failure by vertical shear. In the case of a cofferdam having its steel sheet piling driven deeply into a soil of considerable bearing capacity, this type of failure cannot occur without involving rupture of this underlying soil. Excessive shearing stresses, however, may produce failure by slippage in the interlocks at a and d (Fig. 7–15) accompanied

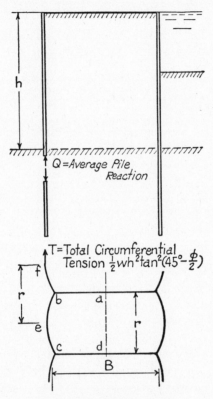

FIG. 7–15. Cofferdam on clay.

by sliding of the fill at the surfaces of contact, $abcd$, with the sheet piling.

If, in Fig. 7–15, Q indicates the average pile reaction, then the sum of all vertical pile reactions on one side of the neutral axis, for a portion of the cofferdam of width r and symmetrical about a diaphragm wall, will be

$$Q\left(\frac{B}{2} + r\right). \qquad (7\text{–}15)$$

At the instant of the first slip in the locks, this force must be equal to the friction in the interlock a, located in the neutral plane of the cell; this friction can be expressed as the product $T \times f$, where f is the coefficient of lock friction. Thus,

$$Q\left(\frac{B}{2} + r\right) = Tf = \frac{wh^2}{2} \tan^2\left(45° - \frac{\phi}{2}\right)rf,$$

$$Q = \frac{wh^2 \tan^2\left(45° - \frac{\phi}{2}\right)}{B + 2r} rf. \qquad (7\text{--}16)$$

The moment formed by these forces is found by adding the moment of forces acting on the curved portion (lever arm is B) to the moment of forces acting on the diaphragm wall (lever arm is $B \div 2$). Thus,

$$QrB + Q\frac{B}{2}\frac{B}{2}. \qquad (7\text{--}17)$$

In order to obtain the moment per unit length of the cofferdam, divide by r. Thus,

$$M_s = QB\left(1 + \frac{B}{4r}\right), \qquad (7\text{--}18)$$

$$M_s = \frac{wh^2}{2} \tan^2\left(45° - \frac{\phi}{2}\right)f \frac{1 + \dfrac{B}{4r}}{1 + \dfrac{B}{2r}} B. \qquad (7\text{--}19)$$

Eq. (7–19) expresses the part of the overturning moment carried by the sheet-pile enclosures of the cells of the cofferdam without the shearing resistance of the fill. To it must be added the overturning moment M_f, carried by the fill within the cells of the cofferdam.

The part of the overturning moment M_f which is carried by the fill can be evaluated in the following manner. Referring again to Fig. 7–15 it is seen that the average shearing resistance between the fill and the vertical surfaces of the sheet piling is

$$F = \tfrac{1}{2}wh^2 \tan^2\left(45° - \frac{\phi}{2}\right) \tan \phi_1, \qquad (7\text{--}20)$$

where $\tan \phi_1$ is the coefficient of friction between fill and sheet piling. The overturning moment resisted by the fill is

$$M_f r = FrB + 2F\frac{B}{2}\frac{B}{2}, $$

$$M_f = FB\left(1 + \frac{B}{2r}\right), \qquad (7\text{--}21)$$

$$M_f = \frac{wh^2}{2} \tan^2\left(45° - \frac{\phi}{2}\right) \tan \phi_1 B\left(1 + \frac{B}{2r}\right). \qquad (7\text{--}22)$$

The total moment which can be resisted by a unit length of the cofferdam can be found by adding Eqs. (7–19) and (7–22). Thus,

$$M = \frac{wh^2}{2} \tan^2\left(45° - \frac{\phi}{2}\right)B\left[\frac{1 + \dfrac{B}{4r}}{1 + \dfrac{B}{2r}}f + \left(1 + \frac{B}{2r}\right)\tan\phi_1\right]. \qquad (7\text{–}23)$$

This equation does not usually represent the most serious condition of internal shear in the cofferdam. It should be supplemented by an equation which expresses the relationship between the shear on the steel contact surfaces and the shear on the neutral plane which can be assumed to coincide with the center plane. The total friction forces F on the vertical boundaries of the fill on one side of the neutral plane must equal the total shearing resistance on the neutral plane in the fill. Thus,

$$\left(2\frac{B}{2} + r\right)F = r\frac{wh^2}{2}\tan^2\left(45° - \frac{\phi}{2}\right)\tan\phi. \qquad (7\text{–}24)$$

Substituting in Eq. (7–21),

$$M_f = \frac{wh^2}{2}\tan^2\left(45° - \frac{\phi}{2}\right)B\,\frac{1 + \dfrac{B}{2r}}{1 + \dfrac{B}{r}}\tan\phi. \qquad (7\text{–}25)$$

The total moment is obtained by adding Eqs. (7–19) and (7–25) as follows:

$$M = \frac{wh^2}{2}\tan^2\left(45° - \frac{\phi}{2}\right)\left[\frac{1 + \dfrac{B}{4r}}{1 + \dfrac{B}{2r}}f + \frac{1 + \dfrac{B}{2r}}{1 + \dfrac{B}{r}}\tan\phi\right]B. \qquad (7\text{–}26a)$$

This expression may be used for determining, for a diaphragm type of cellular cofferdam, the minimum width B necessary for safety against internal shear.

In the case of a circular type of dam, an analogous expression can be developed by substituting for the arrangement shown in Fig. 7–5 a series of prismatic boxes of rectangular section, having a width of $B = 1.7r$ and an average spacing of the crosswalls equal to $1.1r$. For this condition the total overturning moment required to produce failure of a circular type of cellular cofferdam on stiff clay will be

$$M = \frac{wh^2}{2}\tan^2\left(45° - \frac{\phi}{2}\right)B\left[\frac{1 + 0.23\dfrac{B}{r}}{1 + 0.46\dfrac{B}{r}}f + \frac{1 + 0.46\dfrac{B}{r}}{1 + 0.92\dfrac{B}{r}}\tan\phi\right]. \qquad (7\text{–}26b)$$

For the circular type of cofferdam the ratio $B \div r$ is equal to 1.7 (see Fig. 7–5). Substituting this value in the preceding expression gives, for this type,

$$M = 0.39wh^2 \tan^2\left(45° - \frac{\phi}{2}\right)B(f + 0.9\tan\phi). \qquad (7\text{–}26c)$$

In order to develop the shearing stresses expressed by the equations, the sheet piling forming the enclosures of the cellular cofferdam must have sufficient penetration into the underlying soil. A penetration of two-thirds of the height h above the excavated level is usually considered adequate. It should also be borne in mind that a first requirement for the stability of the cofferdam is that the clay stratum should be strong enough to sustain the weight of the filled-up cells.

7–7. Numerical Example. Let it be assumed that the cellular cofferdam, shown in Figs. 7–10 and 7–11, is to be built on a deep layer of clay. In addition to the data already indicated, it is known that the coefficient of lock friction f is 0.3 and the coefficient of friction between the fill in the cells and the steel sheet piling is $\tan\phi_1 = 0.4$. In Eq. (7–26a) are substituted $r = 33.75$ (the value already found by limiting circumferential tension), $\phi = 30°$, and the moment produced by the pressure diagram shown in Fig. 7–11; and the following relationship will result:

$$140 \times 20.5 = \frac{100 \times 64^2}{2 \times 1000} \times \tfrac{1}{3}B\left(\frac{135 + B}{135 + 2B}0.3 + \frac{135 + 2B}{135 + 4B}0.577\right),$$

$$B^3 + 50.9B^2 - 5147B - 218{,}300 = 0,$$

$$B = 69 \text{ ft.}$$

If the above values had been substituted in Eq. (7–23), the much smaller value of $B = 46$ ft would have been obtained. As the largest of the two values must govern, the cofferdam should have a width of 69 ft. It is interesting to note that this value for B is smaller than if the cofferdam had been founded on rock as shown in Fig. 7–11.

7–8. Example of Cofferdam Design. In the following paragraphs will be given a brief discussion of design assumptions, main features, and stability computations for what may be considered a typical cofferdam design. The structure is the cellular cofferdam for the Kentucky Dam near the mouth of the Tennessee River. The design of this cofferdam has been presented by A. F.Hedman in a paper published in the *Engineering News-Record*.[*]

[*]See A. F. Hedman, "Cofferdam Design for Kentucky Dam," *Engineering News-Record* (January 1, 1942), p. 50.

Fig. 7–16 shows a plan view of a portion of the first of the two stages of the cofferdam. Although consideration was given to a three-stage cofferdam, it was finally decided to adopt a two-stage project, which would close off approximately one-half of the crossing during each of the

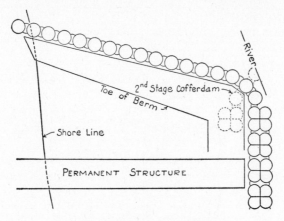

FIG. 7–16. First stage of cofferdam.

two phases. Fig. 7–16 indicates the main arrangement of the cofferdam. Circular cells, backed up by a berm, on the two shore-arms were selected because each cell, being a self-sustaining unit, could be filled immediately after driving while the diaphragm type of cells must be filled in such a manner as to maintain a low difference of head between adjacent cells. Furthermore, each cell would be stable in itself, thus localizing any possible failures.

Fig. 7–17 shows a typical cross section of the shore-arm which consisted of a circular cell (58.89-ft diam) and a berm, whose dimensions are indi-

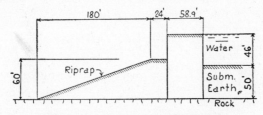

FIG. 7–17. Circular cell with berm.

cated. If a circular cell without a berm had been used, it would have required a diameter of 85 ft for proper safety against sliding or vertical shear, but interlock stresses in a cell that large would have been excessive. As the interlock stresses decrease directly with the diameter of the cell

and as proper stability can be obtained by placing a berm on the dry
side, it was decided to reduce the size of the cell to that shown.

In order to complete, during the first stage, the construction of the
permanent dam to the immediate vicinity of the river arm, it became
necessary to consider for this portion of the cofferdam a unit which would
permit excavation of the berm. The so-called *cloverleaf cell,* which is
shown in plan view in Fig. 7–18, was used for the outstream wall. (This

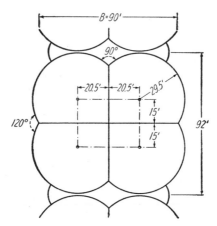

Fig. 7–18. Cloverleaf cell.

type of cell combines, as does the diaphragm type of unit, low interlock
stresses with great width. It has the advantage over the diaphragm
type in that it is a self-sustaining unit and can be filled without maintaining
a low difference of head between adjacent cells.) The radius of the arc
in the cloverleaf cell was practically the same as for the circular cell.

Before proceeding with the design, all decisions and assumptions
regarding the soil characteristics were made. Based on soil tests such
important items as weight of dry and submerged materials, coefficients
of friction for gravel on rock and gravel on steel, and angle of internal
friction were decided upon. The following numerical values were used:

(1) Weight of dry material = 110 lb/cu ft,
(2) Weight of submerged material = 65 lb/cu ft,
(3) Coefficient of friction, gravel on rock = 0.5,
(4) Coefficient of friction, gravel on steel = 0.4 corresponding to an
angle of external friction $\phi_1 = 21°51'$,
(5) Angle of internal friction (for dry or saturated material) = ϕ =
28°51′, tan ϕ = 0.55.

The coefficient of friction, steel on steel, for the piling interlocks was
taken as 0.3, and the slope of the berm as 3:1, or $\delta = 18°26'$.

In order to analyze the cofferdam for stability, vertical shear, and interlock stresses, the following assumptions were made:

(1) Water pressure to rock was used.

(2) Horizontal earth pressure per foot of cofferdam was computed according to Coulomb's theory.* Thus, for the active pressure,

$$P_A = \tfrac{1}{2}wh^2 \; \frac{\cos^2 \phi}{\left[1 + \sqrt{\dfrac{\sin (\phi + \phi_1) \sin \phi}{\cos \phi_1}} \right]^2} , \qquad (7\text{-}27)$$

and for passive pressure,

$$P_P = \tfrac{1}{2}wh^2 \; \frac{\cos^2 \phi}{\left[1 - \sqrt{\dfrac{\sin (\phi - \delta) \sin \phi}{\cos \delta}} \right]^2} , \qquad (7\text{-}28)$$

where ϕ = angle of internal friction,
    ϕ_1 = angle of external friction,
    δ = angle of slope of berm with horizontal. (See Fig. 1–9.)

(3) The distribution of the active pressure was assumed to be triangular with the resultant one-third of the height above base. The distribution of the passive pressure was assumed to be parabolic with the resultant one-half of the height above base.

(4) The allowable stresses in the piling were: tension 32,000 psi on the webs and 12,000 lb/lin in. on the interlocks.

(5) The factors of safety were: 1.25 for sliding and shear and 1.33 for tension in the interlocks.

As the sheet piling for the cofferdam cells exceeded in length the usual dimension of 80 ft, splices were made in the field and made watertight on the river side. The designer made the following recommendations to the construction superintendent:

(1) Rock below the cofferdam should be grouted to insure tightness against seepage and uplift.

(2) Adequate weep holes should be provided in the cells for drainage to provide safer saturation conditions than computed, if possible.

(3) Berms should be carefully and adequately drained.

(4) Berm slopes should be rip-rapped from foundation rock to prevent erosion.

(5) The area in which the cloverleaf cells are to be set should be dredged in order to make the driving distance of the piles as short as possible. This precaution would do much toward preventing

---

*The external friction was completely disregarded for the passive pressure and only partly included for the active pressure.

interlocks from parting during driving operations; and, since these cells are contemplated to stand part of the time with a small berm, engaged interlocks in this area are imperative.

Determination of the width, B, of the cloverleaf cell is shown in Fig. 7–19. With the berm removed, the water on the upstream side was

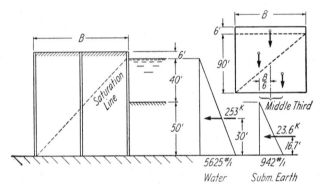

FIG. 7–19. Analysis of cloverleaf cell.

allowed to rise only to a level 6 ft below the top. A straight saturation line was assumed and the resultant of all stresses was required to fall within the middle third. The width can be found thus,

$$B \times 6 \times 110 \times \frac{B}{6} + \tfrac{1}{2}B \times 90 \times 65 \times \frac{B}{3}$$

$$= (253 \times 30 + 23.6 \times 16.7) \times 10^3$$

$$B = 86 \text{ ft.}$$

The average width was approximately 90 ft as shown in Fig. 7–18. Subsequent investigations of interlock tension and internal shear indicated adequate safety margins for these quantities.

PROBLEMS

7–1. Design a cellular cofferdam of the circular type for a hydrostatic pressure of 70-ft head. Allowable interlock tension equals 8 kips/lin in. Interlock friction is 0.3. Fill inside the cells: $W = 100$ lb/cu ft; $\phi = 34°$. Find radius of cell and adjust it to a driving distance of 15 in. (*Ans.:* 48.5 ft.)

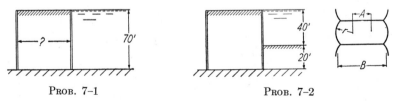

PROB. 7–1   PROB. 7–2

7-2. It is desired to design a cellular cofferdam of the diaphragm type for the following data: dry soil inside cell = 105 lb/cu ft; submerged soil width on upstream side = 50 lb/cu ft; angle of internal friction for both dry and submerged soil ϕ = 28; allowable interlock tension = 6 kips/lin in.; coefficient of lock friction f = 0.25. It is required to find theoretical values for: distance between crosswalls; radius, r, of circular arcs; and distance, A, between centers of circular arcs. ($Ans.: A = 7$ ft.)

7-3. Design a cellular cofferdam of the diaphragm type from the following data: weight of water, 62.5 lb/cu ft; weight of soil inside cell, 100 lb/cu ft; angle of internal friction inside cell, 34°; dry weight of submerged soil outside cell, 94 lb/cu ft; voids in this soil, 32 per cent; angle of internal friction of this soil, 24°; allowable interlock tension, 6 kips/lin in.; coefficient of lock friction, 0.25. Find A and r and adjust to driving distance of 15 in. ($Ans.: A = 4.3$ ft.)

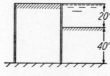

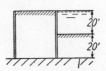

PROB. 7-3   PROB. 7-4

7-4. Use same data as in Prob. 7-3, except pressure on upstream side is due to 20 ft of water and 20 ft of submerged soil. Explain negative value of A. ($Ans.: -64.87$ ft.)

SINGLE-WALL COFFERDAM

CHAPTER 8

SINGLE-WALL COFFERDAMS

8-1. Introduction. The single-wall cofferdam, also called the braced cofferdam, consists of an enclosure of steel sheet piling, the inside of which is unwatered and excavated for the purpose of building a structure. The external pressure from water and soil necessitates internal bracing of the steel sheet-piling enclosure. The cofferdam should be braced laterally and vertically. The lateral bracing should consist of horizontal wales and struts, while the vertical bracing (its function is to prevent the enclosure from "folding-up") can be of cross-members, such as tie rods connecting to the lateral struts.

The single-wall cofferdam should be designed so that, when completed, it can successfully resist the lateral pressure; but, it should be kept in mind that the most dangerous stresses in the sheet piling are set up during the excavation and unwatering. These stresses, moreover, usually occur in locations where bracing and reinforcing are impracticable, such as below the line of excavation. For this reason the procedure of construction of the cofferdam demands the attention of the designer even more than the analysis of the finished cofferdam.

8-2. Structural Arrangements. Fig. 8-1 shows typical details of a single-wall cofferdam resting on a river bottom. The rectangular enclosure is formed by interlocking steel sheet piling of high beam strength. The sheet-piling units are supported laterally by tiers of rectangular wale frames consisting of four horizontal girders and a number of struts. Timber or structural steel may be used for wale frames, and the connections should be adjustable to allow for elimination of clearances between sheet-piling wall and wale frame during the assembly. At the same time it is imperative that all connections possess a high degree of rigidity to insure stability against eccentric loads, caused by differences in lateral pressure intensities and also by impact from accidental contacts with the excavating and hoisting equipment used during the construction.

Bracing in several vertical planes is also highly desirable; it should, of course, be located between the upper tiers of the wale frames. The wale frames are usually hung from beams placed across the tops of the steel sheet piling.

Great care and accuracy are necessary in locating and driving the steel sheet-pile units. Wood piles, braced by batter piles, must first be driven on the inside or outside (sometimes on both sides) of the contemplated cofferdam enclosure and connected with at least two lines or temporary wales to form guides for the steel sheet piling. The sheet piles are then set in place and, at intervals, a pair of piles are driven and bolted to a temporary wale to hold the wall. After closure has been effected, the piles can be driven to their final positions and permanent wale frames installed.

Because a cofferdam is practically always a temporary structure, which has served its purpose after the completion of the permanent construction

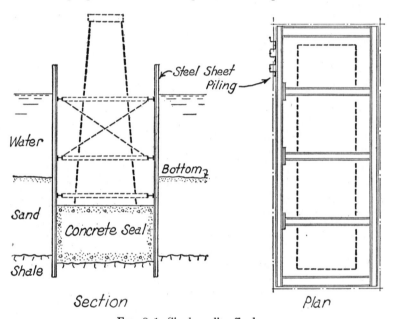

FIG. 8-1. Single-wall cofferdam.

located in its enclosure, the eventual recovery of sheet piling and bracing should receive attention during the planning stages. Complete recovery is not often possible; wale frames in the bottom seal and portions of the cross struts above the top of the seal are usually retained in the concrete. Parts of the steel sheet piling may be salvaged by cutting the wall (by underwater burning) just above the top of the concrete seal.

8-3. Computations. The load to which a cofferdam is exposed is either hydrostatic water pressure, earth pressure, or a combination of the two. These pressures can readily be expressed by the Rankine and Coulomb formulas.

Almost invariably the first step in the design is to find the lowest position in which the top wale can be placed in order to develop the full beam strength of the sheet piling in the top span under the external pressure. The most economical arrangement is that illustrated in Fig.

8–4, where the top of the wall forms a cantilever section. If the pressure increment is defined by p, the section modulus per unit width of sheet piling by S, and the safe working stress in steel by f, it is readily seen that

$$S = \frac{\frac{1}{6}ph^3 \times 12}{f}. \tag{8-1}$$

If the height h is expressed in feet, the pressure increment p in pounds per square foot, and the two other quantities in pounds and inches, then

$$h = \sqrt[3]{\frac{fS}{2p}}. \tag{8-2}$$

The second span h_1 in Fig. 8–4 should be such that the maximum bending moment in this span will not exceed the maximum bending moment in the cantilever span, which is $\frac{1}{6}ph^3$. The sheet-piling wall constitutes a continuous beam subjected to the action of lateral loads. In order to obtain an economic distribution of bending moments, the supporting wales must be located in such a manner that there is no rotation of the tangents to the elastic beam curve at these supports. In Fig. 8–2

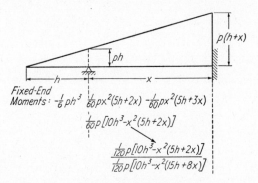

Fig. 8–2. Economical second span.

the span adjacent to the overhang is called x and the sheet-piling wall is assumed fixed at the second support. The resulting structure is analyzed by the method of moment distribution. Equating the final moments at the two supports gives:

$$-\frac{1}{6}ph^3 = \frac{1}{120}p[10h^3 - x^2(15h + 8x)],$$

$$8x^3 + 15hx^2 - 30h^3 = 0. \tag{8-3}$$

This equation has one real positive root, namely, $x = 1.12h$.

Subsequent spans h_2, h_3, h_4 can now be evaluated, when it is noted that for each of these spans the relative increase in lateral pressure is comparatively small. In Fig. 8–3 is shown a span of length x, a distance H from the top of the wall. A rectangle of equal area has been substituted

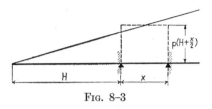

for the trapezoidal pressure diagram. If no rotations of the continuous beam occur at the two supports shown and if, at the same time, the maximum bending moment is to equal the maximum moment in the top cantilever, then

Fig. 8–3

$$\frac{1}{12}p\left(H + \frac{x}{2}\right)x^2 = \frac{1}{6}ph^3; \quad x^3 + 2Hx^2 - 4h^3 = 0. \tag{8–4}$$

For the span h_2,

$$x^3 + 2h(1 + 1.12)x^2 - 4h^3 = 0; \quad x = h_2 = 0.885h. \tag{8–5}$$

Subsequent spacings are listed in Fig. 8–4.

For calculating the horizontal load on the wales the approximate

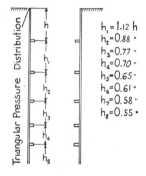

Fig. 8–4. Spacing of wale frames.

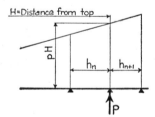

Fig. 8–5

method indicated by Fig. 8–5 is generally satisfactory. Using the notation indicated, the uniform lateral load P on the frame is

$$P = \tfrac{1}{2}pH(h_n + h_{n+1}). \tag{8–6}$$

The wale frames should be analyzed for uniformly distributed loads along their perimeter, as indicated in Fig. 8–6, which gives general expressions for bending moments. The connections between the outside wales and the cross struts have been assumed as hinged, while the four corner connections have been assumed rigid. Rigid connections for the cross struts would not appreciably change the values of the bending moment.

Of great importance is the complete rigidity of the corner connections, which materially reduces the bending moments at other points of the frame.

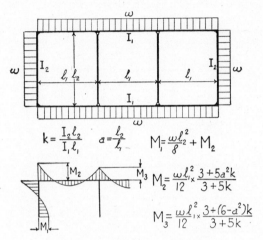

$$k = \frac{I_2 \ell_2}{I_1 \ell_1} \qquad a = \frac{\ell_2}{\ell_1} \qquad M_1 = \frac{\omega \ell_2^2}{8} + M_2$$

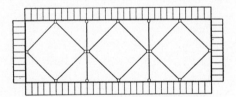

$$M_2 = \frac{\omega \ell_1^2}{12} \times \frac{3 + 5a^2 k}{3 + 5k}$$

$$M_3 = \frac{\omega \ell_1^2}{12} \times \frac{3 + (6 - a^2)k}{3 + 5k}$$

FIG. 8–6. Analysis of wale frame.

In order to reduce the effective spans of the wale girders, and at the same time maintain large openings for excavation, a system of knee braces can often be used to advantage as shown in Fig. 8–7.

FIG. 8–7. Knee-braced wale frame.

8–4. Cofferdams in Water. Single-wall cofferdams have been used with considerable success in rivers and inlets, but numerous failures have also been reported; and great care is needed in designing and planning for excavation and unwatering. It will often be found necessary to complete the concrete seal at the bottom of the cofferdam before any water is pumped from the inside. This procedure will necessitate the use of underwater concrete and a final inspection of the uncovered bottom by a diver.

If the conditions of the bottom are such that no appreciable penetration can be effected into the bottom and if friction between the outside submerged soil and the sheet piling cannot be depended upon, then the bottom seal must be sufficiently heavy to prevent any accidental floating of the unwatered cofferdam. Fig. 8–8 is representative of this condition. To counter any buoyancy, the minimum value x of the depth of the bottom seal can be determined from

$$62.5D = 150x; \quad x = 0.42D. \tag{8–7}$$

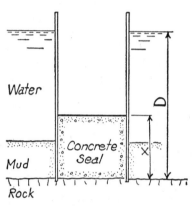

Fig. 8–8

It is impossible to make a single-wall cofferdam watertight, and continuous pumping is required to keep it unwatered. In the course of dewatering, it will usually be found that as the water is lowered inside the cofferdam the leaks in the interlocks will become smaller, due to the bending and shearing stresses developed in the sheet piling. Deposits of rock dust or coal dust in the water adjacent to the outside face of the cofferdam will also tend to close the leaks by clogging up the joints.

Single-wall cofferdams can ordinarily be built to withstand a head of about 50 ft of water and be unwatered before the bottom concrete seal is poured in the dry. Beyond this depth it will usually be found necessary to complete the excavation and construct the bottom seal by underwater concreting before the inside is dewatered. A head of about 75 to 85 ft of water and earth may be resisted in this manner, depending on the character of the soil to be removed from the inside of the cofferdam. If the single-wall cofferdam is built to form a circular well, which will be stressed mainly in circumferential compression, a depth of more than 100 ft can be obtained. Bracing rings must be added on the inside of the sheet piling to prevent buckling of the sheet piling. Contrary to the rectangularly shaped cofferdam in which a high section modulus of the steel sheet piling is imperative, the straight web type is more adaptable to the circular single-wall cofferdam.

It is important to guard the struts and other members of the wale frames against being dislocated during the construction. The openings in the wale frames serve as hoisting wells for excavation buckets. These

(a) Before bucket caught a strut.

(b) After collapse.

FIG. 8-9

will often swing considerably, and unless they are confined by vertical guides, may catch or hit a strut, which if removed may cause complete collapse of the outside sheet piling. An example of this is shown in Fig. 8–9 where the bucket shown in (*a*), while being hoisted up, dislodged one of the struts, which resulted in the failure of the cofferdam, shown in (*b*).

The importance of investigating the stresses in a single-wall cofferdam during the excavation of its enclosure has already been pointed out. The examples that follow will illustrate typical designs and procedures of construction.

Example 1. Let it be desired to construct a single-wall cofferdam through 20 ft of water and 28 ft of submerged sand to a firm stratum, as shown in Fig. 8–10. It is, furthermore, desired to unwater the inside after excavation has been completed and before the bottom seal has been constructed. Also to be taken into consideration: the penetration of the sheet piling in the subsoil is too small to be of any value for lateral support; cantilever action should be assumed below the last wale frame.

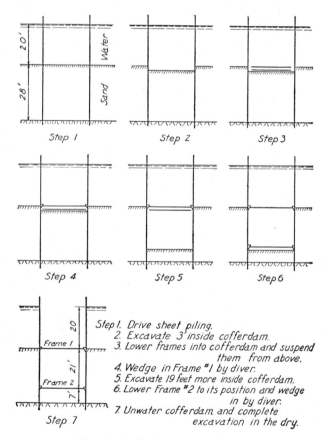

Step 1. Drive sheet piling.
2. Excavate 3' inside cofferdam.
3. Lower frames into cofferdam and suspend them from above.
4. Wedge in Frame #1 by diver.
5. Excavate 19 feet more inside cofferdam.
6. Lower Frame #2 to its position and wedge in by diver.
7. Unwater cofferdam and complete excavation in the dry.

Fig. 8–10. Single-wall cofferdam 1.

Maximum bending stresses in the steel sheet piling and wale frames must not exceed 24,000 psi. The sand is assumed to have a submerged weight of 56 lb/cu ft and an angle of internal friction of 25°.

The position of the first wale frame is found by Eq. (8–2) by assuming that the strongest sheet-pile unit (the MZ-38 of U. S. Steel Corp.; the ZP-38 of the Bethlehem Steel Co.) will be employed. This unit has a section modulus of 46.8 in.^{3}/ft width of wall. The distance from the top must, therefore, not exceed

$$h = \sqrt[3]{\frac{24,000 \times 46.8}{2 \times 62.5}} = 20.8.$$

This frame can be placed 20 ft from the top of the water. The pressure diagram is then drawn up for the excavated and unwatered cofferdam, as shown in Fig. 8–11, and the position of the bottom wale frame is fixed as high above the bottom as the allowable steel stress will permit. Thus,

$$\frac{(3644 - 85x)\,\dfrac{x^2}{2} + 85\,\dfrac{x}{2}x\,\dfrac{2}{3}x}{46.8}\,12 = 24,000,$$

$$x = 7.4 \text{ ft.}$$

When the excavation and unwatering have been completed, the loading and moment diagrams for the steel sheet piling will be as shown in Fig. 8–11.

Now it remains for the designed to outline the procedure of excavation and erection of the wale frames so that at no time will the stresses in the sheet piling be dangerous to the safety of the partially completed cofferdam.

It requires no computations to see that to remove the water inside the cofferdam down to the intended position of the first wale frame will compel the sheet piling to act as a cantilever of much greater span than that found from Eq. (8–1), because the equivalent point of support will be a considerable distance below the top surface of the submerged sand. The wale frames must therefore be placed in position, or "wedged in" as sometimes termed, while the water is still in the cofferdam; divers must be employed for this phase of the work. If the wale frames are completely assembled before being lowered, the work to be performed by the diver will be materially reduced.

Keeping in mind that a second wale frame is subsequently to be put in position and that, if assembled on land, its passage down through the inside of the cofferdam will be blocked by the first wale frame, it is seen that the second frame should be either lowered before or suspended underneath the first wale frame. With the water remaining inside the cofferdam, excavation of the sand to make room for the two wale frames will not produce any serious stresses in the steel sheet piling. This operation is indicated in Steps 2 and 3 of Fig. 8–10, and Step 4 shows the top frame wedged-in, and thus providing a support for the sheet piling at this point.

With the first frame in position, underwater excavation can now proceed inside the cofferdam. Step 5 shows enough sand removed to permit the lowering of the bottom frame from its suspended position to its final location. Before it can be brought into contact with the inside of the cofferdam, however, it will be necessary for the steel sheet piling to span from the top frame to the point of junction with the subsoil (either rock or very dense clay).

This condition (Step 5, Fig. 8–10) is shown in detail in Fig. 8–12, which indicates active and passive pressure due to the submerged soil. If it is assumed that there is no penetration of the sheet piling into the subsoil, additional resistance to lateral movement is due only to friction between the rock and the piling. This force is

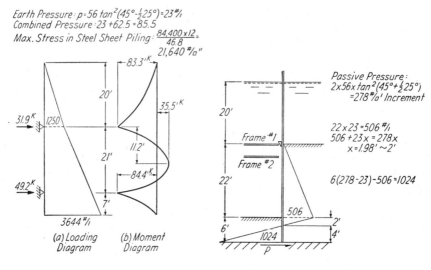

FIG. 8–11. Moments in single-wall cofferdam 1.

FIG. 8–12. Excavation inside cofferdam 1.

indicated by P, and can be found by taking moments about the support provided by Frame No. 1; thus,

$$\tfrac{1}{2}506 \times 22 \times \tfrac{2}{3}22 + \tfrac{1}{2}506 \times 2 \times 22.67 = \tfrac{1}{2}1024 \times 4 \times 26.67 + 28P,$$

$$P = 1375 \text{ lb.}$$

If the coefficient of friction between steel and rock is assumed to be 0.5, it is seen that a vertical downward force of 2750 lb must be provided by the weight of steel sheet piling, wale frame, details, and equipment. An evaluation of these items will show that this can readily be supplied. A subsequent investigation of bending moments due to the pressures in Fig. 8–12 will result in actual stresses not exceeding 50 per cent of allowable values.

Example 2. It is desired to construct a single-wall cofferdam in 40 ft of water and 20 ft of submerged mud as shown in Fig. 8–13. Due to the comparatively great depth of water and small depth of supporting soil and its small passive pressure, it is decided that a concrete seal should be poured underwater. It is assumed that the penetration of the sheet piling into the bottom soil is sufficient to prevent any floating of the pumped-out cofferdam but not sufficient for lateral support; before the seal is constructed, cantilever action of the sheet piling must be assumed

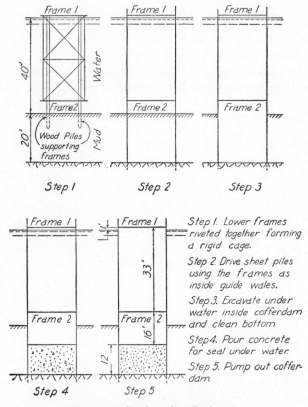

Step 1. Lower frames riveted together forming a rigid cage.

Step 2. Drive sheet piles using the frames as inside guide wales.

Step 3. Excavate under water inside cofferdam and clean bottom.

Step 4. Pour concrete for seal under water.

Step 5. Pump out cofferdam.

FIG. 8–13. Single-wall cofferdam 2.

FIG. 8–14. Bird's-eye view of single-wall cofferdam.

below the bottom frame. Maximum bending stresses in the steel sheet piling must not exceed 24,000 psi. Equivalent liquid pressure of the submerged mud is assumed to be 20 psf.

It is proposed to construct this cofferdam by using the inside steel wale frames as guides during the driving of the steel sheet piling. This is the reverse of the procedure of the preceding example, where the wale frames were brought inside the enclosure. A photograph of a cofferdam, constructed in this manner, is shown in Fig. 8–14. Several advantages accrue from this procedure, the chief one being the absence of any wedges between the wall and the frames; imperfect contact will be corrected when the water is pumped out and the outside pressure is exerted. If a thick layer of mud should prevent the bottom of the cage formed by the wale frames to be placed in its final position, it may be necessary to dredge the site beforehand.

After the steel sheet piling has been driven to form a closed wall, it is planned to excavate underwater the mud inside. This condition is shown in Step 3 in Fig. 8–13; here, the steel sheet piling acts as a beam supported by the two wale frames and subjected to the outside pressure of the submerged mud. The stress analysis for this condition is shown in Fig. 8–15; if the heaviest available section

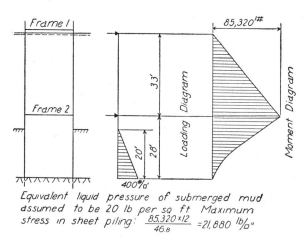

Equivalent liquid pressure of submerged mud assumed to be 20 lb per sq ft Maximum stress in sheet piling: $\frac{85,320 \times 12}{46.8} = 21,880 \ lb/_{\Box}"$

Fig. 8–15. Single-wall cofferdam 2.

(MZ-38 or ZP-38, having a section modulus $S = 46.8$ in.[3]) is chosen for the sheet piling, the maximum bending stresses are well within the permissible value of 24,000 psi.

There remains to investigate the stresses developed in the steel sheet piling after the seal has been constructed and the water removed from the inside. In this case the sheet piling forms a continuous beam fixed at one end and simply supported at the other end. The analysis is completed in Fig. 8–16. The analysis indicates an overstress of the steel sheet piling due to the long span between the two wale frames. It becomes necessary, therefore, to supplement the bracing cage by an additional frame midway between the two frames originally contemplated. The analysis for this condition is shown in Fig. 8–17.

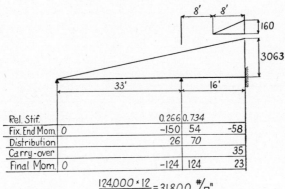

Rel. Stif.			0.266	0.734	
Fix. End Mom.	0		-150	54	-58
Distribution			26	70	
Carry-over					35
Final Mom.	0		-124	124	23

$$\frac{124,000 \times 12}{46.8} = 31,800 \ ^{\#}/_{\square}{}''$$

This stress is excessive

FIG. 8–16. Cofferdam 2 (two wale frames).

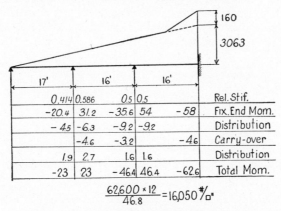

0.414	0.586	0.5	0.5		Rel. Stif.
-20.4	31.2	-35.6	54	-58	Fix. End Mom.
-4.5	-6.3	-9.2	-9.2		Distribution
	-4.6	-3.2		-4.6	Carry-over
1.9	2.7	1.6	1.6		Distribution
-23	23	-46.4	46.4	-62.6	Total Mom.

$$\frac{62,600 \times 12}{46.8} = 16,050 \ ^{\#}/_{\square}{}''$$

FIG. 8–17. Cofferdam 2 (three wale frames).

PROBLEMS

8–1. Assume that the steel sheet piling (MZ-38) of a single-wall cofferdam can be considered fixed at the level where it penetrates into a hard stratum, and that it is subjected only to hydrostatic outside and inside pressure. Plot a curve which gives the relationship between h and D if the maximum bending stress in the steel must not exceed 20,000 psi, h being the difference which can be allowed between inside and outside water levels, and D the outside depth of the water. (*Check: D = 20, h = 12.*)

PROB. 8–1

8–2. Use same data as in Prob. 8–1, except that a wale frame has been placed at elevation of outside water level before lowering of inside water level is commenced. (*Check: D* = 33, *h* = 10.)

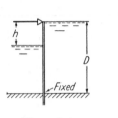

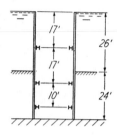

PROB. 8–2   PROB. 8–3

8–3. Find the size of steel sheet piling necessary in the single-wall cofferdam shown. The maximum bending stress must not exceed 24,000 psi and no lateral support can be expected from penetration into the rock. Assume that submerged soil has a pressure increment of 24 psf. (*Ans.*: MZ-32.)

WORM'S-EYE VIEW OF BOTTOM OF STEEL CAISSON, SHOWING EXCAVATION WELLS

CHAPTER 9

OPEN AND PNEUMATIC CAISSONS

9–1. Introduction. Caissons may be defined as enclosing shells, which serve as a means for getting a foundation to its final position. Caissons may be circular in cross section, or square or rectangular. As a

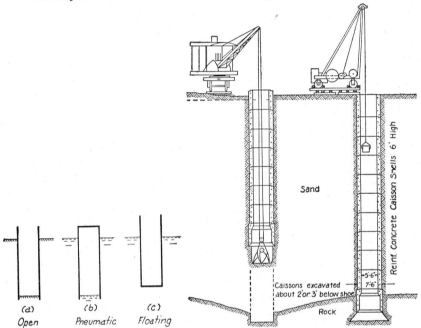

FIG. 9–1. Types of caissons.   FIG. 9–2. Caisson construction.

general rule, it will prove economical to select a cross section which has a minimum perimeter, hence the frequent use of the cylindrical caisson.

The fundamental difference between the open caisson and the pneumatic caisson is, as shown in Fig. 9–1, that the pneumatic caisson has a closed top and is thus able by the use of compressed air to provide a space below the surface from which water and earth are excluded. The pneumatic caisson is simply an inverted bucket and, if turned over, would become a floating box caisson, as shown in Fig. 9–1(c), which could be floated to its final location and subsequently sunk to its terminal elevation.

Open caissons are used in dry ground or where only moderate amounts of water are encountered. The procedure of construction may be as shown in Fig. 9–2. A bottom section of the caisson shell, equipped with a cutting edge, is placed on the top surface of the ground and the earth is removed from its inside. As the support is removed, the shell will sink down by its own weight, and during its descent additional sections are joined to it. When it has reached its final elevation, the interior is filled up with concrete.

It is possible to enlarge the bottom bearing area of the open caisson and thus reduce the unit pressure on the supporting subsoil. Fig. 9–3 shows the usual arrangement of the *caisson bell* and desirable dimensions.

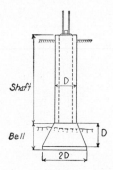

FIG. 9–3. Belled-out caisson.

It is important to keep the caisson in its correct, vertical position during the process of sinking. Large caissons are generally easier to control than small ones, and caissons with built-out bottoms are usually hard to keep plumb. The best way to correct the position of the caisson would be to lift it up and put it down again; however, this is usually impracticable and so tipping is quite often arrested by placing blocks under the portion of the cutting edge which is sinking faster than the rest.

Caissons have been constructed of reinforced concrete, steel, and timber. The first of these is by far the most common; steel shells are always used in connection with concrete in order to obtain sufficient weight for sinking. Timber caissons, while extensively built in the past (they were quite common forty years ago) now are of only academic interest.

Open caissons have been used for many years in the construction of building and bridge piers. They are more rapidly and economically sunk than pneumatic caissons, but they cease to be effective where the material is such as to flow into the excavation faster than it can be dredged; for such conditions, the pneumatic caisson is superior.

9–2. Pneumatic Caissons. These have already been defined as inverted boxes, in which compressed air is utilized to keep water and mud from entering during the sinking.

The most pronounced advantage of the pneumatic caisson as compared with the open caisson lies in the easy access to the bottom of the shaft. Control of the caisson is readily exercised during the process of sinking; obstructions, such as boulders under the cutting edge, can be quickly removed. When the final elevation is reached, the foundation

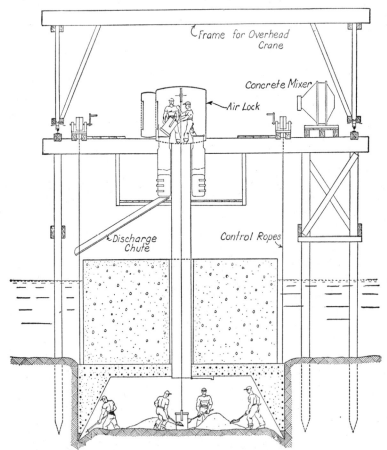

Fig. 9–4. Pneumatic caisson equipped with air lock.

bed can be prepared and inspected and the working chamber filled with concrete deposited in the air instead of under water. The chief disadvantage is that the work at the bottom of the shaft must be carried out under air pressure which is sufficient to balance the pressure of the surrounding water in addition to the atmospheric pressure, or practically the full hydrostatic head from the cutting edge to the surface of the water.

The principle employed in the construction of a pneumatic caisson is shown in Fig. 9–4. The working chamber, at the bottom of the shaft, is made airtight and communicates through the shaft with an airlock, which should be placed above water level. The working chamber and the shaft are filled with compressed air at a pressure that will balance or slightly exceed the water pressure at the depth to which the cutting edge has penetrated. This inside pressure must, of course, be increased as the caisson moves down and as the head of water outside the caisson increases.

The roof of the working chamber must be sufficiently strong to support the weight of the concrete pier and also sufficiently airtight to prevent any serious leakage of air. Sometimes reinforcement is placed in the concrete immediately over the roof to make it strong enough to sustain the loads.

The airlock is usually made of steel and consists of a chamber with two doors; one opens to the outside atmosphere and the other to the shaft leading down to the working chamber. One of these two doors must always be closed tight while the airlock is being filled with compressed air, or when the pressure is being reduced to that of the atmosphere. The doors are placed in such a manner that the unequal air pressure will always force them against their frames, which have rubber linings to prevent the escape of air.

When the shaft needs to be extended, a gate is closed at the bottom in the working chamber to prevent the escape of air. The airlock is then unbolted from the shaft, the additional section is attached and the airlock shifted to the top of the new section.

The vertical shaft can be made of concrete as an integral part of the pier, as is often done in modern designs (see Fig. 9–8).

The maximum depth of a pneumatic caisson is about 120 ft under water. At this depth the air pressure would be

$$120 \times 62.5 = 7500 \text{ lb/sq ft} = 52 \text{ psi.}$$

As the atmospheric pressure is 14.7 psi, the additional air pressure is about three and one-half atmospheres. This is about the limit of human endurance; some men can work only half an hour in this pressure, and some cannot stand it at all. Considerable time must also be allowed for decompression (the gradual reduction of pressure to normal). The deepest pneumatic caisson ever sunk in the United States (123.5 ft below water) was for one of the piers for the Santa Fe Railway crossing of the Colorado River near Needles, California.*

Placing the caisson in its correct position requires considerable care and attention. If there is a tidal variation at the site, then the caisson can sometimes be placed tentatively at low tide and, if any correction is necessary, refloated at high tide.

To eliminate the necessity of transporting the caisson shell after its completion and, at the same time, to insure its correct location and

---

*See *Engineering News-Record* (June 21, 1945), p. 4.

facilitate control during sinking, a procedure known as the *artificial island method* has been used. A steel sheet-pile cofferdam is first driven and, within its enclosure, a fill is placed to form an artificial island on which to start the cutting edge of the caisson.

Pneumatic caissons are often started as open caissons and continued in this manner until the presence of water necessitates the use of compressed air. It will usually be found advantageous to equip the caisson with two shafts and two sets of airlocks; one for the personnel and the other for removing the excavated material. If the material is sand, then it can generally be removed by the blowout method, which makes use of the difference in air pressure between the working chamber and the outside air. No suction is required; a flexible hose connected to a pipe leading up to the open air is all that is required.

The working chamber is filled with concrete after the caisson has reached its final level. The airlock should be used for transporting the concrete, and the air pressure should be maintained until the concrete has obtained sufficient strength to resist the hydrostatic uplift.

9-3. Computations. In sinking, the whole weight of the caisson is at first carried on the cutting edge; but, as lower levels are reached, more and more of the load is resisted by friction of the surrounding soil. This friction on the embedded surface of the caisson, or skin friction, depends on the soil characteristics and depth, and on the nature and the extent of the surface. Also, it will depend on whether the outside of the caisson is made of steel, timber, or concrete and on whether the shaft is plumb or out of plumb when sunk. It is possible to reduce this skin friction by the use of a water jet. Likewise, the air leaking under the cutting edge of a pneumatic caisson will materially reduce the skin friction. Although flaring out the bottom of the caisson tends to reduce the surface friction, it is not to be recommended because of the loss of guidance. Pneumatic caissons should always be made with vertical sides.

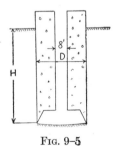

FIG. 9-5

In Fig. 9-5 is shown a caisson having an outside diam of D and sunk to a depth of H below the top surface. The diam of the inside shaft has been made 8 ft, which is usually sufficient to allow for ladders and hoisting equipment. Assume that there is no support under the cutting edge; then, equating the force per unit area of embedded surface to the coefficient of skin friction f gives

$$\frac{\frac{\pi}{4}(D^2 - 8^2)H \times 150}{\pi DH} = \frac{D^2 - 8^2}{D} 37.5 = f. \qquad (9\text{-}1)$$

From Eq. (9–1), it is possible to find the outside diam required to attain a given depth if the coefficient of skin friction c is known for this depth. In general it can be said that the frictional resistance per square foot of embedded surface will rarely be less than 250 nor more than 1000 lb/sq ft. It is usually increased somewhat with the depth. For sand and gravel carrying large amounts of water (river, lake, and sea bottoms) it is quite low, varying from 250 to 750 lb/sq ft.*

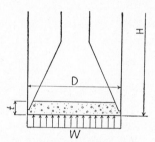

FIG. 9–6. Strength of seal.

In evaluating the total bearing capacity of caissons supported in deep layers of clay, an allowance is sometimes made for the support due to skin friction. In such cases only a portion of the skin friction, usually about 300 lb/sq ft can be counted on.

The thickness of the concrete seal placed in the bottom of the caisson must be such that it can safely withstand the hydrostatic uplift when the inside air pressure is removed. For a round caisson, as shown in Fig. 9–6, the seal can be assumed to act as a simply supported circular plate subject to a uniformly distributed load, in which the maximum stress will occur at the center in both radial and tangential directions and will equal

$$\frac{3W}{8\pi t^2}(3 + \mu), \qquad (9\text{-}2)$$

where μ is Poisson's ratio (usually 0.15 for concrete) and W is the total load and equals, according to Fig. 9–6,

---

*See H. S. Jacoby and R. P. Davis, *Foundations for Bridges and Buildings* (New York, 1941), p. 351. Also E. S. Blaine, "Practical Lessons in Caisson Sinking," *Engineering News-Record* (February 6, 1947), pp. 85–87.

$$W = H \times 62.5 \times \frac{\pi}{4} D^2. \qquad (9\text{--}3)$$

The thickness t should be such that the tensile stress in the concrete is below the allowable value, say 300 psi.

9–4. Structural Arrangements. The terminating rim of the caisson, which makes contact with the soil in direct bearing, is called the cutting edge. The cutting edge is usually made up of structural steel angles or plates. Fig. 9–7 shows two possible make-ups. In Fig. 9–7(a) the shapes

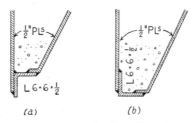

Fig. 9–7. Cutting edges.

are arranged to provide a sharp cutting edge; in Fig. 9–7(b) a blunt cutting edge is provided. It is claimed that the sharp edge gives a greater rate of sinking and reduces the loss of air escaping from the working chamber, but it is also considerably more vulnerable to damage from obstructions; so, the blunt edge is more widely used.

Fig. 9–8 shows the typical features of a reinforced concrete caisson. There is a gradual taper from the small inside opening occupied by the shaft to the cutting edge which is of the blunt type. In the shaft, recesses are provided at intervals, which enable ready shifting of the horizontal diaphragm and thereby prevent the compressed air in the lower part from escaping. The lower portion of the caisson adjacent to the cutting edge is usually quite heavily reinforced, while the upper part is reinforced only near the outside. Compressed air is supplied to the working chamber by means of a pipe embedded in the concrete, while another pipe of larger diameter, communicating with the outside air, affords a means of disposing of sand removed from under the caisson.

As the caisson must be built up in sections, considerable attention must be given to the correct design and execution of the construction joints between the concrete liftlines. Besides insuring bond by a thorough surface cleaning of the hardened concrete, reinforcement must be extended through the joints and large precast concrete key blocks (usually six per joint) placed at the top of each lift. The height of a concrete lift can usually be made approximately the same as the diameter of the caisson. The sinking of the caisson must be interrupted during the construction and curing (usually six days) of the additional sections. This interruption of the excavating and sinking process is, of course, a decided disadvantage and can be eliminated if facilities exist for precasting, transporting, and

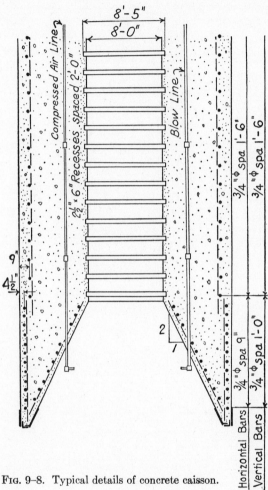

FIG. 9–8. Typical details of concrete caisson.

assembling the caisson sections, with suitable devices for connecting the reinforcement of the various sections.

Example 1. It is desired to sink two round caissons through 100 ft of sand and water to bedrock. The two caissons form the lower part of a bridge pier sustaining a total reaction of 6000 tons from the superstructure. The bedrock can safely carry 20 tons/sq ft. Due to the complete submergence of the sand, the coefficient of skin friction may be taken as 350 lb/sq ft. Find the outside diameter of the caisson and the thickness of the concrete seal which will be placed at its bottom upon reaching bedrock.

The caissons will be sunk by the use of compressed air. In computing the outside diameter from Eq. (9–1), it is necessary to reduce the downward force, due to the weight, by the hydrostatic uplift, which acts over the entire cross section of the caisson. Thus,

$$\frac{\frac{\pi}{4}(D^2 - 8^2)150 - \frac{\pi}{4}D^2\,62.5}{\pi D} = 350,$$

$$D = 22 \text{ ft.}$$

In computing the thickness of the bottom seal, it is assumed that maximum tensile stress when the air pressure is removed from the working chamber will not exceed 300 psi. According to Eq. (9–2),

$$300 = \frac{3 \times 6250\,\frac{\pi}{4}\,22^2}{8\pi t^2}(3 + 0.15),$$

$$t = 54.6 \text{ in. or } 4\tfrac{1}{2} \text{ ft.}$$

The total pressure on the bedrock will be the sum of the reaction from the superstructure plus the weight of the caisson divided by the cross-sectional area of the caisson. Thus,

$$\frac{6000}{\frac{\pi}{4}\,22^2} + \frac{150 \times 100}{1000} = 30.8 \text{ kips/sq ft.}$$

Example 2. It is desired to find the depth of a caisson supported in a deep layer of clay and carrying a load of 2000 kips. A bell is to be constructed at the

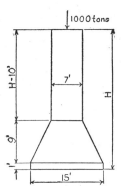

Fig. 9–9.
Numerical example.

lower end of the shaft, as shown in Fig. 9–9. Soil characteristics of the clay are:

Weight: w = 120 lb/cu ft,
Angle of friction: ϕ = 8°,
Cohesion: c = 1700 lb/sq ft,
Skin friction, ultimate value: f = 600 lb/sq ft,
Skin friction, supporting value: f = 300 lb/sq ft.

In order to take advantage of the increase with depth of the bearing capacity of the soil, use will be made of the equation which was developed in the chapter on "Soil Bearing Capacity" and which expresses for cohesive soils the relationship of supporting capacity to the physical characteristics given above. If p denotes the unit pressure exerted at a level H below the top surface, then

$$H = \frac{p}{w} \tan^4\left(45° - \frac{\phi}{2}\right) - \frac{2c}{w} \times \frac{\tan\left(45° - \frac{\phi}{2}\right)}{\cos^2\left(45° - \frac{\phi}{2}\right)} ; \qquad (9\text{-}4)$$

solving for p,

$$p = Hw \tan^4\left(45° + \frac{\phi}{2}\right) + 2c \frac{\tan^3\left(45° + \frac{\phi}{2}\right)}{\cos^2\left(45° - \frac{\phi}{2}\right)} ; \qquad (9\text{-}5)$$

substituting the known values for w, ϕ, and c gives

$$p = 210H + 9088;$$

and selecting a factor of safety of 2,

$$p = 105H + 4544.$$

The outside shaft diam will be made 7 ft, as this will give a unit stress of $2,000,000 \div 5541 = 361$ psi, due to the superimposed load and an additional 1 psi for each linear foot of shaft length. It will be assumed that the total supporting capacity of the caisson can be expressed as the sum of bearing on the bottom of the truncated cone, known as the *bell*, and the frictional resistance existing between the earth and the cylindrical surface of the vertical shaft. Thus (see Fig. 9-9),

$$\frac{\pi}{4} 15^2(105H + 4544) + \pi 7(H - 10)\, 300 = 25,150H + 737,000. \qquad (9\text{-}6)$$

The total vertical load, which must be transmitted to the soil, is the sum of the superimposed load and the weight of the caisson. The latter can be written as the sum of the vertical shaft, the truncated cone of the bell, and its lower cylindrical part. Thus,

$$2,000,000 + \left[\frac{\pi}{4} 7^2(H - 10) + 893 + 177\right]150 = 5770H + 2,103,000. \quad (9\text{-}7)$$

Equating (9-6) and (9-7) and solving gives $H = 70.5$ ft.

The vertical shaft will be 60.5 ft long and will have an outside diam of 7 ft and an inside diam of 5 ft. As the weight of this shell is not sufficient to overcome the skin friction, additional assistance must be provided in the form of weights on its top or by other means. As the end of the shaft reaches its final elevation, the difference between the sum of the skin friction forces and the weight of the shell will be

$$61\pi 7 \times 600 - \frac{\pi}{4}(7^2 - 5^2)61 \times 150 = 634{,}000 \text{ lb.}$$

It is seen that, before the shaft can be sunk, about 320 tons of weight must be added to the weight of the shell. In order not to block the entrance to the shell

Fɪɢ. 9–10. Weighting top of caisson shell to assist in sinking.

during the excavation, it is necessary to build these weights in the form of square slabs with holes of the same diam as the inside of the shell.

Probably the most expensive item in connection with the sinking of caissons through deep and dry soil is that of artificially weighting the shell to promote downward movement. If the caisson shell consists of connecting sections, as shown in Fig. 9–10, then this weighting material must be removed and replaced each time a new section is added to the caisson.

The skin friction can be considerably reduced by the use of water and air jets, and by keeping the caisson moving down uninterruptedly. Another method for bringing down the caisson shaft consists of making the shell of steel plate and drilling it through the soil before excavating its inside. The bottoms of such *rotating caissons* are equipped with cutting teeth, usually formed by a gas torch and bent alternately inward and outward to give a set as in a saw. Rotating caissons have been drilled as much as 70 ft through sand, clay, and boulders to rock to form foundation units for buildings.*

9–1. Given a circular concrete caisson having a square inside shaft 7 ft × 7 ft. Find the outside diam needed to overcome a skin friction of 275 psf. Find the thickness of the concrete seal at a depth 90 ft below the water surface, if tension in the concrete cannot exceed 250 psi.

9–2. Redesign the caisson in Example 9–2, if the soil characteristics are as follows:

$$\text{Weight: } W = 100 \text{ lb/cu ft,}$$
$$\text{Angle of internal friction: } \phi = 20°,$$
$$\text{Cohesion: } c = 200 \text{ psf,}$$
$$\text{Skin friction, ultimate value: 600 psf,}$$
$$\text{Skin friction, supporting value: 300 psf.}$$

---

*See "Rotating Caissons Drill Their Way to Rock," *Engineering News-Record* (July 11, 1935), pp. 37–41.

CHAPTER 10

FLOATING CAISSONS*

10–1. Introduction. Floating caisson shells are shaped as open boxes with sides and bottoms, but without tops. They are usually built on dry land, launched, and towed to the site; then they are weighted and lowered onto the prepared and leveled bed, where they form part of the substructure, their interior usually being filled up with sand, gravel, or concrete.

Sometimes floating caissons are called box caissons or stranded caissons. Their origin may be traced to the old method of filling a barge with stones and then scuttling it over the selected site.

They may be built from steel, timber, or reinforced concrete. The latter is by far the most frequently used. Floating caissons are especially suitable where a foundation is to be laid on a prepared gravel bed with no danger of scour.

Floating caissons have been extensively used in Europe and in other parts of the world where European engineering influence has been felt. They have been used to great advantage in harbor and river development in the United States, Canada, and the Panama Canal Zone. They can be constructed on ways along the shore and launched in the same manner as a ship and towed into position, or they may be lifted off land and put into the water by means of a derrick.

Since the caissons are apt to plunge low in launching unless long and expensive ways are used, the maximum stresses are usually experienced during launching and can be so considered in designing the structure.

Concrete has proved to be an excellent material for floating caissons. Reinforced concrete caissons possess great stiffness and substantial strength, which permits of their being towed long distances in rough water without danger. While it is possible to launch concrete caissons in fresh water ten days after their manufacture, it is better to allow for a longer period when the caissons are to be subjected to sea water action.

The construction of concrete caissons at a more or less permanent yard permits of the installation of a suitable plant and the organization of a good working force, both of which will materially reduce the cost of

---

* The term "floating caissons" was used for the first time in American technical literature by H. S. Taft in his paper entitled "Floating Concrete Caissons," *Professional Memoirs, Corps of Engineers, United States Army* (1915), Vol. 7, p. 145. It has also been used extensively in Great Britain; see D. H. Lee, *Sheet Piling, Cofferdams, and Caissons* (London, 1945), p. 150.

manufacturing and launching the caissons and hence the total cost of the structure.

10–2. Structural Arrangements. It is best to have small caissons mono-cellular; however, it is desirable for large caissons to have numerous compartments in order to decrease their dead weight without making the side walls too thin and hence to provide sufficient buoyancy. The cross-walls can be made of substantial thickness without any appreciable effect upon buoyancy. Two advantages accrue from the division of the inside box: the outside wall is strengthened against the hydrostatic pressure, and increased control is gained over the caisson during the

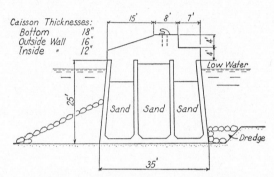

FIG. 10–1. Floating caisson for breakwater.

process of sinking it. The latter is usually accomplished by filling water into the interior. By confining this water to certain compartments the caisson will be much steadier, and any tendency to tilt can immediately be corrected.

As a general rule it can be stated that, for economy, the caisson should be only slightly lighter in weight than buoyancy requires. Since it is possible to sink the caissons quickly to position by means of water ballast, they become safe against moderate wave action in a very short time after arriving at their final location. In the case of a large caisson with a number of compartments and its top above water, it is often possible to pump out the compartments, one at a time, and fill them with concrete, thus avoiding underwater construction.

Fig. 10–1 shows a typical arrangement for a breakwater in which a caisson floated to the site forms the main element. While the sides facing adjacent caissons are made vertical, the two sides facing the exposed and sheltered areas have slight batters. Reinforcements should be placed in both side of the bottom and exterior and interior walls. Special attention should be given to all corners, which should be chamfered and well reinforced.

It is usually necessary to remove some of the bottom material and produce a level surface. After the caisson has been placed in its final position the compartments are filled up with sand and gravel, and concrete is placed on top to form the upper part of the breakwater. It is essential of course that the vertical reinforcement in the caisson walls extends into the mass concrete. Fig. 10–1 shows how attachment of mooring cleats will enable small vessels to berth alongside the sheltered face. Protective rip-rap should be placed as shown, in order to prevent scour of the bottom adjacent to the breakwater. It is usually possible to place adjacent caissons less than 2 ft apart and fill the spaces between them with concrete (see Fig. 10–2).

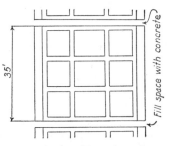

Fig. 10–2. Plan view of floating caissons.

10–3. Stable Flotation. The depth of flotation of the caisson after launching preferably should allow for from 5 to 10 ft of the walls to remain above water. At the same time, care must be taken to insure that the position of the empty caisson in the water is that of a stable floating body. This will be illustrated for the floating caisson shown in Fig. 10–1. Computations based on the dimensions listed in Figs. 10–1 and 10–2 will disclose a total volume of reinforced concrete equal to 8600 cu ft or 645 tons. The depth of flotation x can now be found by equating to this weight the weight of the volume of water displaced by the floating caisson or

$$645 \times 2000 = 64 \frac{x}{3} \left[35^2 + 35 \left(35 - \frac{x}{3} \right) + \sqrt{35^3 \left(35 - \frac{x}{5} \right)} \right].$$

This equation, if solved by trial, gives

$$x = 17.3.$$

In order to explain the principles involved in stable and unstable flotation, reference is made to Figs. 10–3 and 10–4, which illustrate some elements of hydrostatics. The stability of any structure depends upon the equilibrium of the external forces which act upon it. In the case of a floating body, these external forces are essentially, and for all practical purposes, two. They are gravity, due to the intrinsic weight of the body, acting vertically downward, and buoyancy, or the component of hydrostatic pressure, acting vertically upward. It is true that, in addition, there are the horizontal components of the hydrostatic pressure, but in still water, whatever the shape and size of the body, the components must exactly balance one another; they can therefore be disregarded.

As the buoyancy of a floating body is always equal and opposite to its weight, only two forces of the same magnitude need be considered in the stability investigation. In ordinary statics, equilibrium would be assured by the coincidence of the lines of action of these two forces, equal in magnitude and opposite in direction. This requirement can be fulfilled by any symmetrical body, weighing less than an equal volume

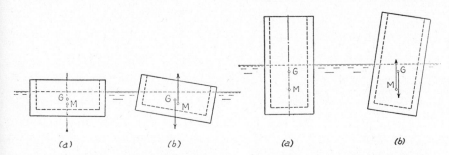

(a)   (b)   (a)   (b)

FIG. 10–3. Stable floating caisson.   FIG. 10–4. Unstable floating caisson.

of water and placed in the liquid in a position which makes its centerline vertical.

But the extreme mobility of water, and the absence in a floating body of any resistance to disturbance, involve another phase of equilibrium. It is obvious that there must be not only perfect balance at any instant, but also a disposition on the part of the body to right itself, or to recover its initial position, in the event of a slight displacement. Both of these points have to be taken into consideration in the design of floating caissons.

The calculations necessary for the purpose are much simpler for floating caissons than they are for ships, since the former are usually constructed to some regular geometrical figure which permits of the easy determination of its center of gravity and also of the center of buoyancy. In contrast, the calculation of the weight of an ordinary ship and the point at which it may be assumed concentrated, as well as the displacement and its geometrical center, are matters of considerable complexity.

In Fig. 10–3 (a) is shown a rectangular floating caisson partly immersed in water. Its center of gravity is designated G and the center of buoyancy is designated M. The two resultant forces, weight and hydrostatic uplift, lie in the same vertical line and the condition of equilibrium is thus fulfilled.

Now, let it be assumed that the caisson has acquired a slight displacement, with the result that it has taken up the position shown in Fig. 10–3 (b). The center of gravity G remains unchanged with respect to the surface of the water and the top of the caisson; the latter has been rotated a small angle about the point G. The center of buoyancy M has been removed to a point which is the centroid of the trapezoid formed by the submerged part of the caisson and readily determinable by simple geometrical construction. As the center of buoyancy M no longer lies vertically

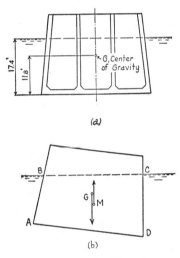

FIG. 10–5. Stability of floating caisson.

below the center of gravity G, there obviously now exists a couple, the moment of which is the weight of the caisson times the horizontal distance between the two centers. The moment is a righting couple and tends to bring the caisson back to its original position.

However, suppose the caisson is shaped as indicated in Fig. 10–4(a), having a great height and a comparatively narrow base. In the upright position, the primary condition of equilibrium obtains as before. But, when a slight displacement takes place, as in Fig. 10–4(b), the moment called into existence is an overturning moment instead of a righting moment and the caisson has a tendency to capsize; hence, the unstable condition.

Fig. 10–5 indicates the stability investigation for the floating caisson shown in Figs. 10–1 and 10–2. Depth of flotation and center of gravity are recorded in Fig. 10–5(a). A small displacement, in the form of a rotation about the center of gravity G, has been produced in Fig. 10–5(b) and the center of buoyancy M found as the centroid of the quadrangle ABCD. It follows that the caisson floats in a stable position.

10–4. Computations. While floating in the water, the walls and bottom of the caisson are subject to bending stresses due to the outside hydrostatic pressure. To successfully resist these stresses, slab thick-

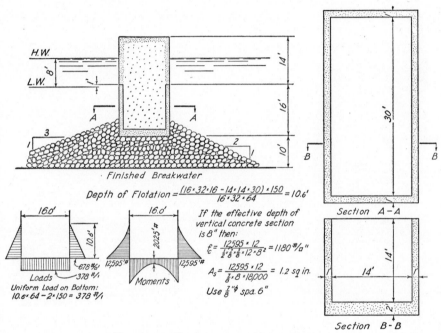

FIG. 10–6. Floating caisson for breakwater.

nesses and amounts of reinforcement must be computed. As the pressures are resisted in two directions—horizontally by the rigid circumference of the box and vertically by cantilever action to the bottom of the caisson— the exact analysis of the stresses is one of considerable complexity. The floating caisson will develop stresses equal, but in opposite directions, to those in a rectangular watertank.

Reliable expressions for the stresses can be obtained by the usual approximations, and, in the case of the long rectangular floating caisson shown in Fig. 10–6, excellent accuracy of analysis is obtained by treating this frame as two vertical cantilevers fixed to the bottom slab and completely disregarding the stiffening effect of the end walls. It should be noted that practical consideration would require several modifications of the breakwater section shown in Fig. 10–6, such as rounded inside corners of the caisson and slight sloping of the upper portion consisting of concrete placed on top of the caisson.

10–5. Floating Steel Caissons. Although concrete has been used extensively for floating caissons, they can also be built of wood or steel. Steel shells may be used advantageously where additional excavation

Courtesy of Dravo Corporation

FIG. 10–7. Floating caisson, partly open at bottom.

under the caisson becomes necessary after its grounding, since cutting edges, excavating shafts, and other details are constructed more readily in steel than in concrete. Furthermore, the comparative lightness of the steel shell makes it possible to reduce the displacement by openings in the bottom and at the same time to have sufficient freeboard to permit towing it to its final location.

Fig. 10–7 shows a steel caisson, partially open at the bottom, which was used for the construction of a bridge pier.* This particular boxlike caisson had five vertical shafts, which communicated with a work chamber extending under its entire bottom. The steel *floater* weighed approxi-

---

See K. C. Cox, "Floating Caissons Form Pier Foundations for Anacostia River Bridge," *Civil Engineering* (December 1946), p. 532.

Courtesy of Dravo Corporation

FIG. 10–8. Launching of floating caisson.

mately 80 tons and was launched in a manner similar to that used in side-launching ships (see Fig. 10–8). In its final location the caisson was sunk by pouring concrete ballast into it, and excavation of its bottom chamber was carried out by jetting and clamshell buckets. Finally the chamber was filled with concrete, placed by a tremie pipe under water.

PROBLEMS

10–1. A floating caisson of reinforced concrete has the following outside dimensions 20 ft × 20 ft × 20 ft. Thickness of walls and bottom is 15 in. (a) Find depth of flotation in fresh water. (b) Find caisson's centroid and center of buoyancy. (*Ans.*: 13.5 ft, 8.45, 6.75 from bottom.)

10–2. What should be the depth of water inside the floating caisson in Fig. 10–6 if it is desired to increase the depth of flotation to 15 ft? (*Ans.*: 5.4 ft.)

10–3. In preceding Prob. 10–2 find the centroid of the caisson, partially filled, and its new center of buoyancy. (*Ans.*: 5.23 ft from bottom.)

10–4. It is desired to find the depth of water, x, which must be placed in the 24 compartments of the floating caisson in Fig. 12–10 in order to make the centroid of the partially filled caisson, C, coincide with the center of buoyancy, B. (*Ans.*: $x = 10.3$ ft.)

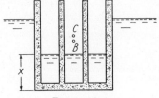

PROB. 10–4

CONSTRUCTION OF BREAKWATER

CHAPTER 11

BREAKWATERS

11–1. Introduction. A breakwater is a structure built within the domain of the sea and submerged for the greater part of its bulk. As the name implies, its function is to break up large waves, preventing them from exerting their destructive influence upon the area sheltered for the reception of shipping. The breakwater must have great strength and stability to withstand the wave pressures. The intensity of these external forces which make for disruption is enormous, exceeding beyond all comparison the power of the most intense wind on land structures.

11–2. Types of Breakwaters. Practically all breakwaters fall within the limits of three types, namely: (a) the wall, (b) the mound or heap, and (c) the cellular cofferdam type.

The first of these involves the construction of a masonry or concrete wall with vertical or nearly vertical faces. Fig. 11–1 shows a concrete

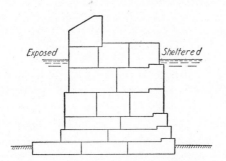

Exposed   Sheltered

FIG. 11–1. Concrete block breakwater.

block breakwater built up of precast concrete sections of considerable weights (usually more than 100 tons) and arranged in such manner that all joints stagger and keyways prevent any horizontal sliding of the blocks. It is advisable to make the top of the bottom course almost level with the bottom of the sea and extend it some distance beyond the side facing the ocean; this will prove to be a potent protection against scour. Blocks of natural stone can also be used. They are heavier than concrete and, for this reason, have claims for preference. They are also less liable to disintegration; but it is expensive to procure them in the large dimensions, and their irregular shapes make it impossible to bed them systematically.

The bottom surface of the sea generally requires some treatment before it is ready to receive the first course of the wall structure, and the service of divers usually will be needed. The bottom can be made level by depositing a layer of underwater concrete, placed by a tremie or in bags and arranged to form a bottom course. Where the bottom has a considerable slope, it is advisable to dress it down to level surfaces forming a series of steps.

The blocks are usually made from precast concrete. The weights range from 5 tons upwards according to the capacity of the available hoisting equipment. Blocks weighing as much as 350 tons have been used for breakwater construction in Europe. Careful and extended curing of the blocks is, of course, essential.

The wall type of breakwater should be used only where the supporting soil is such that the probability of differential settlements may be dis-

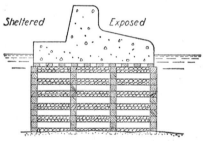

FIG. 11–2. Crib breakwater.

counted. When the wall is founded directly on a firm, homogeneous stratum, such as rock or hard shale, horizontal bonding of the blocks should be provided in addition to the vertical key joints already mentioned. There are several ways of arranging these joints, and usually the blocks are molded to special forms with corresponding projections and recesses.

The joints between the blocks may be filled with mortar by pressure grouting similar to grouting in dams. To prevent the escape of the mortar, however, all the face joints must be caulked. This can be done by forming slightly dovetailed grooves near the outer edges of the blocks and ramming them with wood splines or rolls of canvas containing neat cement, which should be allowed to harden before grouting.

The wall type of breakwater can also be constructed as a floating caisson, towed to its location and filled with sand and gravel and a superstructure built on its top, as explained elsewhere in this volume. Closely related to this type of breakwater is the one shown in Fig. 11–2, which consists of a timber crib filled with stone and surmounted by a concrete roof which forms the top of the structure. Both durability and appearance require that no parts of the crib extend above low water level. Such forms of breakwaters are used only in comparatively shallow water and in moderately exposed positions. Depths of 15 ft of water probably mark the limit to which they may advantageously be applied.

Fig. 11–3 shows a breakwater of the mound type. It consists of a heterogeneous mass of natural and, frequently, undressed stones. These stones are generally deposited at random and without any regards for bonding. The mass of natural stone is often supplemented by precast blocks, usually of cubical shape. The mound breakwater is generally capped by several courses of regularly cut natural stones as shown in Fig. 11–3.

Stones of large size should be used for mound breakwaters. Most specifications will require that in the seaward slope no stone shall be used weighing less than 3 tons and that the average weight of stone in each cargo shall be not less than 4 tons. In the harbor slope, smaller

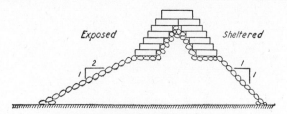

FIG. 11–3. Rubble stone breakwater.

stones may be permitted—usually from ½ ton to 4 tons. The regularly cut capstones will generally vary from 10 to 40 tons.

Mound breakwaters should be built up in layers. The material may be deposited directly on the bottom of the sea without any preliminary dredging operations, for the stones will spread themselves sufficiently to distribute their weight within the limits of support, or they will sink until they reach some firmer substratum by which the settlement becomes arrested.

Where there is an abundance of large stones or where quarries lie conveniently close, the mound breakwater will commend itself because of the facility with which it can be formed and the economy resulting from the use of undressed stone.

The mound breakwater lacks in the quality of permanence, especially its upper portion which is constantly under the influence of the hydro-dynamic action of the striking waves.

Subsidiary classes of breakwaters form a series of gradations between the wall and the mound types of structures. In fact, the combination of wall and mound in varying proportions constitutes by far the bulk of breakwaters. In some cases the mound predominates and is simply capped by a slight superstructure; in other cases, it is reduced to a minimum, becoming merely a foundation layer for a massive wall.

Cellular breakwaters have been used a great deal lately, but only on inland waterways, lakes, and rivers. They consist of a series of enclosures formed by steel sheet piling similar to cellular cofferdams. Their chief advantage is that ordinary sand, a much cheaper fill, can be used for the inside of the cells. The piles, moreover, are easily driven to reach firm layers under the bottom, and dredging of the site can be eliminated.

11–3. Wave Pressures. The function of a breakwater is to provide a sheltered area of water. The forces that act upon it are, therefore, its weight (including buoyancy) and the static and dynamic pressures created by the striking waves.

No elaborate statement is needed to explain the difficulties involved in producing a satisfactory analysis of wave pressures. A purely mathematical approach* will usually give pressures and stresses which experi-

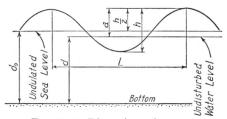

FIG. 11–4. Dimensions of waves.

ence and actual measurements indicate to be too small. The method, which will be outlined in the following, has been developed by D. D. Gaillard and D. A. Molitor† and is based to a large extent upon observational data, which are in themselves quite approximate. However, the resulting shears, overturning moments, and stresses will, if based on correct heights and lengths of waves, prove to be on the safe side.

The nomenclature that will be used in the wave pressure formulas is partly explained in Fig. 11–4, which shows the principal dimensions of wave motion in water. The height h of the wave depends on two factors, the wind velocity V, which is the source of the wave motion, and the *fetch* D of the wave. The fetch is the distance over which the wind acts in creating the wave and can, of course, never exceed the distance from the breakwater to the windward shore; it usually can be assumed to be less than 300 mi, even though the distance to the windward shore may be greater. If V is expressed in mph and D in mi, then the wave height h in ft may be estimated by the formula

$$h = 0.17 \sqrt{VD}. \qquad (11\text{--}1)$$

*See, for instance, *Le Genie Civil* (January 26, 1929), pp. 81–84.
†See *Trans. A.S.C.E.* (1935), pp. 984–1017.

According to observations, the length L of the waves can be expressed in terms of wave height h and wind velocity V; thus,

$$L = 840 \frac{h}{V}. \tag{11-2}$$

It is sometimes erroneously assumed that the wave crest and the wave trough are equal distances above and below the undisturbed water level. But observations show that the mean of the two lies above the still water level; and, if the distance from the bottom to the undulated water level is d_o, then

$$\frac{d_o}{L} = \frac{d}{L} + 2\left(\frac{h}{L}\right)^2. \tag{11-3}$$

Also, according to observations, the distance from undisturbed water level to the wave crest is

$$a = \frac{h}{2} + \frac{h^2}{L}. \tag{11-4}$$

If the wave is completely obstructed by a vertical wall, then the height h_o above the undisturbed water level to which it will rise will be

$$h_o = 2a. \tag{11-5}$$

The total hydrodynamic pressure which is delivered to a submerged plate by water of velocity V is

$$p = kw \frac{V^2}{2g}. \tag{11-6}$$

The total velocity of the striking wave consists of the combined velocity of propagation V and the maximum orbital velocity V_o of a wave particle, so that Eq. (11-6) should be modified to represent the maximum pressure exerted by a wave of given dimensions. Thus,

$$p_{max} = \frac{kw}{2g}(V + V_o)^2, \tag{11-7}$$

in which the following notation is used:

p = pressure in lb/sq ft,
w = unit weight of water, 62.5 and 64 lb/cu ft for fresh and salt water, respectively,
V = velocity of propagation of the wave in fps,
V_o= maximum velocity (fps) of wave particle in its orbit,
k = an empirical constant, which for ocean waves may be assumed to be 1.8 and for fresh water waves varies from 1.3 to 1.7,
g = gravity acceleration, 32.2 fps².

The velocity of propagation can be computed from the formula

$$V = 2.26 \sqrt{L \tanh \frac{2\pi d_o}{L}}, \qquad (11\text{–}8)$$

and the maximum orbital velocity of a wave particle by

$$V_o = \frac{7.11h}{\sqrt{L \tanh \frac{2\pi d_o}{L}}}. \qquad (11\text{–}9)$$

The hyperbolic function in Eqs. (11–8) and (11–9) may, in the absence of tables, be computed by

$$\tanh x = \frac{\sinh x}{\cosh x} = \frac{x + \dfrac{x^3}{3!} + \dfrac{x^5}{5!} + \cdots}{1 + \dfrac{x^2}{2!} + \dfrac{x^4}{4!} + \cdots}. \qquad (11\text{–}10)$$

For the usual problems in wave pressure determination, excellent accuracy can be obtained by including three terms in both numerator and denominator of Eq. (11–10).

Finally, the point of application of the maximum pressure has been found from observations to be

$$h_1 = 0.12h \qquad (11\text{–}11)$$

above the undisturbed water level.

Waves striking a breakwater obliquely produce less pressure than those that strike normally; the following reduction formula can be used,

$$p_n = p \sin^2 \alpha, \qquad (11\text{–}12)$$

where α is the angle between direction of wind and face of breakwater, p the maximum pressure as estimated by Eq. (11–7), and p_n the reduced normal pressure per square foot of vertical wall.

There remains now to construct a diagram indicating the variation of wave pressures on the exposed side of the wall. Based on actual measurements, the diagram in Fig. 11–5 is generally accepted as being on the safe side. The variation is according to a straight line between point A, which represents the height of the completely obstructed wave, and point B, which determines the location of maximum pressure. Between points B and C (trough of wave), the variation is according to a parabola. In computing the overturning moment on the breakwater, the resultant of pressure area ABD may be taken as one-half of AB and BD, and its location at the centroid of the triangle. The resultant of the parabolic pressure area BDC may be taken as two-thirds of this area and its location as five-eighths of BC above C.

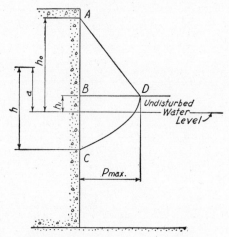

FIG. 11–5. Wave pressure diagram.

11–4. Numerical Example. Let it be desired to find the width of a massive concrete breakwater having a depth of water equal to 30 ft. The wind velocity is 60 mph and the fetch of the waves is estimated at 100 mi.

Using the nomenclature explained in the previous sections, it is found that wave height h and wave length L will equal

$$h = 0.17 \sqrt{60 \times 100} = 13.2 \text{ ft,}$$

$$L = \frac{840}{60} \, 13.2 = 185 \text{ ft.}$$

Height a of wave crest above undisturbed water level will be

$$a = \frac{13.2}{2} + \frac{13.2^2}{185} = 7.5 \text{ ft.}$$

The obstructed wave will rise to a height of $2 \times 7.5 = 15$ ft above the level of the still water. Other quantities to be computed include

$$\frac{d_o}{L} = \frac{30}{185} + 2\left(\frac{30}{185}\right)^2 = 0.214,$$

$$\tanh 2\pi \, \frac{d_o}{L} = \tanh 1.346 = 0.873.$$

The velocity of propagation and orbital velocity of wave particle can now be evaluated by Eqs. (11–8) and (11–9). Thus,

$$V = 2.26 \sqrt{185 \times 0.873} = 28.7 \text{ fps,}$$

$$V_o = \frac{7.11 \times 13.2}{\sqrt{185 \times 0.873}} = 7.4 \text{ fps.}$$

The maximum pressure and its point of application above the undisturbed water level are

$$p_{max} = \frac{1.8 \times 64}{2 \times 32.2} (28.7 + 7.4)^2 = 2345 \text{ lb/sq ft,}$$

$$h_1 = 0.12 \times 13.2 = 1.5 \text{ ft.}$$

In order to completely obstruct the striking waves, the breakwater should rise 15 ft above the undisturbed sea level. The total overturning moment about the base is, according to Fig. 11–6,

$$2345 \left[\tfrac{1}{2}13.5(\tfrac{1}{3}13.5 + 1.5 + 30) + \tfrac{2}{3}7.2 (24.3 + \tfrac{5}{8}7.2)\right] = 893,500 \text{ ft-lb.}$$

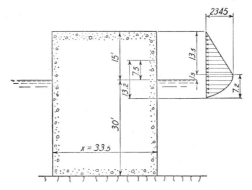

FIG. 11–6. Numerical example.

The weight of the breakwater in terms of the unknown width x and allowing for buoyancy is

$$15x \, 150 + 30x(150 - 64) = 4830x.$$

If, for stability, it is required that the resultant of lateral wave pressure and weight must fall within the middle third of the base, then

$$4830x \, \frac{x}{6} = 893,500,$$

$$x = 33.5 \text{ ft.}$$

The total shearing force which must be resisted by the breakwater is equal to the area of the pressure diagram or

$$(\tfrac{1}{2}13.5 + \tfrac{2}{3}7.2)2345 = 27,100 \text{ lb.}$$

Sliding resistance caused by the friction between the base and the bottom soil should exceed this total horizontal pressure by a substantial amount, usually by 100 per cent. In order not to produce rupture in the bottom soil underneath the base, the angle between a vertical line and the resultant of wave pressure and wall weight should be less than the angle of internal friction of the soil in its submerged condition.

The use of a carefully designed and manufactured concrete mixture is probably more important in a breakwater than in any other type of substructure. Not only will it be subjected to constant wetting and drying in the warm seasons, but during the winter to freezing and thawing as well. Moreover, the destructive agents of the sea water are always present. Aside from damage due to these causes, an additional source of disruptive forces exists in walls subjected to the impact of striking waves.

Courtesy of Portland Cement Association

FIG. 11–7. Wave action on breakwater.

During wave impact, water-filled cavities are subjected to intensive hydraulic pressures. Likewise air confined within holes, fissures, and minute cracks is compressed to create high internal pressures; if these pressures are constantly repeated, they are bound to exert a most disruptive influence, however local and of however short duration they may be. The desirability of preserving an intact face of a monolithic sea wall serving as a breakwater is, therefore, clearly apparent as is also the necessity for reinforcement at the exposed face, generously protected by concrete.

The severity of the impact of wave action against a breakwater of rectangular cross section is illustrated in Fig. 11–7, which shows the waves breaking over a massive mole at the entrance to the harbor at Aberdeen, Scotland. It is interesting to note that the spray has nearly obscured the lighthouse tower in the left background.

The wave action against a sloping wall, or a stepped wall, usually will be less severe than against a vertical surface. This contrast in the manner of turning back waves is illustrated in Fig. 11–8, which shows, in the foreground, a completed portion of a sea wall and, in the back-

Courtesy of Portland Cement Association

FIG. 11–8. Difference in wave action against vertical-faced cofferdam and step section of sea wall.

ground, a vertical-faced cofferdam used during its construction. Spray is visible where waves hit the cofferdam, while portions of the same waves are dissipated without turbulence by the stepped wall.

PROBLEM

The accompanying figure illustrates a method of computing wave pressures on vertical walls, originated by the French mathematician G. Sainflou* and used

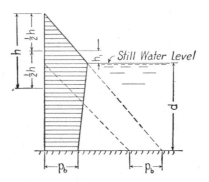

*See G. Sainflou, "Essai sur Les Digues Verticales," *Annales des Ponts et Chausses* (1928), Part 4, pp. 5–48.

extensively in Europe and South America. The Sainflou method assumes that the wave pressure extends to the bottom of the wall and can be represented by the crosshatched area. The point of maximum pressure h_1 is given by the expression

$$h_1 = \frac{\pi h}{4L} \coth \frac{2\pi d}{L},$$

and the pressure intensity at the bottom of the wall is P_b multiplied by unit weight of water, where

$$P_b = \frac{h}{2 \cosh \dfrac{2\pi d}{L}}.$$

The symbols h and L are defined by Eqs. (11–1) and (11–2).

Derive a general expression for the overturning moment at the bottom of the wall, and find the numerical value of this moment in case of a water depth $d = 9$ ft, a wave fetch $D = 30$ mi, and a wind velocity of $V = 55$ mph.

Courtesy of Raymond Concrete Pile Company

REINFORCED CONCRETE PILES FOR WHARF STRUCTURE

CHAPTER 12

WHARVES AND PIERS

12-1. Introduction. Wharves and piers are structures located in or at the edge of water deep enough to permit vessels to tie up against them and load or discharge cargo; their function is to afford direct connection between the water and land carriers.

Similar to a breakwater, the greater part of wharves or piers is located below water and ground level, and they may therefore be classified as substructures that serve as the foundation for the transit sheds, warehouses, cranes, conveyors, railroad tracks, and pavements.

A wharf is usually the name for a landing place for vessels if the structure has water on only one side. A pier is a structure that projects from the shoreline out into the water. A pier has water on both sides. Wharves and piers are generally termed port structures, while a breakwater is usually referred to as a harbor structure. It is not always possible to adhere to these distinctions, since at a number of ports the terms docks, quays, and slips are also widely used. A dock may be either a wharf or a pier; on the Great Lakes, for instance, the iron-ore and coal terminals are often referred to as *ore docks* and *coal docks*. Quays are sometimes used to designate the wharves and piers which form a system of basins, and slips are the open water spaces between piers.

12-2. Wharf Structures. The main feature of the wharf is the vertical drop in elevation at its water edge. It follows that the main forces, which must be resisted by a wharf, are horizontal ones due to lateral earth and water pressures and to the pulls and thrusts of docking vessels.

Typical wharf structures are shown in Fig. 12-1. To resist the earth pressure and create a deep water frontage, a massive retaining wall can be used as indicated in Fig. 12-1(a); it may be constructed inside a cofferdam, or as a floating caisson. Economy can be achieved by varying its cross section or by building it of precast concrete blocks. More economical, however, is the structure in Fig. 12-1(b). This also confines the earth behind a vertical wall, but the enclosing element is a sheet-piling wall—usually of steel, although other materials can be used. Stability of this wall is achieved by driving it down deep below the sea bottom and supporting it by a wale girder tied by horizontal steel rods to some anchorage that is well behind the wall. This anchorage may be a row of vertical sheet piles, combinations of vertical and batter piles, or concrete slabs which, by engaging large earth masses, resist the horizontal movement of the anchor rods.

A different principle in wharf design is employed in Fig. 12–1(c). Instead of retaining the earth by a vertical structure, the transition between the two levels is made by the natural slope of the ground, and the wharf structure is made to bridge over this slope. The chief characteristic of this structure is the absence of any lateral earth pressure; the only horizontal forces resisted by the structure are the pull exerted by ships drawing themselves towards the wharf by means of rope and mooring posts, and the thrusts transmitted to the deck (top surface of dock)

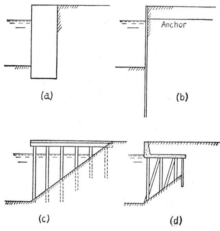

FIG. 12–1. Wharf types.

when the slowly moving ship is brought to a standstill by contacting the wharf. This type of structure can be supported on piles, cylindrical caissons, or even solid piers spaced at certain intervals.

The structure shown in Fig. 12–1(d) combines features of (a), (b), and (c). An earth-filled platform terminates in a low retaining wall at one end while its other end supports laterally a short sheet-piling wall. A horizontal earth thrust, although smaller than that which would occur in Fig. 12–1(b), must be resisted either by flexure in the vertical piles and cylindrical piers or by anchorages similar to those in (b). Instead of building separate pile cluster anchorages behind the main structure, these can be incorporated in it as shown in Fig. 12–1(d) by addition of batter piles under the platform. This type of wharf is sometimes called a *relieving platform* because, by allowing the natural slope to extend under it, the platform will materially relieve the total lateral earth pressures.

12–3. Bulkhead Wharves. An example of a wharf of the retaining wall type is shown in Fig. 12–2. The bulkhead has been formed of precast concrete caissons that can be built on shore, launched, towed to the site, and sunk to rest onto a prepared level. If the shell is made comparatively narrow, it will be necessary to flare out the base so that the resultants of vertical and horizontal forces will fall within its middle third. The outside portion of the caisson shell will be subjected to a greater pressure than the portion facing the rear and may therefore be made of greater thickness. The prepared bottom level consists of a 2-ft cushion of broken stone, and rip-rap protects the front of the base against

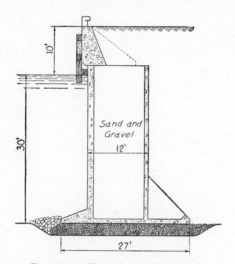

FIG. 12–2. Typical wharf structure.

possible scour. The bulkhead is capped by a retaining wall, which is widened at intervals so as to transmit to the reinforced concrete walls of the caisson the upward and horizontal pulls transmitted through the mooring posts.

All wharf structures should be provided with a fender system, which will protect the wharf, as well as the mooring ship, against damage from the impact of contact. Fig. 12–2 shows this bumper system, for which timber is the most commonly used material; it is attached to the retaining wall and the upper part of the caisson. The attachment should be such that individual units of the fender system can readily be replaced, because these members are subjected not only to repeated shocks and impact but also to frequent wetting and drying.

Fig. 12–3 shows steel sheet piling for a wharf of the type referred to in Fig. 12–1(*b*). The wale frame, which can be seen just above the waterline, is supported at intervals by steel piles driven into the ground below and sloping away from the sheet piling. The usual continuous wall anchorage proved impracticable in this case due to the close proximity

FIG. 12–3. Steel sheet piling for wharf.

of existing buildings. By resisting extraction, the sloping steel piles in Fig. 12–3 act as supports for the wale girder.

Fig. 12–4 shows the structural arrangement for a sheet-piling wharf supported laterally by a continuous wall anchorage. Along inland waterways especially, this type of wharf has proved very efficient and economical. The steel tie rods which support the wale frame should be equipped with turnbuckles, and the anchorage placed as low as possible, consistent with economical erection. The most economical location will usually be found to be just above low water, where the work can be performed in the dry. It is also well to keep, when practicable, the top elevation of wales and tie rods within the zone of saturation of the soil to retard corrosion. The wale and the anchor rod should never be more

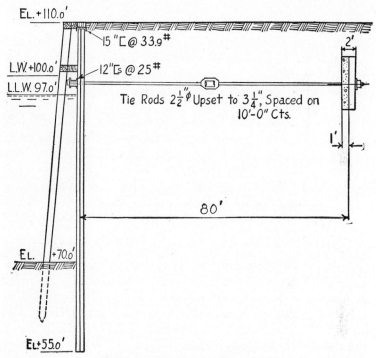

EL.+110.0'

15"$\subset$@ 33.9$^{\#}$

L.W.+100.0'

L.L.W. 97.0'

12"$\subset$s @ 25$^{\#}$

Tie Rods $2\frac{1}{2}"^{\phi}$ Upset to $3\frac{1}{4}"$, Spaced on 10'-0" Cts.

2'

1'

80'

EL. +70.0'

EL.+55.0'

FIG. 12–4. Steel sheet-piling wharf.

than 18 in. under water level, because below this level divers must ordinarily be employed.

The determination of the proper distance between the anchor rods is not difficult if it is recalled that the total load on the wall is the same, regardless of the number of rods; and, for that reason, the total amount of steel in the rods is the same, regardless of their spacing. Rods of small diam should, in general, be avoided. On the other hand, anchor rods that are too large will result in bigger spacings and higher bending moments in the wale girders. The center-to-center distance between tie rods should equal an even number of widths of sheet piles. As a rule the distance between tie rods should be selected so that their diam will lie within the most economical range, which is from $1\frac{1}{4}$ to 3 in. It is customary to add $\frac{1}{4}$ in. to the diam to allow for corrosion, or else the rods should be wrapped in tarred burlap.

The wale usually consists of two steel channels and can be attached to either the inside or the outside of the sheet-piling wall. The holes in the sheet piling for the anchor rods should be made after the piling is driven because of the difficulty of driving every sheet pile to exact grade. Likewise, after driving, the sheet-piling tops will often have to be flame-cut to exact height.

The anchorage should be located far enough back of the bulkhead to be in stable soil. The angle of internal friction of the soil or fill, drawn from the intersection of the bottom of the channel and the sheet-piling wall, locates the plane of stable soil. The face of the anchor wall should, preferably, be from 10 to 15 ft back of this plane.

The anchor wall can be made as a continuous steel, wood, or reinforced concrete wall. The total resistance offered by this wall may be estimated as the difference between intensity of passive and active earth pressure at the elevation of the anchor rod, multiplied by area of contact. Some-times attempts are made to have the anchor rod pass through the center of earth resistance, which coincides with the centroid of the trapezoid representing the earth pressure intensity on the vertical contact face of the anchor wall.

The anchorage for a steel sheet-piling wall may also be constructed of bearing piles sloping alternately in two directions. The anchor rod pull replaced by two equivalent forces will be balanced by the resistance of these piles to further penetration and extraction.

Steel sheet-piling wharves should be equipped with fender systems as shown in Fig. 12–4. All holes for connection bolts should be drilled after the sheet piling has been driven.

The foundations for mooring posts are more difficult in the case of a sheet-piling wharf than for a wharf of the type shown in Fig. 12–2, where an attachment can be made directly to the concrete section. The self-supporting pile clusters on the sheet-piling wharves can be used inside the bulkhead, or the mooring posts can be rigidly attached to the sheet piling.

The fill behind the sheet piling should be placed very carefully, as the manner in which it is deposited may materially affect the lateral pressures. The fill should never be placed towards the bulkhead, because such a method usually pushes a mud wave against the wall, which greatly increases the lateral pressure when the mud wave is finally confined. The best method is to fill, in layers, the whole distance between the anchorage and the bulkhead, endeavoring to keep the surface of the fill as nearly level as possible. In this manner the mud wave may be largely eliminated and the passive resistance increases on the anchorage as the active pressure increases on the outside wall.

12–4. Pile and Caisson Wharves. It was shown, in Fig. 12–1(c), that the earth pressure due to the difference in level between the top of the wharf and the bottom of the channel can be eliminated by bridging over the natural slope between these two surfaces.

FIG. 12–5. Caissons for wharf structure.

Fig. 12–5 shows the cylindrical caissons which are to support a wharf of this type. Steel rails have been used for reinforcement and will tie the caissons to the deck.

The chief advantages of pile wharf structures are economy and rapidity of construction, as compared with filled structures which usually require considerable time to settle. Another advantage is that a pile structure presents a smaller obstruction to the tidal prism. It does not affect materially the amount of water which flows in and out of a harbor with the changes of tide. A fourth advantage is the greater elasticity of pile structures; they absorb more readily the kinetic energy of moving vessels brought into contact with the wharf.

Fig. 12–6 shows a typical structure for a pile wharf, built of reinforced concrete except for the fender timbers in front and some very short steel sheet piling in the rear.

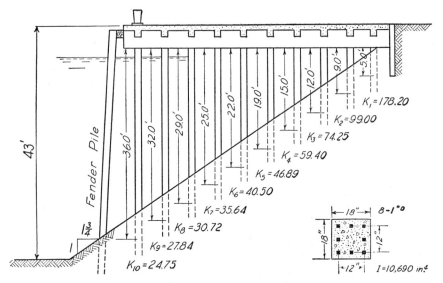

FIG. 12–6. Wharf structure on piles.

The relieving platform structure shown in Fig. 12–1(d) may be built with or without anchorage. The horizontal earth pressure has usually been reduced sufficiently to be resisted by flexure of the vertical piles or piers. If additional later stability is needed, batter piles can be located under the platform and far enough back to prevent their projecting into the channel and creating obstructions for the shipping.

The structural analysis of a relieving platform may be made by breaking up the investigation into two parts. First, the sheet piling is analyzed in the ordinary manner as a beam simply supported by the platform and at some depth below its intersection with the outside ground surface where equality exists between active and passive earth pressures. Finally, the pile group under the platform can be analyzed for the forces acting upon it, including the reaction from the sheet piling.

12–5. Pier Structures. Pier construction is the most economical waterfront, if the total length of berthing space is the deciding factor; and when the space will permit, as in a wide river, this type of structure is often adopted.

One advantage of the pier system is a comparatively inexpensive structure having waterfront on both sides. In a large harbor built on the rocky shore of valuable urban land, such as Manhattan, there is no choice but to build piers. If the piers cannot be long, they need not be more than of a certain moderate width. The width, which depends on the length, is an important problem in the functional design of piers. The longer the pier, the wider it must be. The reason for this is that the longer the pier is, the more traffic must be handled at the shore end. It is a mistake to construct piers at right angles to the stream. Piers should be inclined downstream at an angle of approximately 45° to the shore-line to permit easy docking of large vessels when a strong current is running.

Fig. 12–7 shows typical structural arrangements for piers. Fig. 12–7(a) consists of fill placed between parallel walls of sheet piling tied together

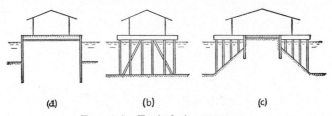

(a)   (b)   (c)

FIG. 12–7. Typical pier structures.

by anchor rods above low water. The anchorage for such a pier presents a much simpler problem than the anchorage for a wharf, due to the presence of the equal and opposite reactions from the two walls. It is usually necessary to support the anchor rod on a few bearing piles in order to prevent excessive sagging. As a pier is frequently designed for a large surcharge load, the resulting lateral pressures become quite large for great depths. For this reason the type shown in Fig. 12–7(a) may not prove economical for large depths.

In the case of a large depth the structure shown in Fig. 12–7(b) will merit consideration. It is simply a bridge built into the dredged area and consists of a deck supported on piles or cylindrical piers (constructed as caissons). As lateral earth pressure has been completely eliminated for this structure, the only horizontal forces to be considered will be those due to the movement of vessels alongside the pier; for their effective resistance, it may be necessary to supplement the vertical bearing piles by batter piles.

The arrangement shown in Fig. 12–7(c) is generally applicable to a wide pier situated in deep water. It may be interpreted as an application of the principle of the relieving platform. Piles are used on both sides of the pier for distances sufficient to bring the natural ground slope up to elevations where a small amount of sheet piling will retain the center portion of the fill. It is customary, as shown in Fig. 12–7(c), to tie the two parts of the structure together by anchor rods and thus completely eliminate any need for batter piles.

Some typical pier and wharf structures are shown in Fig. 12–8. They form parts of the port of Portland, Oregon. The wharf between the projecting piers consists of cellular cofferdams of the diaphragm type.

12–6. Design Loads. A waterfront structure should be designed to resist both vertical and horizontal forces. The dead load (a vertical force) is caused by the weight of the structure itself, including fill and any permanent construction which may be supported by it, such as transit sheds, warehouses, and cargo transfer equipment.

The live load (also a vertical force) is due to the transfer and storage of cargoes before they are loaded on sea or land carriers. This surcharge load, which is assumed applied to the deck, will depend on the nature of the cargoes; it may vary from 100 to 1000 psf.

Lateral earth pressure due to retained fill or natural soil is usually an important item. The theories of Rankine and Coulomb are universally used for evaluating the pressure intensities, and although sometimes they give too high and conservative values, they will, if carefully and judiciously applied, yield stresses that are on the safe side.

Hydrostatic pressure due to water is not an important item, as it is usually counterbalanced by being present on both sides of the bulkhead walls. For massive structures the hydrostatic uplift or the buoyancy is a very important factor to include. The unit weights of 62.5 and 64 lb/cu ft should be used for fresh and salt water, respectively.

The lateral forces assumed to act on a waterfront structure should always include the effects of ships tying up alongside it. In order for a vessel to attain a position parallel to the waterfront, it is customary for it to pull itself toward the wharf by means of its hoisting winches, ropes, and the mooring posts or bollards located on the wharf. This horizontal pull in the direction of the ship cannot, of course, exceed the capacity of the winch, which may vary from 10 to 50 tons. With the spacing of the mooring posts known (usually from 50 to 100 ft), an accurate evaluation can be made of the mooring post pull.

In approaching the waterfront the ship will be brought to a standstill by making contact with the fender system of the structure. Although the speed of the vessel is extremely low, a considerable amount of kinetic energy is delivered to the structure because of its sizable tonnage.

Collision between a ship and a structure of the gravity-wall type will not, as a rule, result in any injury to the wharf, since the energy will be dissipated in the large mass of concrete and fill. However, in the case of a structure supported on piles, the energy of the moving vessel must be absorbed by the elasticity of the structure itself; stresses which have been

FIG. 12–8. Typical pier and wharf structures.

set up must be accounted for. Allowance for the effect of ships' impact on waterfronts is sometimes made by the inclusion of a horizontal force directed toward the shore and of some arbitrary magnitude, such as 50 to 100 tons.

12–7. Ship Impact. In the following discussion a procedure is presented for expressing the stresses in structures on piles as functions of the kinetic energy of an approaching vessel. The analysis can easily be extended to substructures consisting of cylindrical caissons or combinations of caissons and piles.

Reference is first made to Fig. 12–9 which shows a beam, whose axis is fixed against rotation at both ends. If the top of the beam is permitted to move horizontally while the axis remains fixed in the vertical direction, then the deflection of the top due to the application of a load P is

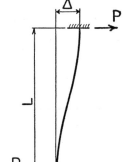

$$\Delta = \frac{PL^3}{12EI}, \tag{12-1}$$

where I is the moment of inertia of the cross section and E is the modulus of elasticity. The strain energy which is consumed by the beam in producing this deflection is

$$\tfrac{1}{2}P\Delta = \frac{P^2L^3}{24EI}. \tag{12-2}$$

Fig. 12–9

A moving ship contacting a wharf such as the one shown in Fig. 12–6 will cause horizontal deflections of several pile bents and will come to rest when its total kinetic energy has been converted into strain energy of the deflected bents. The total strain energy of a bent can be written as the sum of energies stored in each pile. If the piles are assumed fixed at points below the groundline and fixed-free at the pile cap (see Fig. 12–9), it is seen that

$$\frac{P_1{}^2L_1{}^3}{24EI} + \frac{P_2{}^2L_2{}^3}{24EI} + \frac{P_3{}^2L_3{}^3}{24EI} + \cdots = \frac{1}{N} \times \frac{W}{2g} v^2, \tag{12-3}$$

where N = number of bents sharing impact of ship,
  W = displacement of ship, lb,
  g = gravity acceleration, 386.4 in./sec^2,
  v = velocity of ship, in./sec.

Expressing equal deflections of the tops of all piles,

$$\frac{P_1L_1{}^3}{12EI} = \frac{P_2L_2{}^3}{12EI} = \frac{P_3L_3{}^3}{12EI} = \cdots, \tag{12-4}$$

$$P_2 = P_1\left(\frac{L_1}{L_2}\right)^3; \quad P_3 = P_1\left(\frac{L_1}{L_3}\right)^3; \quad \cdots. \qquad (12\text{–}5)$$

Substituting (12–5) in (12–3),

$$P_1{}^2L_1{}^3 + P_1{}^2\frac{L_1{}^6}{L_2{}^3} + P_1{}^2\frac{L_1{}^6}{L_3{}^3} + \cdots = 12EI\,\frac{Wv^2}{Ng}, \qquad (12\text{–}6)$$

$$\frac{P_1{}^2L_1{}^2}{K_1{}^4}\,\Sigma K^3 = \frac{12EW}{Ng}\,v^2. \qquad (12\text{–}7)$$

where $K = I \div L$ denotes the stiffnesses of the piles. If

$$C = v\sqrt{\frac{3WE}{Ng\Sigma K}}, \qquad (12\text{–}8)$$

then the maximum bending moments in the piles will be

$$M_1 = \tfrac{1}{2}P_1L_1 = CK_1{}^2; \quad M_2 = \tfrac{1}{2}P_2L_2 = CK_2{}^2; \quad \cdots. \qquad (12\text{–}9)$$

It is seen that the maximum bending stresses will occur at the top and bottom of the rear pile and are directly proportional to the velocity of the moving ship and also directly proportional to the square root of the displacement.

In the case of a timber platform supported on timber piles, the latter should be assumed hinged at the top and Eq. (12–7) becomes

$$\frac{P_1{}^2L_1{}^2}{6EK_1{}^4}\,\Sigma K^3 = \frac{1}{N} \times \frac{W}{2g}\,v^2, \qquad (12\text{–}7a)$$

and the maximum bending moments occur at the bottoms of the piles and are

$$M_1 = P_1L_1 = CK_1{}^2; \quad M_2 = P_2L_2 = CK_2{}^2; \quad \cdots, \qquad (12\text{–}9a)$$

where C is given by Eq. (12–8).

The deflection of a pile bent caused by the complete absorption of the kinetic energy, for piles fixed at the top and bottom, is

$$\Delta = \frac{P_1L_1{}^3}{12EI} = \frac{CI}{6E} \qquad (12\text{–}10)$$

If the piles can be assumed hinged at the top, the deflection of a pile bent is

$$\Delta = \frac{P_1L_1{}^3}{3EI} = \frac{CI}{3E}. \qquad (12\text{–}10a)$$

Of the quantities involved in computing the stresses and deflections, the unsupported pile length L and the number of pile bents N are not clearly defined and may vary somewhat with local conditions. If driven into firm material, a pile usually can be considered as fixed at a point $\overline{5}$ ft below the groundline; and in soft material, 10 ft below. The number of pile bents that can be assumed to share the impact of a mooring ship, parallel to its front face, can safely be taken as the number of bents in one-half the length of the vessel.

12–8. Numerical Example. Maximum bending stress and deflection will be found for the case of a ship of 10,000 tons displacement striking the front of the wharf, shown in Fig. 12–6, while moving sideways at a rate of $\frac{1}{4}$ in./sec. The number of bents that can be counted on to share the impact is assumed to be ten; hence,

$$C = \frac{1}{4} \sqrt{\frac{3 \times 2 \times 10^7 \times 3 \times 10^6}{10 \times 386.4 \times 7529 \times 10^3}} = 19.67 \text{ lb/in}^5.$$

$$M_1 = 19.67 \times 178.2^2 = 624.500 \text{ in.-lb.}$$

If, in Fig. 12–6, it is assumed that the modular ratio $n = 10$, then this moment will be found to produce a maximum compressive stress of 664 psi. Contact with the moving ship will deflect the wharf

$$\Delta = \frac{19.67 \times 10,692}{6 \times 3 \times 10^6} = 0.012 \text{ in.}$$

If, for comparison, it is assumed that timber piles 12 in. in diameter are substituted for the concrete piles and that the timber bents are spaced apart one-half of the distance between the concrete pile bents, then

$$C = \frac{1}{4} \sqrt{\frac{3 \times 2 \times 10^7 \times 15 \times 10^5}{20 \times 386.4 \times 6500}} = 335 \text{ lb/in.}^5,$$

$$M_1 = 335 \times 16.96^2 = 96,330 \text{ in.-lb.}$$

The maximum fiber stress due to this moment is 568 psi. While this stress is of the same magnitude as the stress in the concrete piles, the deflection of the timber structure will be much greater, namely,

$$\Delta = \frac{335 \times 1018}{3 \times 15 \times 10^5} = 0.076 \text{ in.}$$

This is in accordance with the fact that timber wharves possess greater elasticity than concrete wharves.

12–9. Example of Pier Design. In Fig. 12–10 is shown a pier, constructed in water whose depth may vary from 44 ft to 37 ft. Bottom conditions are such that 4 tons/sq ft can be carried without making any allowance for buoyancy. The deck of the pier should be 46 ft wide and be designed for a live load of 500 psf.

It is, of course, impossible to arrive at a solution for a problem of this nature, or for any design for that matter, without detailed knowledge of location, availability of materials, labor, transportation, and a number of other factors. For the sake of illustration, a design which makes use of a floating caisson is suggested in Fig. 12–10.

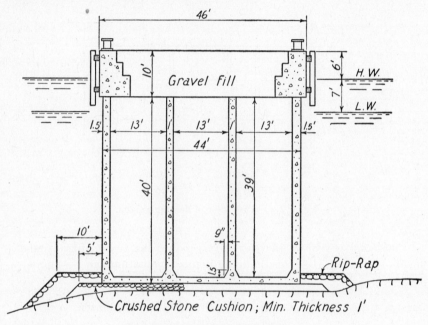

FIG. 12–10. Example of pier design.

The top of the caisson will extend 3 ft above low water and be 4 ft below high water. Retaining walls will be built on top of the caissons, and the space between them as well as the compartments of the caisson will be filled up with gravel and sand. It is worthy of mention that an earth-filled structure lends itself most readily to the installation of piping and electric conduits, which can be laid in the fill without any attachment to the load-carrying members. The problem of supporting railroad tracks is also greatly simplified by the use of earth fill.

Of great importance is the proper preparation of the bottom before placing the caisson. A stone cushion is laid on the bottom; and rip-rap, placed along the edges, is protection against scour. The caissons can usually be placed with a clear space of not more than 2 ft between adjacent units. Concrete slabs may then be constructed to bridge this gap, being fixed to one caisson and able to slide on the other so that possible expansion can be taken care of. The retaining walls can be built continuously over the caissons.

The caisson shell is shown in Fig. 12–11.   Thicknesses are governed by the bending stresses caused by the hydrostatic pressure acting on the floating caisson.   Sharp corners have been completely eliminated and 2 in. of concrete protection provide for all steel reinforcement.

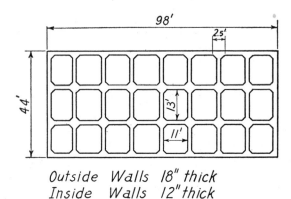

Outside Walls 18" thick
Inside   Walls 12" thick

Fig. 12–11. Plan view of floating caisson.

The total weight of the caisson, assuming the twenty-four compartments empty, is 3100 tons and the depth of flotation can be figured as follows:

$$44 \times 98 \times x \times 64 = 62 \times 10^5; \quad x = 22.5 \text{ ft.}$$

The center of gravity of the caisson is found to be 18.4 ft above the bottom.   A stability investigation, as explained elsewhere in this volume, will disclose that the empty caisson is floating in an unstable position, because the weight and the uplift form an overturning couple.   It will therefore be necessary to fill water into the compartments before the caisson is towed to the site.   Let it be desired to find the depth of water in the twenty-four compartments, which will give the caisson a freeboard of 5 ft or a draft of 35 ft.   An investigation will disclose stable flotation in this case.   As the cross-sectional area of one compartment is 140 sq ft, the following equation will give the depth x of water inside the caisson:

$$140 \times 24 \times x \times 64 + 62 \times 10^5 = 35 \times 44 \times 98 \times 64,$$

$$x = 16 \text{ ft,}$$

which expresses that the sums of the weights of inside water and outside shell must equal the weight of displaced water.   Fig. 12–12 shows the caisson floating in the stable position, and wall and bottom thicknesses should be checked for hydrostatic pressures in this position.

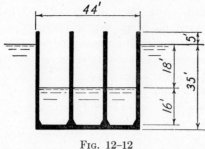

FIG. 12-12

12-10. Example of Wharf Design. As an example of the preliminary analysis of a wharf structure, let it be desired to investigate the type of wharf shown in Fig. 12-13. Anchorage for the sheet piling is provided by batter piles arranged in clusters and connected to the sheet piling by

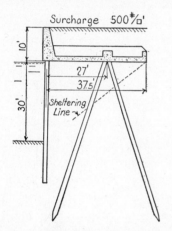

FIG. 12-13. Sheet piling with earth plate.   FIG. 12-14. Pressure diagram.

concrete earth plate and low retaining wall. This type of structure is usually called *sheet piles with plate*. The earth plate serves a twofold purpose. It transfers the horizontal pull from the upper end of the sheet piles to the pile clusters, and the weight of the earth above the plate prevents the rear piles from becoming tension piles. Furthermore, the earth pressure on the sheet piles will be greatly reduced due to the fact that there is no overburden above the bottom of the earth plate.

The evaluation of the earth pressure acting on this structure is, as might be supposed, a very complicated matter and very few data are available on this subject. There is no doubt about the fact that the earth plate *shelters* the sheet piling below it, but how far down this sheltering effect is felt is at best a matter of guesswork. It is possible to draw an arbitrary line from the back edge of the plate and assume that the earth pressures on the sheet piling above this line are proportional to the distances from the bottom of the earth plate and below this line to the distances from the ground surface (including the surcharge). The angle of this line with the horizontal is at present a matter of judgment; it may be argued that the angle of repose is a natural selection, but it is generally taken as a higher value (between 30° and 45°).* In the example shown in Fig. 12–13, it will be assumed that a line making a slope of 80 per cent can be used as such a shelter line. It will be assumed that the angle of internal friction $\phi = 28°$, that the weight of the dry fill is 100 lb/cu ft, and that the weight of the submerged fill is 55 lb/cu ft. The earth pressure diagram will then be as shown in Fig. 12–14.

If the earth plate is made long enough to reach the point where a shelter line through the point D intersects it, then the two ordinates of the pressure diagram at this point will be

$$30 \times 55 \times \tan^2\left(45° - \frac{28°}{2}\right) = 1650 \times 0.364 = 600 \text{ psf,}$$

$$(500 + 10 \times 100 + 30 \times 55) \times 0.364 = 1147 \text{ psf.}$$

If the passive earth pressure increment can be assumed to be 304 pfs, then the point of equivalent support can be figured thus:

$$1147 + 20x = 304x; \quad x = 4 \text{ ft.}$$

Point of zero shear and maximum bending moment can now be figured in the usual manner and the maximum bending moment in the sheet

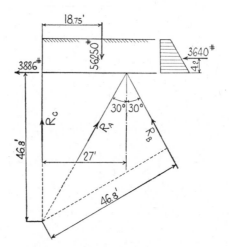

FIG. 12–15. Pile pressures.

*See G. P. Manning, *Reinforced Concrete Design* (New York, 1936), p. 351.

piling is found to be 51,000 ft-lb. Depth of penetration can be determined from the reaction at the lower end of the equivalent beam thus:

$$1.1\left(4 + \sqrt{\frac{6 \times 7400}{304 - 20}}\right) = 18.2 \text{ ft.}$$

Fig. 12–15 shows the earth plate subjected to the following forces:

(a) Weight of plate, earth, and surcharge,
(b) Reaction from sheet piling,
(c) Earth pressure on retaining portion of earth plate.

If the sheet piling as well as the two batter piles are assumed to be hinged at both ends, then all the direct loads can be found by statics using the following computations (see Fig. 12–15):

$$R_A \times 46.8 = 56{,}250 \times 18.75 + 3640 \times 42.6 + 3886 \times 46.8,$$

$$R_A = 29{,}700 \text{ lb.}$$

$$R_B \times 46.8 = 56{,}250 \times 18.75 - 3640 \times 51 - 3886 \times 46.8,$$

$$R_B = 14{,}700 \text{ lb.}$$

$$R_C \times 27 = 56{,}250 \times 8.25 + 3640 \times 4.2,$$

$$R_C = 17{,}750 \text{ lb.}$$

If each cluster is made up of three piles, two sloping toward the front and one toward the rear, and if the clusters are spaced 9 ft on centers, then the final loads are

A piles: $29{,}700 \times 9 \times \frac{1}{2} = 133{,}650$ lb $= 67$ tons;

B piles. $14{,}700 \times 9 = 132{,}300$ lb $= 66$ tons.

The sheet piling will be subjected to a direct load of 17,750 lb and will, due to this and the bending moment, develop a combined stress of (assuming MZ–38*):

$$\frac{17{,}750}{11.2} \pm \frac{51{,}000 \times 12}{46.8} = 14{,}660 \text{ psi Comp.;} \quad 11{,}500 \text{ psi Ten.}$$

This stress should now be less than the allowable value.

12–11. Use of Master Piles. Where high pressures and long spans of steel sheet piling are encountered, it is often advantageous to use a combination of sheet piling and regular rolled shapes known as *master pile construction*. This scheme is especially favorable if the piling must be installed on rock into which it is difficult to penetrate.

---

*MZ-38, sheet pile manufactured by U.S. Steel Corp. (See Appendix 1.)

Fig. 12–16 shows a plan view of sheet piling which forms arcs connected to heavy rolled sections; the latter are known as the master piles and are anchored by large steel rods near their tops and firmly secured at their bottoms. The numerical example, which follows, will explain details of arrangement and computations.

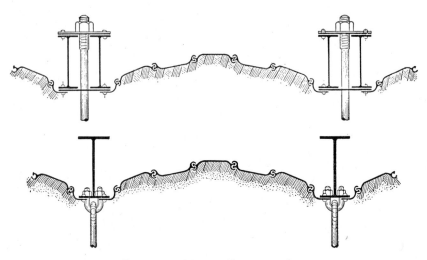

FIG. 12–16. Master pile construction.

Fig. 12–17 shows the cross section of a pier consisting of retaining walls and a large relieving platform on piles. The portion of the waterfront is made of steel sheet piling driven to form arcs between structural steel sections, 18WF105, anchored near the top and doweled into the rock as shown in Fig. 12–19. Soil properties are as follows: fill above platform, $w = 100$ lb/cu ft, $\phi = 28°$; natural soil below platform, submerged weight $w = 50$ lb/cu ft, $\phi = 22°$. The entire wharf is to carry a surcharge of 1000 psf.

An analysis of the retaining wall is shown in Fig. 12–18. It is seen that the horizontal and vertical forces on this unit are resisted by the two rows of vertical piles under its base and the horizontal steel rods tying together the master piles.

Fig. 12–19 indicates the analysis for the lower part. First the active pressure diagram is drawn up. For the small radius of 8 ft, 0 in. of the arcs it will be ascertained that the interlock tension is quite small. The triangular load acting on the master piles (spaced also 8 ft, 6 in.) will be the sum of two parts: (1) the components of the tension produced in the two connected arcs, and (2) the direct pressure on the back of the master pile, whose width is increased to 24 in. by the split-steel sheet piling section

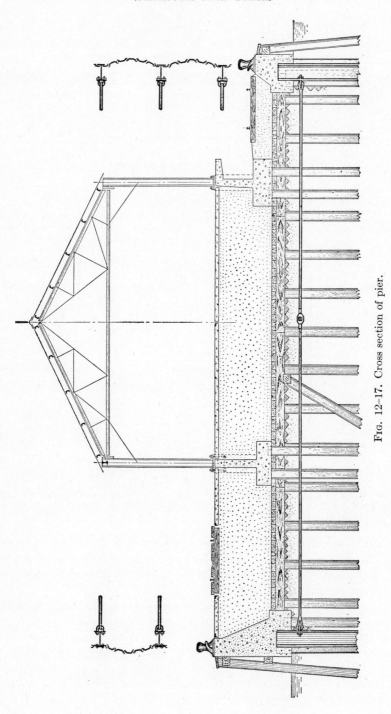

Fig. 12-17. Cross section of pier.

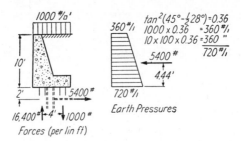

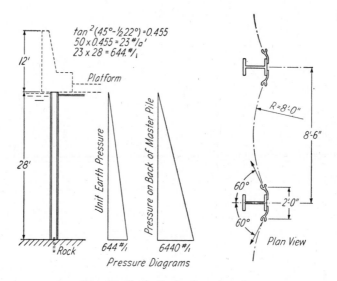

FIG. 12–18. Analysis of retaining wall.

FIG. 12–19. Analysis of master pile.

welded to its inside flange. The tension in the bottom of the circular arcs is equal to

$$t = pr = 644 \times 8 = 5152 \text{ lb/ft,}$$

and the total pressure on the master pile,

$$2 \times 644 + 2 \times 5152 \cos 60° = 6440 \text{ lb/ft.}$$

The maximum bending moment due to the triangular load is

$$M = 0.1283 \times \tfrac{1}{2}6440 \times 28 \times 28 = 324{,}000 \text{ ft-lb,}$$

which will produce a bending stress in an 18WF105 equal to

$$f = 324{,}000 \times 12 \div 202 = 19{,}250 \text{ psi.}$$

The cross-sectional area needed for dowels at the bottom can be found by dividing the reaction, 60 kips, by the allowable shearing stress; thus,

$$60,000 \div 10,000 = 6 \text{ sq in.},$$

which can be supplied by two 2-in. round bars. Details of the bottom connection are shown in Fig. 12–20.

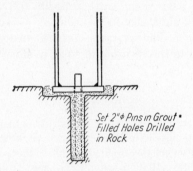

Set 2"ϕ Pins in Grout ·
Filled Holes Drilled
in Rock

Fig. 12–20. Base connection for master pile.

12–12. Subsoil Failures of Wharves. Fig. 12–21 shows a type of failure which may endanger the stability of a wharf structure. Since cohesive soils normally have a relatively small angle of internal friction and since cohesion gives a constant addition to the shear strength regardless

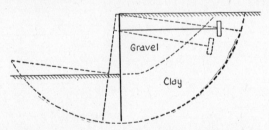

Gravel

Clay

Fig. 12–21. Subsoil failure of anchored bulkhead.

of the depth, this type of failure is particularly apt to occur if the wharf is built on a deep layer of clay. A failure of this nature is similar, in many respects, to slope or embankment failures which have been extensively covered by writers on soil mechanics.*

The method presented in the following chapter and applied to abutments may also be used for investigations relative to the probability of such failures occurring under waterfront structures. It is generally assumed that the surface of rupture is a circular arc and that rupture occurs at once along the whole failure line (which is, strictly speaking, not correct). As

*See D. P. Krynine, *Soil Mechanics* (New York, 1941), pp. 244–260.

indicated in the numerical example in Chap. 13, Sec. 13–9, it is not possible to establish, without trials, the center and radius of the most dangerous circle. Several sliding circles must be investigated. However, it will usually be found that this center lies vertically above or slightly in front of the wall. This location is approximate, of course, but it can be used as a first trial. When water lies on the outside of the wharf, its weight must be transformed into equivalent earth pressure. If a water table exists back of the wall, this must also be considered, as well as any surcharges on top of the wharf. The average shearing stresses are subsequently found and compared to the shearing resistances along the potential failure lines.

PROBLEMS

12–1.   The wharf structure shown on the accompanying sketch is supported on reinforced concrete piles 15 in. × 15 in. and all of the same length. The front piles form a continuous sheet-piling wall, while the spacing of each of the two rows of batter piles is 10 ft on center. The backfill consists of sand having an angle of internal friction of 25° in both dry and submerged condition, and dry and submerged weights of respectively 100 and 60 lb/cw ft. The wharf can carry a live load of 400 lb/cu ft, and active pressure can be assumed to exist between points A and B (point of equal active and passive intensity). If all piles are assumed hinged at both ends, find stresses and bending moments.

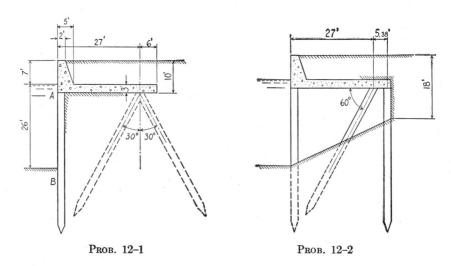

PROB. 12–1   PROB. 12–2

12–2.   Data are same as Prob. 12–1 except that sheet-piling wall is formed by rear row while front piles and batter piles are spaced 10 ft on center.

CHAPTER 13

BRIDGE PIERS AND ABUTMENTS

13-1. Introduction. Piers and abutments provide the links between bridge superstructures and the supporting soil. They are essentially blocks of concrete or stone masonry, and a very large proportion of their mass is below ground or water level.

The term *pier* is generally used to designate the intermediate foundation units over which the superstructure passes, while the end supports are called *abutments*. It follows that the latter are combinations of piers and retaining walls.

Generally speaking, the economy of design of an entire bridge project will demand that the cost of a pier, including excavation, should not exceed the cost of the superstructure of one span. This ratio governs broadly the length of the span between piers; and, when the cost of a pier and its foundation exceeds this ratio, the length of the span should be increased.

The design of abutments is, to some extent, standardized; but there is a wide latitude in the design of piers, their chief characteristic being massiveness and the ability to resist vibrations and heavy vertical and lateral loads.

13-2. Structural Arrangements. The centerline of a pier should, except under special circumstances, be made to coincide with the centerline of the superstructure. Fig. 13-1 shows the main portions of a bridge pier.

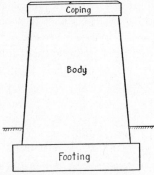

FIG. 13-1. Typical bridge pier.

The coping forms the upper part of the pier. It projects a small amount, from 4 in. to 1 ft depending on the height of the pier, beyond the middle part called the body. The coping course serves to protect the pier against the weather and its top should be shaped so it will permit rapid run-off of rain water. The depth of the coping is usually about 2 ft, its width from 6 to 8 ft, and its length should be at least 4 ft in excess of the extreme width of the superstructure, measured from out to out of bearing plates.

Sometimes the coping course is followed by a belting course, having a smaller offset than the coping. For very high and heavy piers, several belting courses may be employed. The chief functions of the belting courses are to strengthen the coping and to improve the architectural appearance of the pier.

The main part of the pier is called the body or the stem. Its top dimensions are governed by the dimensions of the coping less its projections. The sides of the pier stem are usually battered. This batter may vary from $\frac{1}{4}$ in./ft for very tall piers to 1 in./ft for short ones. If the

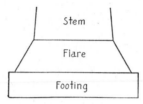

Fig. 13–2. Pier with enlarged footing.

pier is located in a stream and presents an obstruction to current and ice, the ends should be shaped to reduce its resistance to these factors. Extensive tests and observations have indicated that, for both upstream and downstream ends of the pier, the semicircular shape affords the minimum obstruction consistent with practical construction. Almost as good is the 45° upstream and downstream end. A pier with specially shaped ends will very materially reduce the tendency to scour of the bottom of the stream adjacent to the pier. In localities where heavy ice movement occurs, it is advisable to build the upstream end into a 45° nose. This nose should be protected from a point not less than 4 ft above extreme high water to 4 ft below extreme low water by a steel angle, properly attached to the concrete.

The bottom part of the pier is called the *footing* and serves to transfer the load from the pier to the foundation. The footing is usually made of rectangular shape and projects at least 1 ft beyond the bottom of the stem. The dimensions of the footing depend upon the character of the underlying material; and, as the dimensions of the bottom of the body of the pier is governed mainly by the width of the superstructure, it may be necessary to insert a flare between stem and footing to take care of discrepancies in sizes, as shown in Fig. 13–2.

The pier footing may be supported directly on the soil underneath, or it may rest on piles, which can be driven under water if necessary. It is also possible, and quite common, to support the pier on caissons, either several separate caissons or one large caisson having a number of compartments.

A pier foundation must be capable of carrying the total dead and live load of the bridge without appreciable settlement and, furthermore, the foundation must be carried to such depth as to be beyond the reach of any scouring action of the current. In the case of arched continuous girder bridges, any marked settlement would have serious results. In the case of statically determinate superstructures a moderate settlement would not have the same serious consequences so long as the settlement is due to a compression of the subsoil within its elastic limits. Failures of bridge piers are seldom caused by excessive settlement. The chief danger, and one which may occur years after completion of the structure, is that due to scouring action of the current around and under the pier, the equilibrium of the supporting soil will gradually be destroyed.*

Scour of the bottom of a river is caused by a change in the permanent water level. The construction of piers and abutments will generally decrease the effective cross-sectional area of the stream, thus inevitably increasing the velocity and raising the water level (usually very slightly) in the stream above the bridge. Furthermore, the existence of piers as obstructions to the stream flow will set up eddies around the piers and may possibly cause crosscurrents below the river crossing. The combined effect of increased velocity and eddies may disturb the equilibrium of the bottom material and lead to scouring.

Scouring of a river bed may happen on even the smallest stream, if its normal state is interfered with. It is probably true that the scouring of bottom material around the substructures has been the occasion of more bridge failures in the past than any other cause. In the early days of bridge building, there was more tendency to set up scouring action around the piers, due to the comparatively shorter spans and, consequently, relatively large obstructions of the water area. The general use in modern bridges of longer spans and slender piers does not cause severe constrictions of the water areas, as a rule, but the problem still remains and should be given serious attention in any submerged pier design.

In order to avoid failure due to undermining by scour, the pier must be carried to a depth below the lower limit of erosion. Although no reliable rules have, as yet, been established, some observations appear to indicate that a simple relation exists between the distance ΔH through which the level of the water rises and the distance ΔT by which the scour reduces the elevation of the deepest portions of the river bed. It has

---

*See Karl Terzaghi, "Failure of Bridge Piers Due to Scour," *Proceedings*, International Conference on Soil Mechanics (1936), Vol. 2, p. 264.

been suggested that ΔT in soils with little or no cohesion is likely to assume values of the order of three or four times ΔH.

Before the year 1880, stone masonry was used almost exclusively for bridge piers, but concrete has been used extensively since then; and, at the present time, piers are built either entirely of concrete or of a concrete hearting and stone facing.

A dense and durable concrete is necessary for pier construction. Large-size aggregates can be used. It will be found advantageous to use a small amount of reinforcing near the surface of the pier. This will have the effect of reducing the probability of surface cracks due to temperature and shrinkage. There are some advantages in using a facing of stone masonry, among these being the saving in the expense of forms, the greater speed of construction, a more attractive appearance, and the elimination of surface cracks.

If the pier is supported on piles, the footing should extend at least 6 in. down over the pile tops, and there should, preferably, be not less than 1 ft of concrete between the face of the pile and the outside of the footing. Reinforcement in both directions immediately above the pile tops is very essential. Sometimes structural shapes, such as old rails spaced 1 ft apart, are used for this reinforcement.

The footing of the pier may be placed inside a single-wall cofferdam which may form part of the permanent construction. If necessary, piles can be driven inside the cofferdam and mass-concrete then laid on the piles.

13-3. Loads. Due to the comparatively simple shape of a bridge pier, its structural analysis will not as a rule present any difficulties. There are, however, a number of conditions and combinations of circumstances for which the bottom pressures must be determined. In the structural analysis of piers, these circumstances are:

(1) The dead load of the superstructure.

(2) The live load on the superstructure.

(3) The weight of the pier itself reduced by the hydrostatic uplift caused by the surrounding water, if any.

(4) Lateral forces, acting perpendicular to the centerline of the superstructure. These forces include the wind on the superstructure as well as on the traffic passing over the bridge; the centrifugal force in the case of a railroad bridge on a curve; the wind pressure on the portion of the pier extending above water or ground surface; pressure due to water current; pressure due to floating ice.

(5) Longitudinal forces, acting in a direction parallel to the centerline of the bridge. In the case of a railroad bridge, it is necessary to investigate the action of forces caused by the stopping and starting of trains. In the case of arch bridges, unbalanced horizontal thrusts come within this category.

The forces due to dead load and live load on the superstructure as well as the weight of the pier itself can, of course, be estimated with great accuracy. As to whether porosity of rock, soil, or concrete in the absence of seams or cracks is sufficient to permit of full hydrostatic uplift, there has been a vast amount of discussion. The question seems to be decided conclusively by recent experimental observations[*] which show that the effective porosity, so far as creation of uplift is concerned, is to all intents and purposes 100 per cent. In computing the weight of the pier, therefore, its volume below the waterline should be multiplied by the difference in unit weights of concrete and water. The presence of hydrostatic uplift in the surrounding soil upon which the pier rests will also affect the computations of bearing power, because it follows that the surcharge due to the water above the subsoil cannot be counted upon to increase its internal frictional resistance. Likewise, all soil weights should be figured as submerged weights.

The impact produced by the live load of traffic on the bridge can usually be neglected in analyzing substructures.

In computing the lateral wind forces acting on the superstructure and on the exposed portion of the substructure, a wind pressure of 30 lb/sq ft can generally be assumed.

In the case of railroad bridges, centrifugal forces should be provided for in accordance with the American Railway Engineering Association Specifications of 1940, which state that on curves the centrifugal force (assumed to act 6 ft above the rail) shall be taken equal to a percentage of the live load, computed by the formula

$$C = 0.00117S^2D, \tag{13-1}$$

where
C = percentage of live load,
S = speed, mph,
D = the degree of the curve.

The maximum speeds which can be assumed for the different degree of curves is given in the table below:

Degree	Speed (mph)	Degree	Speed (mph)
1	100	6	50
2	87	7	43
3	71	10	39
4	61	15	32
5	55	20	27

[*] Karl Terzaghi, "Simple Tests Determine Hydrostatic Uplift," *Engineering News-Record* (June 18, 1936), pp. 872–875.

In the case of highway bridges no provision for centrifugal force need be made.

In railroad bridges, longitudinal forces resulting from accelerating or braking trains on the structure may become quite big. According to the Specifications of the American Railway Engineering Association, the longitudinal force resulting from the starting and stopping of trains shall be 20 per cent of the load on the engine drivers and 5 per cent of the load on the remainder of the train. This force shall be taken on one track only and shall be assumed to act 6 ft above the top of the rail. The braking and traction forces act in the direction of the length of the bridge.

The pressure exerted by a current is a direct function of its kinetic energy and can be computed by the formula

$$P = mwa\,\frac{v^2}{2g}, \tag{13-2}$$

where
P = total pressure on surface, lb,
m = constant,
w = unit weight of water, 62.5 lb/cu ft,
a = area of wetted surface, sq ft,
v = velocity of current, fps,
g = gravity acceleration, 32.2 fps².

Inasmuch as the unit weight of water is almost twice the gravity acceleration, Eq. (13-2) may be written

$$p = mv^2, \tag{13-3}$$

where p is the intensity of pressure. The value of the constant m depends on the shape of the pier; it is much smaller for rounded ends than for flat ends. A value of $m = 1.5$ will always be on the safe side.

The velocity of the current reaches a maximum at some slight depth below the surface, the surface velocity being checked by adverse winds; but for practical purposes the maximum velocity may be assumed to occur at the surface, and it may further be assumed that the curve of the velocity diagram is a straight line. The velocity then varies uniformly from a maximum at the surface to zero at the depth where scouring ceases to have effect. According to Eq. (13-3) the curve of pressure will be a parabola and the distance from the center of pressure to the top surface will be one-fourth of the total depth over which the current pressure is active.

The maximum pressure due to floating ice will be the crushing strength of the ice which varies from 300 lb to 800 lb/in. It is customary to assume the ice 1 ft thick at the surface of the water.

13–4. Numerical Example. It is desired to compute and tabulate the pressures which will occur under the bridge pier shown in Fig. 13–3. The

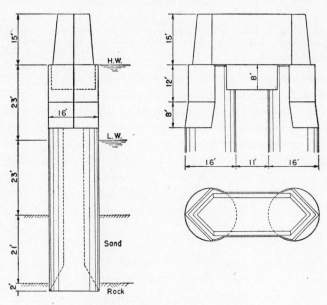

Fig. 13–3. Bridge pier on caissons.

pier, which supports a single-track railroad bridge, consists of a cap resting on two cylindrical caissons. The caissons have been sunk through 23 ft of water and 21 ft of sand to penetrate 2 ft into bedrock. In the direction of the current, on both upstream and downstream faces, the cap and upper part of the caissons have been shaped to form 45° ends. The maximum current velocity will be assumed to be 12 fps at the surface of high water; and the maximum depth of scour will be assumed to be 50 ft below this mark. Other assumptions will be made as the external forces are computed.

The moment of inertia and the section modulus of the two cross-sectional areas of the caissons (assumed to work together in unison) will be

$$I = 2\left(\frac{\pi 16^4}{64} + \frac{\pi 16^2}{4} 13.5^2\right) = 79,600 \text{ ft}^4; \qquad (13\text{–}4)$$

and the section modulus will be

$$S = 79,600 \div 21.5 = 3700 \text{ ft}^3. \qquad (13\text{–}5)$$

The dead and live loads from the superstructure will be assumed to be 800 tons and 1000 tons, respectively. The weight of the two caissons and the cap is approximately 2500 tons and, as the cross-sectional area of one caisson is 201 sq ft, the following uniform pressures will be produced on the bedrock immediately under the caissons:

$$\text{Dead load, pier: } 5000 \div 402 = 12.4 \text{ kips/sq ft,}$$
$$\text{Dead load, superstructure: } 1600 \div 402 = 4.0 \text{ kips/sq ft,}$$
$$\text{Live load, superstructure: } 2000 \div 402 = 5.0 \text{ kips/sq ft.}$$

Buoyancy at high and low water will be, respectively: $67 \times 62.5 = 4188$ lb/sq ft and $44 \times 62.5 = 2750$ lb/sq ft.

The wind pressure on the superstructure and on the traffic passing over it may be estimated by multiplying the total exposed area by the intensity of wind pressure (usually 30 lb/sq ft); finally, this force should be multiplied by the distance from its point of application to the bottom

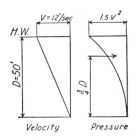

FIG. 13–4. Pressure of current.

of the caissons. It will be assumed that this total wind moment is 1850 ft-kips. If divided by the section modulus in Eq. (13–5), the maximum tensile and compressive stresses due to wind are found. Thus,

$$\frac{1850 \times 10^3}{3700} = 500 \text{ lb/sq ft.} \tag{13–6}$$

The maximum pressure due to current velocity is found by Eq. (13–3) and equals

$$1.5 \times 12 \times 12 = 216 \text{ lb/sq ft.} \tag{13–7}$$

Fig. 13–4 shows the variations of this current pressure between surface of high water and the level at which the velocity is assumed to be zero. The total current pressure will be

$$\tfrac{1}{3}216 \times 50 \times 16 = 57{,}600 \text{ lb,} \tag{13–8}$$

and the moment with respect to the bottom of the caissons is

$$57.6 \left[\tfrac{3}{4}50 + 17\right] = 3139 \text{ ft-kips;} \tag{13–9}$$

and, by dividing by the section modulus,

$$\frac{3139 \times 10^3}{3700} = 850 \text{ lb/sq ft.} \tag{13–10}$$

The ice pressure, which is usually much more severe than the current pressure, will be figured for a crushing strength of 400 psi, for a layer thickness of 8 in.; and the customary reduction factor of one-half due to the rounded ends will be used. Thus,

$$\tfrac{1}{2}400 \times 8 \times 12 \times 16 = 307{,}000 \text{ lb,} \qquad (13\text{--}11)$$

and the moment produced by it is

$$307 \times 67 = 20{,}569 \text{ ft-kips.} \qquad (13\text{--}12)$$

This moment will produce the following maximum pressure or uplift:

$$20{,}569 \div 3700 = 5.5 \text{ kips/sq ft.} \qquad (13\text{--}13)$$

The force due to traction and braking, which acts on the pier in the direction of the centerline of the superstructure, will be figured for a locomotive having a tractive effort of 40,000 lb followed by two coaches weighing 50 tons each; the length of the span will permit only these three units at the same time. The force will be

$$40 + 0.05 \times 200 = 50 \text{ kips.} \qquad (13\text{--}14)$$

This force will be assumed to act 6 ft above the rail tops or 10 ft above the top of the pier. Hence the moment is

$$50 \times 92 = 4600 \text{ ft-kips.} \qquad (13\text{--}15)$$

This moment will produce bending about a line connecting the centers of the two caissons, and the effective section modulus in this direction will be

$$2 \times \frac{\pi 16^3}{32} = 804 \text{ ft}^3. \qquad (13\text{--}16)$$

Maximum pressures and uplifts due to traction and braking on the bridge will be

$$4600 \div 804 = 5.7 \text{ kips/sq ft.} \qquad (13\text{--}17)$$

It should be noted that the pressure given in Eq. (13–17) acts at a point that is 90° from the point of maximum pressures given in Eqs. (13–10) and (13–13). The requirement that under no circumstances must there be any tension under the caissons will be found to be fulfilled, if it is remembered that no traction force can occur without full live load on the bridge.

The combination of dead load, maximum buoyancy, current, ice, and wind will give the following maximum and minimum pressures:

$$12{,}400 + 4000 - 4188 + 850 + 5500 + 500 = 19{,}062 \text{ lb/sq ft.}$$

$$12{,}400 + 4000 - 4188 - 850 - 5500 - 500 = 5362 \text{ lb/sq ft.}$$

Sliding of the bases of the caissons should also be investigated, although it will generally be found that bridge piers have adequate safety against this type of failure. For the bridge pier in this particular example, the total lateral force due to current, ice, and wind will be 58 + 307 + 25

= 390 kips, while dead load minus buoyancy will amount to 4916 kips. This gives a ratio between horizontal and vertical forces equal to 0.08, considerably under the coefficient of sliding for concrete on rock.

13-5. Abutments. An abutment is a structure that carries one end of a bridge span and, at the same time, laterally supports the embankment that serves as an approach to the bridge. In the case of a river crossing, an abutment often has a third function—namely, to protect the embankment against scour of the stream.

Fig. 13-5 shows the most important types of bridge abutments. In (a) is shown the simplest and most economical type called the breast

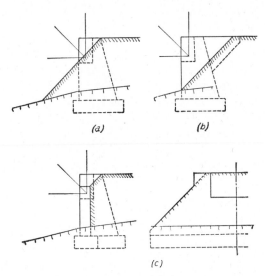

(a)   (b)

(c)

FIG. 13-5. Abutment types.

abutment or buried abutment. It is simply a pier, which has had its thickness increased to resist the lateral thrust of the material in back of it and which has been provided with a recess in front for the purpose of supporting the end span of the bridge. The retained material flows around in front of this type of abutment and is not protected against scour in the case of water flowing under the end span.

In Fig. 13-5(b) is shown a so-called **U**-abutment. In order to prevent the fill from spilling in front of the abutment, two parallel wings have been attached to its rear so as to form a **U**-shaped inclosure. These wings may be designed as reinforced concrete cantilevers and connected by horizontal ties through the fill. (See also Fig. 13-11.)

Fig. 13-5(c) shows a side view and a front view of a wing abutment. In this type, the tops of the wings are sloped to conform to the natural slope of the retained fill. The angle of the wings with respect to a vertical plane through the longitudinal axis of the bridge can be made 90° as shown in Fig. 13-5(c), or any other amount which may prove suitable under the local conditions. If the wings are swung back so as to become parallel to the centerline of the bridge, the wing abutment will become a **U**-abutment.

The wing abutment is probably the most widely used and also the one which offers the greatest protection to the embankment. The **U**-abutment can be used to advantage where rock foundation is found near the ground surface. In this case the wings can often be stepped to conform to the natural slope, thereby avoiding the costly cantilever arrangement. The buried abutment can be advantageously used for grade crossings and viaducts, where there is no need of protecting the embankment against the action of water.

Concrete abutments should have surface reinforcement similar to piers. A coping, similar to a bridge pier coping, is usually provided under the bridge seat; and stone facings will materially improve the architectural appearance of the abutments.

Proper drainage of the fill immediately behind the abutment is of primary importance. Water collecting behind the abutment not only increases the lateral earth pressure but, by alternately freezing and thawing it, materially reduces the durability of the concrete. Gravel fill, drains, and weep holes through the wall near the groundline are the elements of a good drainage system.

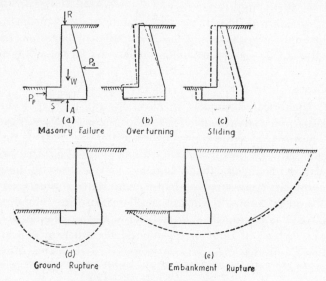

(a)
Masonry Failure

(b)
Overturning

(c)
Sliding

(d)
Ground Rupture

(e)
Embankment Rupture

Fig. 13-6. Abutment failures.

13-6. Stability of Abutments. In Fig. 13-6(a) are shown the forces which act on a typical abutment: the reaction R, which is delivered by the bridge superstructure and is made up of dead load and live load; the weight W of the abutment; the active earth pressure P_a behind the wall and the passive pressure P_p in front of it; and finally, the soil reactions A and S under the base.

A bridge abutment or a retaining wall may fail or become unable to perform its function in several ways, as indicated in Fig. 13–6. The masonry may fail in any of the orthodox manners of tension cracks, crushing, or shear. If the vertical forces R and W are too small to balance the overturning moment of the lateral earth pressures, the wall will tip over as shown in (b). If these same vertical forces are unable to mobilize sufficient shearing resistance between base and soil, a forward movement will take place and the wall is said to fail by sliding. This condition is shown in Fig. 13–6(c).

In addition to these types of failures, ruptures may occur in the adjacent soil. If the shearing resistance of the soil immediately under the wall is low, the weight of the abutment may produce failure along some curved surface extending from the rear edge of the base to some point on the lower ground surface in front of the abutment (see (d) of Fig. 13–6). It is readily seen that the active earth pressure on the back of the wall will counteract this movement of the abutment. It can only occur prior to the placing of the fill or if the active earth pressure is arrested for some reason.

If the soil is deficient in cohesion, internal friction, or both, it is possible for the fill to rupture in the embankment as well as in the underlying soil, as shown in Fig. 13–6(e). This movement is also a rotational movement, and the wall and all the earth about it move out as a unit. If the wall rests on piles, this sliding plane must be below the points of the piles.

13–7. Numerical Example. In the following will be demonstrated what is often referred to as the classical design of an abutment. This principle states that: to prevent tension on the back side of the footing and to make sure that the maximum compression on the front side of the footing shall not be greater than twice the average pressure, the resultant of the lateral earth pressures and the weight of the masonry and bridge must fall inside the middle third of the base. In this computation, live load shall only be included if it tends to aggravate the situation; that means that under ordinary circumstances the live load should be disregarded on the bridge span but considered as surcharge on the embankment.

It should be noted that, if the abutment rests on rock or solid material where settlements will not occur, it will not be serious if the resultant falls a little outside the middle third, provided of course that the allowable pressure on the soil is not exceeded.

Let it be desired to find the width of the base of the bridge abutment shown in Fig. 13–7. All dimensions are given except the projection x

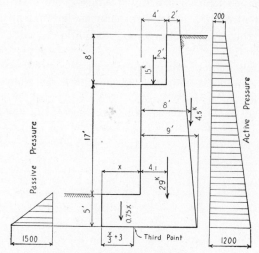

FIG. 13–7. Numerical example.

of the footing beyond the front face. Diagrams for active and passive pressures have been assumed, the former including the effect of the surcharge on the embankment. The dead-load reaction on the bridge seat has been assumed to be 15 kips/linear ft of wall. The other three vertical forces are: the weight of the projection, the weight of the rest of the abutment, and the weight of the fill lying directly over the sloping back of the wall. In order for the resultant of these four forces, augmented by the two lateral earth pressures, to strike at the third point, their moments about this point must be zero. Hence, the equation

$$0.75x\left(\frac{x}{6} - 3\right) + 15(\tfrac{2}{3}x - 1) + 29(\tfrac{2}{3}x + 1.1) + 4.5(\tfrac{2}{3}x + 5)$$

$$= 0.2 \times 30 \times 15 + \tfrac{1}{2}30\tfrac{1}{3}30 - \tfrac{1}{2}1.5 \times 5 \times \tfrac{1}{3}5$$

$$x = 6.0.$$

The soil bearing pressure will, for these forces, increase uniformly from zero at the rear edge to

$$2 \times \frac{0.75 \times 6 + 15 + 29 + 4.5}{6 + 9} = 7067 \text{ lb/sq ft}$$

at the front edge.

13–8. Embankment Ruptures. If an abutment or a retaining wall has been designed for stability, as indicated in Fig. 13–6(a), (b), and (c), it will usually also be safe against the type of ground rupture which is

shown in Fig. 13–6(*d*). However, the embankment rupture shown in
Fig. 13–6(*e*) may occur, even though the wall has been designed to satisfy
the classical requirements. The direct cause of an embankment failure
is insufficient depth of the abutment below the ground surface, combined
of course with the low soil characteristics of the fill and the supporting
earth.

A very rough idea of the required depth can be obtained by the
application of Rankine's theory to the simplified case shown in Fig. 13–8.

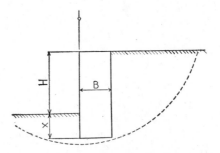

FIG. 13–8.   Embankment failure.

If, at the depth x, it is required that active and passive earth pressures
be equal and it is recalled that the unit weight of concrete is approximately 50 per cent greater than the unit weight of the usual soil, then

$$\frac{3}{2}\,(H+x)\,\tan^2\!\left(45^\circ - \frac{\phi}{2}\right) = x\tan^2\!\left(45^\circ + \frac{\phi}{2}\right), \quad (13\text{–}18)$$

$$x = H\,\frac{3\tan^2\,(45^\circ - \tfrac{1}{2}\phi)}{2\tan^2(45^\circ + \tfrac{1}{2}\phi) - 3\tan^2(45^\circ - \tfrac{1}{2}\phi)}. \quad (13\text{–}19)$$

The factor of safety against rupture of the embankment can be
ascertained by investigating the resisting forces on various circular planes
passing underneath the footing of the wall. In failures of this type, the
wall and the earth move out as a unit, and it is assumed that a sliding
takes place along a smooth curve for which can be approximated a circular arc. It is often necessary to investigate several possible curves
but it will usually be found that the most dangerous plane passes quite
close to the underside of the base. The center of the circle must also be
located by trial, but it will ordinarily be found to lie near a vertical line
through the face of the wall. If the wall rests on piles, this sliding plane
must be below the points of the piles.

13–9. Numerical Example. Let it be desired to investigate a wall
which, for the sake of simplicity, has been assumed to be rectangular in

shape, as shown in Fig. 13–9. The distance between the top and ground surfaces is 25 ft; the wall is assumed to penetrate 12 ft into the ground and have a width of 10 ft. A circle with radius 50 ft is now drawn having its center at a point O, 12 ft above the embankment top, and lying on the vertical line produced by extending the front face of the wall. This circle intersects the surfaces at A and B. If the soil has an angle of internal friction of $\phi = 0°$ and a unit cohesion of $c = 500$ lb/sq ft, what is the factor of safety against rupture along this surface?

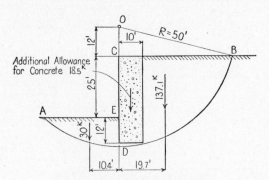

Fig. 13–9. Numerical example.

Rotation about point O is promoted by the forces to the right of this point, namely the segment BCD, which is assumed to have a unit weight of 100 lb/cu ft, and also by the additional weight of 50 lb/cu ft of the rectangular concrete section. The rotation is resisted by the forces to the left of point O, namely segment AED. The total overturning moment is, therefore,

$$1371 \times 100 \times 19.7 + 370 \times 50 \times 5 - 300 \times 100 \times 10.4 = 2,481,000 \text{ ft-lb.} \quad (13\text{–}20)$$

The total length of the circular arc AB is 103.3 ft; the moment of the cohesive forces with respect to O is, therefore,

$$103.3 \times 500 \times 50 = 2,583,000 \text{ ft-lb.} \quad (13\text{–}21)$$

The factor of safety is found by dividing Eq. (13–21) by Eq. (13–20); thus,

$$2583 \div 2481 = 1.04. \quad (13\text{–}22)$$

If the top of the embankment had been subjected to live load, the moment in Eq. (13–20) would have been increased. The factor of safety would consequently have been decreased.

In order to find the actual factor of safety against embankment failure, it is necessary to investigate circular arcs that have centers at other points than O. The factors of safety for the different arcs are then compared and the smallest will represent the actual factor of safety.

Assume next that the soil is a cohesionless material and it is desired to find the angle of internal friction which will give a factor of safety of 1 against rupture and subsequent sliding along the circular arc AB.

This problem, and other problems of a similar nature, can conveniently be solved by dividing the two segments up into parallel strips (Fig. 13–10)

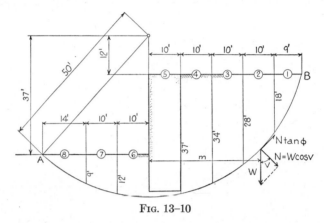

FIG. 13–10

and computing the normal forces N on each element from the weight of earth W and load above it. The arrangement of these computations is shown in Table 13–1. The discrepancy between the overturning moment

TABLE 13–1

(See Fig. 13–10.)

Strip	W (Kips)	cos v	N (Kips)	m (Ft)	Wm (Ft-kips)
1..............	8.1	0.445	3.6	44.5	360
2..............	23.0	0.714	16.4	35	805
3..............	32.0	0.866	27.7	25	800
4..............	35.5	0.954	33.9	15	533
5..............	56.3	0.995	56.0	5	282
6..............	12.5	0.995	12.4	5	−63
7..............	10.5	0.954	10.0	15	−158
8..............	6.3	0.842	5.3	27	−170
			165.3		2389

computed in the table and that evaluated in Eq. (13–20) is due to the approximate distances in Fig. 13–10 on which the tabular values are based.

The frictional resistance on the eight elements of AB can be obtained by multiplying the normal forces N by the coefficient of friction tan ϕ. Finally, by multiplying by the radius of the sliding curve, the resisting moment can be evaluated and equated to the overturning moment. Using for the latter the approximate in Table 13–1 gives:

$$50 \times 165.3 \times \tan \phi = 2389,$$

$$\tan \phi = 0.2892,$$

$$\phi = 16°08'. \qquad (13\text{--}23)$$

As in the previous problem the arc AB represents only one of the possible sliding surfaces, and other circles passing just under the retaining wall should be investigated.

Courtesy of Northern Pacific Railway Company

Fig. 13–11. Bridge abutment.

13–10. General Discussion. In the case of a soil possessing both cohesion c and internal friction ϕ, both items should be included. The expression for the factor of safety is

$$F = \frac{R \, (cL + \tan \phi \, \Sigma \, N)}{M}, \qquad (13\text{--}24)$$

where
F = factor of safety,
N = normal pressure on sliding surface,
M = overturning moment of soil,
R = radius of sliding surface,
L = length of sliding surface.

It is not possible to predict the center of the most dangerous arc without making a few trials. The number of these trials, however, can be materially reduced (four or five will usually be sufficient) when it is remembered that the most critical arc has a center which lies either above or slightly in front of the wall.*

---

*See Karl Terzaghi, "The Mechanics of Shear Failures on Clay Slopes and the Creep of Retaining Walls," *Public Roads* (December, 1929), Vol. 10, No. 10, p. 184.

If the abutment is of the **U**-type, as shown in Fig. 13–11, it is customary to assume an average unit weight for the concrete, less than 150 lb/cu ft, to compensate for the volume of soil inside it.

The danger of an embankment failure will be greatly reduced for the

Courtesy of Sverdrup & Parcel, Consulting Engineers

Fig. 13–12. Bridge piers.

abutment shown in Fig. 13–12, which allows the fill to flow through large openings between heavy columns.

PROBLEMS

The accompanying figure shows dimensions of a cantilever concrete wall which will be part of an excavated floodway channel, normally empty but utilized for short periods each season for diversion of flood waters.

13–1. Determine the pressure under the base of the flood wall if the channel is empty but the ground waterline in the backfill coincides with its top surface. Active earth pressure should be determined by Rankine's theory and hydrostatic uplift can be assumed to vary from zero at A to 100 per cent at B.

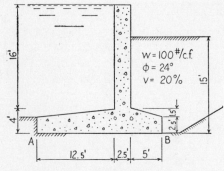

PROB. 13–1

13–2. Determine the pressure under the base if the channel is filled with water to the top of the wall and the backfill is completely drained. Passive earth pressure of the backfill should be determined by Rankine's theory and hydrostatic uplift can be assumed to vary from 100 per cent at A to zero at B.

APPENDIX

APPENDIX 1

STEEL SHEET-PILING SECTION—Z PILES*

Profile	Section Index	District Rolled	Driving Distance per Pile	Weight		Web Thickness	Section Modulus	
				Per Foot	Per Square Foot of Wall		Per Pile	Per Foot of Wall
			In.	Lbs.	Lbs.	In.	In.³	In.³
	MZ 38	P.	18	57.0	38.0	⅜	70.2	46.8
	MZ 32	P.	21	56.0	32.0	⅜	67.0	38.3
	MZ 27	P.	18	40.5	27.0	⅜	45.3	30.2

INTERLOCK WITH EACH OTHER

*Courtesy U.S. Steel Corporation.

STEEL SHEET PILING SECTIONS*

Profile	Section Index	District Rolled	Driving Distance per Pile	Weight		Web Thickness	Section Modulus	
				Per Foot	Per Square Foot of Wall		Per Pile	Per Foot of Wall
			In.	Lbs.	Lbs.	In.	In.³	In.³
	MP 102	P.C.	15	40.0	32.0	½		
	MP 101	P.C.	15	35.0	28.0	⅜		
	MP 117*	C.	15	38.8	31.0	⅜	8.9	7.1
	MP 113*	P.	16	37.3	28.0	½	3.3	2.5
	MP 112	P.C.	16	30.7	23.0	⅜	3.2	2.4
	MP 110	P.	16	42.7	32.0	³¹⁄₆₄	20.4	15.3
	MP 116	P.C.	16	36.0	27.0	⅜	14.3	10.7
	MP 115	P.C.	19⅝	36.0	22.0	⅜	8.8	5.4

(First three rows: INTERLOCK WITH EACH OTHER. Last five rows: INTERLOCK WITH EACH OTHER.)

Minimum interlock strength in direct tension:

MZ 27, 32, 38; MP 110, 115, 116 . . . . 8 kips/in.
MP 117 . . . . 10 kips/in.
Others . . . . 12 kips/in.

*Courtesy U.S. Steel Corporation.

BEARING PILES*

PROPERTIES

WIDE FLANGE
CBP SECTIONS

PROPERTIES OF SECTIONS

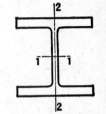

District Rolled	Section Index and Nominal Size	Depth of Section	Weight per Foot	Area of Section	FLANGE Width	FLANGE Thickness	Web Thickness	Axis 1-1 I	Axis 1-1 S	Axis 1-1 r	Axis 2-2 I	Axis 2-2 S	Axis 2-2 r
		In.	Lbs.	In²	In.	In.	In.	In.⁴	In.³	In.	In.⁴	In.³	In.
P.C.	CBP 145 14 x 14½	14.234	117	34.44	14.885	.805	.805	1228.5	172.6	5.97	443.1	59.5	3.59
		14.032	102	30.01	14.784	.704	.704	1055.1	150.4	5.93	379.6	51.3	3.56
		13.856	89	26.19	14.696	.616	.616	909.1	131.2	5.89	326.2	44.4	3.53
		13.636	73	21.46	14.586	.506	.506	733.1	107.5	5.85	261.9	35.9	3.49
P.C.	CBP 124 12 x 12	12.122	74	21.76	12.217	.607	.607	566.5	93.5	5.10	184.7	30.2	2.91
		11.780	53	15.58	12.046	.436	.436	394.8	67.0	5.03	127.3	21.2	2.86
P.C.	CBP 103 10 x 10	10.012	57	16.76	10.224	.564	.564	294.7	58.9	4.19	100.6	19.7	2.45
		9.720	42	12.35	10.078	.418	.418	210.8	43.4	4.13	71.4	14.2	2.40
P.C.	CBP 83 8 x 8	8.026	36	10.60	8.158	.446	.446	119.8	29.9	3.36	40.4	9.9	1.95

*Courtesy U.S. Steel Corporation.

APPENDIX 3

FIXED-END MOMENTS*

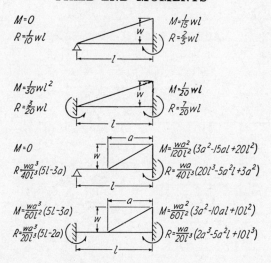

$M=0$

$R=\frac{1}{10}wl$

$M=\frac{1}{15}wl$

$R=\frac{2}{5}wl$

$M=\frac{1}{30}wl^2$

$R=\frac{3}{20}wl$

$M=\frac{1}{20}wl$

$R=\frac{7}{20}wl$

$M=0$

$R=\frac{wa^3}{40l^3}(5l-3a)$

$M=\frac{wa^2}{120l^2}(3a^2-15al+20l^2)$

$R=\frac{wa}{40l^3}(20l^3-5a^2l+3a^2)$

$M=\frac{wa^3}{60l^2}(5l-3a)$

$R=\frac{wa^3}{20l^3}(5l-2a)$

$M=\frac{wa^2}{60l^2}(3a^2-10al+10l^2)$

$R=\frac{wa}{20l^3}(2a^3-5a^2l+10l^3)$

---

*Moments produced in simply supported and fixed-end beams by hydrostatic or equivalent liquid loads. M = moment, R = reaction.

APPENDIX 4

ACTIVE EARTH PRESSURE

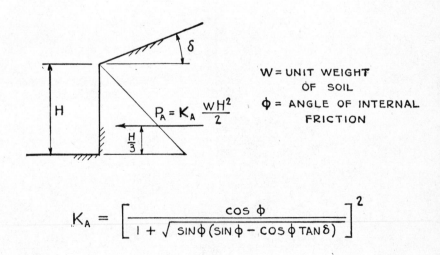

$$K_A = \left[\frac{\cos \phi}{1 + \sqrt{\sin\phi\,(\sin\phi - \cos\phi\,\tan\delta)}} \right]^2$$

TABLE OF VALUES OF K_A

δ		ϕ IN DEGREES							
DEG.	SLOPE	10	15	20	25	30	35	40	45
0	0	.704	.589	.490	.406	.333	.271	.217	.172
5	1:11.5	.769	.635	.524	.431	.352	.284	.227	.178
10	1:5.7	.970	.704	.569	.453	.374	.300	.238	.186
15	1:3.7		.933	.639	.505	.402	.319	.251	.194
20	1:2.7			.883	.572	.441	.344	.270	.204
25	1:2.1				.821	.505	.378	.288	.217
30	1:1.7					.750	.436	.318	.235
35	1:1.4						.671	.369	.260
40	1:1.2							.587	.304
45	1:1.0								.500

APPENDIX 5

PASSIVE EARTH PRESSURE

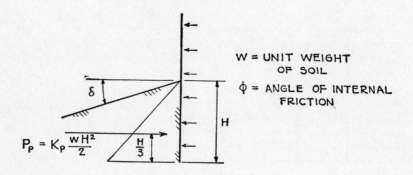

W = UNIT WEIGHT OF SOIL

ϕ = ANGLE OF INTERNAL FRICTION

$$P_P = K_P \frac{wH^2}{2}$$

$$K_P = \left[\frac{\cos \phi}{1 - \sqrt{\sin \phi \, (\sin \phi - \cos \phi \tan \delta)}} \right]^2$$

TABLE OF VALUES OF K_P

δ DEG.	SLOPE	ϕ IN DEGREES							
		10	15	20	25	30	35	40	45
0	0	1.420	1.698	2.039	2.464	3.000	3.690	4.599	5.829
5	1:11.5	1.262	1.504	1.792	2.144	2.577	3.124	3.826	4.747
10	1:5.7	.970	1.295	1.551	1.925	2.224	2.644	3.193	3.897
15	1:3.7		.933	1.299	1.566	1.866	2.223	2.660	3.204
20	1:2.7			.883	1.278	1.553	1.848	2.118	2.629
25	1:2.1				.821	1.230	1.501	1.796	2.140
30	1:1.7					.750	1.162	1.428	1.712
35	1:1.4						.671	1.076	1.331
40	1:1.2							.587	.972
45	1:1.0								.500

APPENDIX 6

EXCERPTS FROM NEW YORK BUILDING CODE, 1949

BEARING VALUES OF SOIL

C26–376. Test Pits or Borings.—*A*. Except as otherwise provided in this title, applications for permits for new structures, and where required, applications for alterations in structures erected before January 1, 1938, shall contain a statement of the character of the soil strata supporting the foundations or footings. Such applications shall include the records of borings or test pits which shall show the nature of the soil in at least one location in every 2500 sq ft of building area. The borings or test pits shall be carried sufficiently into good bearing material to establish its character and thickness. For structures more than one story in height except dwellings not more than two stories in height, or for structures having an average area load exceeding 1000 psf there shall be at least one boring in every 10,000 sq ft of building area carried to a depth of 100 ft below the curb or to a depth which shows 25 continuous feet of material of Class 10 or better, as classified in Section C26–377, below the deepest part of the excavation of the proposed structure or 5 ft into ledge rock.

For structures having an average area load in excess of 2000 psf, supported on rock, either directly or by piles to rock, or piers to rock, all borings shall be carried to a depth of at least 5 ft below the surface of the rock except where ledge rock is completely uncovered. Such structures not bearing on rock, shall have at least one boring in each 10,000 sq ft of building area carried to a depth of 100 ft below curb, or 5 ft into ledge rock.

Records of core borings into rock shall show in all cases the percentage of rock core recovered.

The average area load is the sum of all dead loads and the reduced live load, as specified, divided by the area of the building at the ground level.

Such records shall be specified by a licensed professional engineer or a licensed architect. Samples of the different strata encountered in such borings and test pits, representing the natural state in the ground of such strata, shall be available for the inspection of the superintendent.

B. It shall be unlawful to take washed or bucket samples and all samples, except those of rock, shall be so bottled as to protect them against evaporation. The number, location, and depth of such pits or borings, together with the method used in making and reporting them shall be satisfactory to the superintendent.

C26–377. Presumptive Bearing Capacities of Soil.—*A*. Satisfactory bearing materials shall be ledge rock in its natural bed, natural deposits of gravel, sand, compact inorganic silt or clay, or any combination of these materials. These bearing materials shall not contain an appreciable amount of organic matter or other unsatisfactory material, nor shall they be underlaid by layers of such unsatisfactory materials of appreciable thickness.

B. Fill material, mud, muck, peat, organic silt, loose inorganic silt, and soft clay shall be considered as unsatisfactory bearing materials and shall be treated as having no presumptive bearing value.

C. The maximum allowable presumptive bearing materials shall, except for pile foundations, in the absence of satisfactory load tests or other evidence, be those established in Table I.

TABLE I

CLASSIFICATION OF SUPPORTING SOILS

Class	Material	Maximum Allowable Presumptive Bearing Value (Tons per Sq Ft)
1	Hard sound rock	60
2	Medium hard rock	40
3	Hardpan overlying rock	12
4	Compact gravel; very compact sandy gravel; boulder-gravel formations	10
5	Soft rock	8
6	Loose gravel; sandy gravel; compact sand; gravelly sand; very compact sand-inorganic silt soils	6
7	Hard dry consolidated clay	5
8	Loose coarse to medium sand; medium compact fine sand	4
9	Compact sand-clay soils	3
10	Loose fine sand; medium compact sand-inorganic silt soils	2
11	Firm or stiff clay	1.5
12	Loose saturated sand-clay soils; medium soft clay . .	1

Fordham and Ravenswood gneiss and trap are classed as hard rock. Inwood limestone, Manhattan schist, and massive serpentine are medium hard. Shale, decomposed serpentine, schist, or gneiss are classed as soft rock.

TABLE II

EXPLANATION OF TERMS

(a) Compaction Related to Spoon Blows (Sand)

Descriptive Term	Blows per Ft	
Loose	15 or less	These figures approximate for medium sand, 2½ in. spoon, 300-lb hammer, 18-in. fall. Coarse sand requires more blows; finer, fewer blows.
Compact	16 to 50	
Very compact	50 or more	

(b) Consistency Related to Spoon Blows (Mud, Clay)

Descriptive Term	Blows per Ft	Molding Effort
Very soft	push to 2	Relatively slight finger pressure
Soft	3 to 10	Substantial finger pressure
Stiff	11 to 30	Substantial finger pressure
Hard	30 or more	Not molded by fingers

TABLE III
Soil Sizes

Descriptive Term	Pass Sieve Number	Retained Sieve Number	Size Range
Clay	200	Hydrometer	0.006 mm
Silt	200	Analysis	0.006 to 0.074 mm
Fine sand	65	200	0.074 to 0.208 mm
Med. sand	28	65	0.208 to 0.589 mm
Coarse sand	8	28	0.589 to 2.362 mm
Gravel		8	2.362 mm
Pebble			2.362 mm to 2½ in.
Cobble			2½ in. to 6 in.
Boulder			6 in.

D. When it is shown by borings, or otherwise, that materials of varying bearing values must be used for the support of structures:

(1) The bearing value allowable for footings on the stronger material shall be unchanged;

(2) The bearing value allowable for footings on the weaker material shall be unchanged, provided the weaker material is not more than two classes below that of the stronger material as established in this section; but

(3) If the weaker material is ranked more than two classes below that of the stronger material as established in this section, the bearing value allowable for footings on the weaker material shall be reduced by a percentage equal to five times the number of classes it is below the stronger material in ranking.

C26–378. Soil Tests.—*A. When Soil Tests Are Required.* Where there is doubt as to the character of the soil or should application be made for permission to impose on the soil loads in excess of those specified in Section C26-377, a static load test shall be made in accordance with the rules of the board and at the expense of the owner of the proposed structure. The superintendent shall be duly notified of any such test in order that he may be present either in person or by representative. A complete record of such test shall be filed with the department.

B. Procedure for Soil Tests. In conducting tests to determine the safe sustaining power of the soil, the following regulations shall govern:

(1) The soil shall be tested at one or more places and at such level or levels as the conditions may determine or warrant.

(2) All tests shall be made under the supervision of the superintendent or his representative.

(3) Each test shall be made so as to load the soil over an area of at least 4 sq ft and so that the load is applied continuously throughout the test.

(4) Before any test is made, a sketch of the proposed apparatus and structure to be used in making the test shall be approved by the superintendent.

(5) The loading of the soil shall proceed as follows:

(a) The load per square foot which it is proposed to impose upon the soil shall be first applied and allowed to remain undisturbed and readings shall be taken at least once every 24 hr in order to determine the rate of settlement. The applied load shall remain until there has been no settlement for a period of 24 hr.

(b) After the requirements of clause (a) of this subdivision are met, an additional 50 per cent excess load shall be applied and the total load allowed to remain undisturbed until no settlement occurs during a period of 24 hr, careful measurements and readings being taken at least once every 24 hr in order to determine the rate of settlement.

C26–379. Determination of Results of Soil Tests. The test shall be considered unsatisfactory and the result unacceptable if the proposed safe load shows more than $\frac{3}{4}$ in. of settlement, or the increment of settlement obtained under the 50 per cent overload exceeds 60 per cent of the settlement obtained under the proposed load.

FOUNDATIONS

C26–391. General.—A. The foundation loads of permanent structures shall be carried down to satisfactory bearing material so that the entire transmitted load will be distributed over the bearing area at a unit intensity within the allowable bearing values established by this title. Any type of pile or other foundation construction unprovided for in this title shall meet, in addition to the requirements of this article, all the requirements which may be established by the rules of the board.

B. The provisions of Sections C26–391 through C26–411 apply to vertical loads and forces acting on the foundations but do not make allowance for lateral forces.

FOOTINGS

C26–392. Spread of Footings.—The superintendent shall have authority to permit or require a variation in unit loads between different footings on the same plot, when in his opinion such variation may be desirable or necessary to secure adequate stability in the structure.

C26–393. Levels of Footings.—Where footings are on sloping ground or where the bottoms of footings in a structure are on different levels or are on levels different from the footings of adjoining structures, the plans submitted must include vertical cross sections to natural scale, showing all such variations in level. When such change of level occurs, adequate provision shall be made for the lateral support of the material supporting the higher footing.

C26–394. Wood Footings.—Wood footings may be used only for wood frame structures, if such footings are placed entirely below the permanent water level or for capping wood piles which project above water level in foundations for wood frame structures over submerged or marsh lands.

C26–395. Concrete Footings.—Concrete footing shall be at least 12 in. thick, except that the thickness of such footing may be reduced to 8 in. for wood frame structures. Reinforcing steel shall be protected by at least 3 in. of concrete.

C26–396. Masonry Footings.—A. Masonry footings other than concrete for walls and piers shall be of solid masonry and shall have an area sufficient to distribute the superimposed load in accordance with the bearing capacity of the soil upon which such footings are built. When such footings rest upon other than solid rock, they shall extend at least 4 ft below finished grades. Masonry footings shall be laid in cement mortar or cement-lime mortar, shall be at least 8 in. wider than the foundation wall above, and shall have a depth at least equal to the total projection beyond the foundation walls next above.

B. When brickwork in foundation walls is stepped up from the footings, the maximum offset, if the brickwork is laid in single courses, shall be $1\frac{1}{2}$ in., and, if laid in double courses, 3 in.

C. Footings of concrete masonry shall also conform to the requirements of Sections C26–395 and C26–400.

C26–397. Masonry Foundations.—A. *General.* (1) Foundations wall shall have a thickness at least equal to that of the wall next above, and at least equal to the thicknesses given in inches in the following table:

Type of Structure	Solid Masonry	Hollow Masonry	Hollow Walls of Brick	Rubble Stone Masonry
Private dwellings at most 20 ft high and one-story structures at most 20 ft high	8	12	12	16
Private dwellings over 20 ft high or other structures of more than one story and over 20 ft high	12	16	16	16

(2) Foundation walls of hollow blocks may be used above grade when the upper walls are of wood frame or of hollow building block construction. All other foundation walls shall be of solid masonry, except when the structure is without basement or cellar.

B. Mortar-foundation walls built of masonry units shall be laid in cement mortar or cement-lime mortar.

C. Thickness. (1) In structures over two stories high, except private residences, foundation walls shall be at least 4 in. thicker than the wall section next above, except that when the walls are of hollow units or are hollow walls of brick, the foundation walls may be of the same thickness as the walls next above, provided such foundation walls are built of solid masonry or concrete and that a maximum of two stories above the foundation are of the same thickness. Foundation walls of reinforced concrete shall comply with the requirements of Sections C26–468 through C26–509.

(2) Every foundation wall serving as a retaining wall shall be designed to support safely all vertical and lateral loads to which such foundation wall may be subjected. It shall be unlawful to have tensile stresses in any masonry, except where such masonry is properly reinforced. The maximum compressive stresses due to combined dead, live, and lateral loads shall be within those permitted in Sections C26–355 through C26–362.

(3) When any foundation wall other than a retaining wall extends more than 13 ft below the top of the first-floor beams, such extended portion shall be increased by at least 4 in. for each interval of 13 ft or fraction thereof, except when such portion is adequately braced by an intermediate floor construction.

C26–398. Steel Grillage Footings.—Steel grillage beams may be used in footings; but, when such beams are used on yielding soils, they shall rest upon a bed of concrete, at least 8 in. thick, mixed in compliance with Section C26–311. In all cases, such beams shall be entirely encased by at least 4 in. of concrete of the same quality, and the spaces between beams shall be entirely filled with concrete, or with grout of one to two mixture by volume. The beams shall be provided with proper spacers.

C26–399. Pressure under Footings.—*A.* In the case of loads exerting pressure under the footings of foundations, the full dead loads, including the weight of the foundations, and the figured total live loads from all floors on the lowest tier of columns, piers, or walls shall be taken. For this purpose the reduced live loads, permitted by Section C26–348, may be used.

B. Where a footing is subject to a combination of pressure from wind and from live and dead loads, the normal pressure may be increased by $33\frac{1}{3}$ per cent, provided the area of the footing thus found is at least that required for the live and dead loads alone. Where the pressure on any footing, due to wind, is less than $33\frac{1}{3}$ per cent of the pressure due to live and dead loads, such pressure may be neglected.

C26–400. Design of Footings.—*A.* Footings shall be designed so as to distribute their loads properly within the allowed bearing capacities of soils as established by Sections C26–376 through C26–379 and so as to insure that the stresses in the materials shall be within those fixed by Sections C26–354 through C26–375.

B. In plain concrete footings the stress due to bending away from the face of the supported wall or pier, at any section, on a depth 4 in. less than the footing thickness, shall be within the safe modulus of rupture taken as $0.03f_c'$ for controlled concrete and as 60 psi and 75 psi for average concrete of grades A and B, respectively.

C26–401. Eccentric Footings.—Eccentricity of loading in foundation shall be fully investigated and the maximum loading shall be kept within the approved safe loads of the supporting soil.

C26–402. Weight of Foundations, Fill, and Floors.—The weight of foundations and of overlying fill and floors shall be included in the dead load for which provision shall be made.

C26–403. Depth of Foundations.—Footings, piers, or pile caps exposed to frost shall, unless such footings, piers, and caps are on sound rock, be carried down at least 4 ft below the adjoining ground surface. It shall be unlawful to lay footings in freezing weather, unless adequate precautions are taken against frost action. It shall be unlawful to lay footings, piers, or pile caps on frozen soil.

C26–404. Foundation Piers.—*A.* The minimum diameter of foundation piers shall be 2 ft and the method of their installation and construction shall be such as to provide for accurate preparation and inspection of their bottoms, and to insure sound concrete or other masonry.

B. The design of foundation piers shall be governed by the requirements of Article 8 of this title, and Sections C26–412 through C26–509, provided that for a foundation pier, constructed of plain concrete, the height of which pier exceeds 6 times its least horizontal dimension; except, where the least horizontal dimension is 6 ft or greater, the maximum allowable working stress shall be determined by the following formula:

$$f' = f\left(1.3 - \frac{H}{20D}\right),$$

in which f' is the reduced allowable working stress in psi,

f is the allowable working stress in psi given in Section C26–364 and Section C26–365,

H is the height of the pier in ft, and

D is the least horizontal dimension in ft.

C. The height shall in all cases be at most 12 times the least horizontal dimension, and the compressive stress shall be at most 850 psi.

D. If piers are constructed of reinforced concrete, such piers may be constructed with spiral or vertical reinforcement, as prescribed in Sections C26–468 through C26–509; except that, when all other conditions of such Sections are fulfilled, the provisions of subdivision (h) of Section C26–494 shall be inapplicable. Such construction shall be subject to the following modifications:

(1) The maximum allowance for spiral reinforcement shall be limited to 1 per cent and the maximum stress permitted on the gross section, including vertical reinforcement, shall be limited to 1000 psi.

(2) When such piers are spirally reinforced, and are 6 ft or greater in diameter, or where the ratio of height to diameter of such piers is 12:1 or less, vertical reinforcement may be omitted, the factor "p" in the formula for columns with spiral reinforcement, prescribed in subdivision *C* of the section C26–494, becoming zero.

(3) A minimum of three-quarters of 1 per cent of vertical reinforcement uniformly spaced around the perimeter shall be used in all other cases.

E. Where a pier is circular and entirely encased by a steel shell having a minimum thickness of $\frac{3}{8}$ in., such percentage of the shell thickness as corresponds with the efficiency of the vertical joint may be considered as the equivalent of an equal volume of the spiral reinforcement required by subdivision (c) of Section C26–494. If horizontal joints are spliced, the shell may be considered as the vertical as well as the spiral reinforcement up to the efficiency of the horizontal joints in tension.

F. It shall be unlawful to design the bases of foundation piers so that the presumptive capacity of the bearing material is exceeded. The presumptive capacity of such rock may, however, be increased above that stated in Section C26–377 to equal the unit compression in the pier itself, provided all of the following conditions are satisfied:

(1) Such piers bear on hard sound bedrock which is substantially level and the bearing surface of which is prepared by hand in level or bench areas.

(2)   Such loaded areas are 10 ft or more from the lot line or 40 ft or more below the curb level.

(3)   45° slopes extending downward from the periphery of the bearing areas fall outside of and below any adjoining excavation.

Pile Foundation

C26–405.0   General Requirements.—*A. Definition of a Pile.*   A pile is a structural unit introduced into the ground to transmit loads to lower strata or to alter the physical properties of the ground, and is of such shape, size, and length that the supporting material immediately underlying the base of the unit cannot be manually inspected.

B. General.   All piles shall conform to the requirements of this part and of such other provisions of the Code as are referred to.

C. Evaluation of Supporting Materials for Pile Foundations.   The bearing values of soils supporting pile foundations shall be evaluated by one of the following methods in accordance with the provisions of the sections specified herein:

(1)   The resistance to driving of piles, Section C26–405.2, *H*.
(2)   Pile load tests, Section C26–405.2, *I*.
(3)   The resistance to jacking, Section C26–405.2, *J*.

The above values may be modified as required by Section C26–405.2, Paragraphs *E*, *F*, or *G*.   The presumptive bearing values contained in Section C26–377 shall not apply to pile foundations.

D. Protection of Pile Materials.   Where the boring records or site conditions indicate possible deleterious action on pile materials because of soil constituents or of changing water levels, such materials shall be adequately protected by approved preservatives or impervious encasements which will not be rendered ineffective by driving and which will prevent such deleterious action.

E. Wood Piles.   (1) Wood piles shall be cedar, cypress, Douglas fir, hickory, Norway pine, oak, Southern pine, spruce, Western hemlock, or other similar species approved for such use.   Where required to be protected by preservatives, such treatment shall conform to the preservative treatment herein after specified.

(2)   All wood piles shall be of sound timber suitable for driving, cut above the ground, free from decay, unsound knots, knots in groups or clusters, windshakes and short or reversed bends.   The maximum diameter or any sound knot shall be one-third the diameter of the pile section where the knot occurs, but not more than 4 in. in the lower half of pile length nor more than 5 in. in other parts.   All knots shall be trimmed flush with the body of the pile and ends shall be squared with the axis.   Such piles shall have reasonably uniform taper throughout their length and shall be so straight that a line joining the centers of point and butt shall not depart from the body of the pile.   No bark or wane shall be measured in required dimensions.   The diameter at any section is the average of the maximum and minimum dimensions at that section.   All piles required to be treated shall be thoroughly peeled.

(3)   For temporary structures of a minor character as approved by the superintendent and for lightly loaded Class 4 and Class 5 structures (C26–242 and C26–243) located over submerged or marsh land, untreated wood piles having

minimum diameters of 4 in. at the point and 8 in. at the butt shall be permitted above high-tide level provided that the top 5 ft of each such pile remains exposed for visual inspection.

(4) Wood piles not impregnated with an approved preservative shall not be used unless the cut-off or top level of the pile is below permanent water-table level. The permanent water-table level shall not be assumed higher than the invert level of any sewer, drain, or subsurface structure, existing or planned in the adjacent streets, nor higher than the water level at the site resulting from the lowest draw-down of wells or sumps.

(5) Creosoted timber piles when pressure-treated to a final net retention of not less than 12 lb of creosote per cubic foot of wood may extend above permanent water level when installed and protected in accordance with the following provisions:

   (a) The tops of the cut-off piles shall be below finished ground level and shall be treated with three coats of hot creosote oil and capped with concrete equal to at least Class A concrete (C26–365).

   (b) The preservative shall be Grade No. 1 coal-tar creosote oil as required by United States Federal specification, No. TT-W-571-b. Preservative treatment shall be an empty-cell process, in accordance with the same specification.

F. Rolled Structural-Steel Piles. Rolled structural-steel piles shall conform as to material to the requirements of Section C26–322. Sections of such piles shall be of **H**-form, with flange projection not exceeding 14 times the minimum thickness of metal in either web or flange and with total flange width at least 85 per cent of the depth of the section. No section shall have a thickness of metal less than $\frac{3}{8}$ in. Other structural sections or combinations of sections having flange widths and depths of not less than 10 in. and thickness of metal not less than $\frac{1}{2}$ in. may also be used.

G. Precast Concrete Piles. Precast concrete piles shall be reinforced with longitudinal steel bars equal to at least 2 per cent of the volume of concrete in such piles, and with lateral ties in the form of hoops or spirals of at least $\frac{1}{4}$-in. round rods or wires, spaced 12 in. on centers throughout the length of the pile, except in bottom and top 3 ft, where this spacing shall be reduced to not more than 3 in. The top of this pile may be cut off after driving. Reinforcing steel shall be covered with not less than 2 in. of concrete. All piles shall be properly cured before they are driven.

H. Cast-in-Place Concrete Piles. After installation to final depth and immediately before the placing of the concrete filling, the inside of the tube, shell, or bore shall be free of any foreign matter. Concrete shall be placed by such methods that the entire volume of the tube, shell, or bore is filled. Concrete filling shall not be placed through water, unless the superintendent specifically consents in writing to such placing, after the submission to him of the detailed method of procedure. The concrete cap shall not be poured until at least 1 hr after all piles within the cap group are completely filled.

I. Combination or Composite Piles. Combination or composite piles may consist of two types of piles. The maximum allowable load shall be that allowed for the weaker section. The design of the piles shall be satisfactory to the superintendent. The connection or joint between the two sections shall be so constructed as to prevent the separation of the upper or lower sections during construction and thereafter. The details and methods of making joints shall be submitted to the superintendent and approved by him before any piles of this type are used.

J. Piles Located in Soils Subject to Physical Change or Movement. (1) Structures on piles installed in unstable strata of soil which are or may be subject to lateral movements shall be adequately braced by batter piles or by other effective methods. All such piles, including the bracing piles, shall be driven to satisfactory resistance into materials of Class 11, or better, as classified in Section C26–377.

(2) Piles installed in soils which exhibit considerable subsidence and consolidation during driving shall penetrate to satisfactory resistance into suitable underlying material or shall be driven to rock.

K. Use of Existing Piles at Demolished Structures. (1) Piles left in place, where the structure has been demolished, shall not be used for the support of new construction unless satisfactory evidence can be produced as to the length and driving condition of each pile, which evidence will prove that the piles in question are adequate for loadings in accordance with the requirements.

(2) Where additional piles are required to support the loadings of the new structure, then the existing piles shall be limited to 75 per cent of their rated load-carrying capacity as determined under Subparagraph (1) above, and the additional piles shall be of similar type and shall also be restricted to 75 per cent of the rated load-carrying capacity as determined by the provisions of Section C26–405.2.

L. Minimum Over-all Dimensions. Except as provided in Section C26–405.0, no tapered pile shall be less than 6 in. in diameter at any section, nor have less than a diameter of 8 in. at the butt after cut-off. No pile of uniform section shall have a diameter of less than 8 in., or, if not circular, a minimum dimension of less than $7\frac{1}{2}$ in. Tapered shoes or points of lesser dimensions may be attached to the ends of piles.

M. Minimum Spacing. Except as provided in Subparagraph (4) below, the minimum spacing of piles shall be as follows:

(1) Piles bearing a rock or penetrating into rock shall have a minimum spacing center-to-center of twice the average diameter, or 1.75 times the diagonal dimension of the pile, but not less than 2 ft.

(2) All other piles shall have a minimum spacing center-to-center of twice the average diameter of 1.75 times the diagonal dimenison of the pile, but not less than $2\frac{1}{2}$ ft, except that all piles located in groups or abutting groups that receive their principal support in materials below Class 6, as classified in Section C26–377, shall have their spacing increased above the minimum values by 10 per cent for each interior pile up to a maximum increase of spacing of 40 per cent.

(3) If, because of known obstructions or space limitations, piles are originally designed to be spaced closer than specified above, or if piles along a lot line are located less than one-half of the required spacing from the lot line, the carrying capacity of each pile not sufficiently distant from another pile or from the lot line shall be reduced. The percentage reduction in load-carrying capacity of each pile shall be one-half of the percentage reduction in required spacing.

(4) When the supporting capacity of a single row of piles is adequate for the wall of a structure, effective measures shall be taken to provide for eccentricity and

lateral forces, or the piles shall be driven alternately in lines spaced at least 1 ft apart and located symmetrically under the center of gravity of the loads carried. A single row of piles without lateral bracing may be used for private dwellings not exceeding two stories in height, provided the centers of the piles are located within the width of the foundation wall.

N. Minimum Penetration.   Piles shall penetrate into soil of Class 12 or better, as classified in Section C26–377, at lesat 10 ft below cut-off level and at least 10 ft below ground level.   The pile point shall be at least 10 ft below nearest established curb level when the pile is located 25 ft or less from the lot or property line.   Any embedment of such a pile in soil less than 10 ft below the nearest established curb level shall not be considered as providing any resistance for such pile, and load-carrying determinations for such pile, in accordance with the provisions of Section C26–405.2, shall be made after such embedment is eliminated, by casting off, by excavation, or by other acceptable means.

O. Bracing of Piles.   (1) Tops of all piles shall be embedded in caps not less than 3 in., and the caps shall extend at least 4 in. beyond the edge of all piles.

(2)   Except for single-row piles permitted in Section C26–405.0, *M*(4), every pile shall be laterally braced by rigid connection or to at least two other piles in radial directions not less than 60° apart.   Three or more piles, connected by a rigid cap, provided they are located in radial directions not less than 60° apart, shall be considered as braced.

(3)   Concrete ties for bracing piles shall have minimum dimensions of one-twentieth of the clear distance between pile caps, but not less than 8 in., and shall be reinforced as a column with the bars anchored in the caps to develop full tension value.   A continuous reinforced stone or gravel concrete slab or mat 6 in. or more in thickness, supported by and anchored to the pile caps, or in which piles are embedded at least 3 in., may be used in lieu of ties for bracing if such slab does not depend upon the soil for the direct support of its own weight and any loads which may be carried thereon.

P. Soil under Pile Cap.   The soil immediately below the pile cap shall not be considered as carrying any vertical load.

Q. Pile Caps.   Pile caps shall be designed in accordance with the requirements of Section C26–496 for the pile loads and butt dimensions, considering each pile as a separate reaction concentrated at the butt section.

C26–405.1.   Requirements for Installation of Piles.—*A.   Precautions during Installations.*   Piles shall be installed with due consideration for safety of adjacent structures by a method which leaves their strength unimpaired and which develops and retains the required load-bearing resistance.   If conditions which will cause serious deterioration of piles exist at the site, suitable measure to avoid such damage shall be employed.   Special precautions shall be taken to protect from injury both the butt, and where deemed necessary by the superintendent, the tip of the piles. If any pile is damaged during installation, the damage shall be satisfactorily repaired or the pile rejected.

B. Equipment.   Equipment and methods for installing piles shall be such that piles are installed in their proper position and alignment.   Followers shall be used only upon written permission of the superintendent and only where necessary to

APPENDIX 6 325

effect installation of piles. A follower shall be of steel of such size, shape, length, and weight as to permit driving the pile in the desired location and to the required depth and resistance. Cushion blocks shall be of such material and design that loss of energy is held to a minimum.

C. Tolerances and Modification of Design Due to Field Conditions. If any pile is installed out of plumb more than 2 per cent of the pile length, the design of the foundation shall be modified as may be necessary to support the resulting vertical and lateral forces properly.

In types of piles which will not permit subsurface inspection, a variance from the plumb of more than 2 per cent of the exposed section of the pile, or other evidence which indicates that the piles are not installed within allowable tolerances, shall be considered as sufficient cause for corrective measures.

Where piles are installed out of position and thus receive eccentric loading, the true loading on such piles shall be analytically determined from a survey showing the actual location of the piles as driven, and if the total load on any pile is more than 110 per cent of the allowable load bearing capacity, correction shall be made by installing additional piles or by other methods of load distribution.

Groups of piles shall not be modified by the addition of piles of lesser load values than the piles originally comprising the group.

A tolerance of 3 in. from the designed location shall be permitted in the installation of piles, without reduction in load capacity, provided the piles comply with the requirements of this subparagraph for conditions of eccentricity.

D. Jetting. Jetting shall not be used except when permitted by the superintendent in writing. When jetting is used, it shall be carried out in such a manner that the carrying capacity of the piles already in place and the safety of existing adjacent structures shall not be impaired. Jetting shall be stopped not less than 3 ft above the final expected bottom of the pile. The piles shall be carried down at least 3 ft below the depth of jetting and until the required resistance is obtained. If there is evidence that the jetting has disturbed the load-bearing capacities of previously installed piles, those piles which have been disturbed shall be restored to conditions meeting the requirements of this article by proper redriving or by other acceptable method after the jetting operations in the area have been completed.

E. Piles Installed without Impact. Piles may be installed by methods other than impact-driving, provided the bottoms of such piles bear on or in a material of Class 9 or better, as classified in Section C26–377.

F. Penetration Measurements. Penetration measurements for the purpose of determining resistance to driving shall not be made when pile heads are damaged to an extent which may effect penetration, nor immediately after fresh cushion blocks have been inserted under the striking part of the hammer and such measurements shall be made without interrupting the driving more than necessary for such measurements. Gross penetration per hammer blow is the downward axial movement of the pile as measured at an established point on the pile located not more than 5 ft above the ground surface. Net penetration is the gross penetration less the rebound, or the net downward movement of the established point.

G. Pile Settlement. Gross settlement is the total amount of downward movement of a pile or pile group which occurs under an applied test load. Net settlement of a pile or pile group is the gross settlement minus the rebound which occurs after removal of the applied test load.

H. Resistance. Resistance is defined as the number of hammer blows or the jacking pressure required to cause any definite penetration.

I. Sequence of Installation. Individual piles and pile groups shall be installed in such sequence that the carrying capacity of previously installed piles is not reduced.

J. Heaved Piles. In soils in which the installations of pile causes previously installed piles to heave, accurate level marks shall be put on all piles immediately after installation and all heaved piles shall be re-installed to the required resistance.

K. Splicing of Piles. Splices shall be avoided as far as practicable. Where used, splices shall be such that the resultant vertical and lateral loads at the splices are adequately transmitted. Splices shall be so constructed as to provide and maintain true alignment and position of the component parts of the pile during installation and subsequent thereto. Except for piles which can be visually inspected after driving, splices shall develop not less than 50 per cent of the value of the pile in bending. Proper consideration shall be given to the design of splices at sections of piles which may be subject to tension or to bending.

L. Inspection and Control. The owner shall maintain a competent licensed professional engineer or competent licensed architect acceptable to the superintendent on the site during pile installations to insure and certify that piles are installed in accordance with design and code requirements.

M. Identification of Piles. A plan showing clearly the designation of all piles by an identifying system shall be filed with the department before the installation of piling is begun.

N. Records of Pile Driving. A record shall be kept by the owner's representative of the total penetration of every pile and the behavior of such pile during driving. Any deviation from the designed location, alignment or load-carrying capacity of any pile shall be promptly reported to the engineer or architect and adequate corrective measures shall be taken. Plans showing such deviations and corrective measures shall be filed with the department. Upon the completion of the pile-driving records, together with the records of such additional borings or other subsurface information that were obtained during the installation of the piles, shall also be filed with the department.

C26–405.2. Allowable Load on Piles.—*A. General.* The foundation loads of structures on pile foundations shall be carried down to satisfactory bearing materials, so that the entire transmitted load is supported without causing damaging vertical and lateral movements. The pile groups of a foundation shall be proportioned as to relative size, as nearly as practicable, to produce uniform settlement and shall be designed to support the maximum combination of the following loads:

(1) All dead loads including the weight of the pile cap and any superimposed load thereon.

(2) The reduced live load as specified in Section C26–248.

(3) Lateral force and moment reactions, including the effect of eccentricity, if any, between the column load and the center of gravity of the pile group.

(4) That amount of the vertical, lateral and moment reactions resulting from

wind loads in excess of one-third of the respective vertical, lateral, and moment reactions computed from the dead and other live loads.

B. Allowable Axial and Lateral Loads on Vertical Piles. The maximum load permitted on any vertical pile shall be the allowable axial load described herein applied concentrically in the direction of its axis. No lateral loads in excess of 1000 lb per pile shall be permitted on a vertical pile, unless it has been demonstrated by tests that the pile will resist a lateral load of 200 per cent of the proposed working lateral load without lateral movement of more than $\frac{1}{2}$ in. at the ground surface; and will resist the proposed working lateral load without a lateral movement of more than $\frac{3}{16}$ in. at the ground level.

C. Allowable Lateral Loads on Batter Piles. The resultant of all vertical loads and lateral forces, occurring simultaneously, in the direction of the axis of batter piles shall not produce stresses in excess of those established in this section. The remaining horizontal component shall not exceed 1000 lb per pile unless it is demonstrated, as established in this section, that such piles can safely resist greater lateral loads.

D. Structural Strength of Piles and Limiting Value of Stresses.

(1) *Strength of Unbraced Piles.* That portion of any pile which is free-standing in air or water shall be designed as a column considered to be fixed at a point 5 ft below the soil-contact level in Class 9 material, or better, as classified in Section C26–377, and 10 ft below in any other material.

(2) *Handling and Installing of Piles.* Piles shall demonstrate their capacity to be handled and installed to the desired total penetration and resistance, and to resist the forces caused by the installation of adjacent piles without structural injury.

(3) *Limiting Values of Stresses.* The average compressive stress on any cross section of a pile, produced by that portion of the design load which may be considered to be transmitted to that section, shall not exceed the allowable values listed below. As an alternative method for the purposes of this section, it may be assumed that for piles more than 40 ft in length, installed in material of Class 12 or better (C26–377), 75 per cent of the load of an end-bearing pile is carried by the tip. For friction piles the full load shall be computed at the cross section located at two-thirds of the embedded length of the pile measured from the tip.

(3.1) *Timber Piles.* Cedar, western hemlock, Norway pine, spruce, or other woods of comparable strength: 600 psi. Cypress, Douglas fir, hickory, oak, Southern pine, or other woods of comparable strength: 800 psi. The maximum allowable load on a wood pile having a 6-in. point shall be 20 tons; and on a pile having an 8-in. point or more the maximum allowable load shall be 25 tons.

(3.2) *Concrete.* Concrete for piles shall comply with Section C26–38 and shall be controlled or average concrete. f_c is the allowable axial compressive strength, and f_c' is the 28-day compressive strength of the concrete. f_c' shall not exceed 4000 psi for computation purposes. The modular ratio, n, is defined as $30,000 \div f_c'$.

For controlled concrete: $f_c = 0.25f_c'$.
For average concrete: Class A.
$f_c = 500$ psi, $n = 15$. Class B.
$f_c = 625$ psi, $n = 12$.

The value n is to be applied only to reinforcing steel in precast concrete piles.

(3.3) *Reinforcing Steel.* The steel unit stress $f_s = mf_c$. Reinforcing steel in excess of 4 per cent of the average cross-sectional area of the pile, and reinforcing steel in cast-in-place concrete piles, except as provided in Subparagraph (3.5), shall not be assigned any load-carrying capacity.

(3.4) *Rolled Structural Steel Piles and Concrete-Filled Steel Piles, Shells, or Tubes.* Steel unit stress f_s 9000 psi, provided the pipe, shell, or tube is at least $\frac{1}{8}$ in. thick, and f_c shall be as provided above. Where injurious soil conditions exist, the steel shall be protected as provided for in Section C26–405.0.

(3.5) *Piles Bearing on Rock (consisting of a structural steel shape installed as a full length core, protected by at least 2 in. of concrete, in a concrete-filled steel shell, at least as thick as No. 18 U.S. Standard gage, which is to be left permanently in place).* The pile shall be formed by driving a casing containing a close-fitting temporary core in such manner as to exclude foreign matter from the casing, or by driving an open-ended casing which shall be cleaned to the bottom. The casing shall be driven to rock, or hardpan overlying rock, to a final penetration of not less than 8 blows to the inch of the last 3 in., using a hammer which delivers per blow at least 22,000 ft-lb, either leaving the drive casing permanently in place or placing a light shell within it and withdrawing the drive casing; placing a structural steel shape within the casing or shell; filling the casing or shell with concrete, then immediately driving the H-beam to refusal on rock before the concrete has set, as indicated by a rate of penetration of $\frac{1}{4}$ in. or less under the last five blows, with the hammer striking a blow of 22,000 ft-lb or equivalent. Then, f_s for the core shall be 12,000 psi and f_c for the concrete as provided above, with no load value for the shell. The load on such a pile shall not exceed 100 tons without tests, or 200 tons on the basis of tests as specified below.

E. *Piles Installed Open-Ended to Rock.* Concrete-filled steel pipe or shells installed open-ended to bearing on rock for the loads permitted in this paragraph shall have a minimum steel thickness of 0.3 in. The piles shall be cleaned to the bottom and redriven or rejacked until the piles bear securely, without possibility of sliding, on Class 1 or Class 2 rock (C26–377). The allowable load on such piles, where satisfactory evidence is submitted that they rest on Class 1 or Class 2 rock, shall be determined by either of the following methods:

(1) The load at the top of the pile shall not exceed 80 per cent of the load determined in accordance with the limiting stresses for the combined steel and concrete section provided that the pipe or shell shall be driven to resistance such that the net penetration for the last five blows totals $\frac{1}{4}$ in. or less under hammers having an energy per blow of at least 22,000 ft-lb, unless permission is granted in writing by the superintendent to permit the use of lighter hammers because of limited headroom due to existing overhead structures.

(2) In accordance with the provisions of Paragraph *I* of this section for loading tests if driven, and not more than 50 per cent of the jacking pressure, if jacked.

The maximum allowable load on any single pile of this type shall not exceed that permitted by the limitations for material stresses, soil conditions, and other requirements of Sections C26–405.0, C26–405.1, and C26–405.2, but shall in no case exceed 200 tons.

F. Piles Bearing on Rock, Hardpan or Gravel-Boulder Formations Directly Overlying Rock. Except as provided in the preceding paragraph of this section, the allowable load of piles bearing on rock, hardpan, or gravel-boulder formations directly overlying rock shall be determined in accordance with Paragraph *I* or by formula in accordance with the provisions of Paragraph *H* for loads of 40 tons or less per single pile or shall be found in accordance with the provisions of Paragraph *I* for loads exceeding 40 tons per single pile, provided that in the latter case the piles bearing on rock are driven to resistance such that the net penetration for the last five blows totals $\frac{1}{4}$ in. or less under hammers as specified in Paragraph *H*, and piles bearing on hardpan, or gravel-boulder formations directly overlying rock, are driven to resistance such that the net penetration for the last five blows indicates, in accordance with the formulas in Paragraph *H*, a bearing value not less than the proposed pile load. The maximum allowable load on any single pile of this type shall not exceed that permitted by the limitations for material stresses, soil conditions, and other requirements of Sections C26–405.0, C26-405.1, and C26-405.2, but in no case shall the allowable load exceed 120 tons for piles bearing on rock, nor 80 tons for piles bearing on hardpan or gravel-boulder formations directly overlying rock.

G. Piles Which Receive Their Principal Support Other Than by Direct Bearing (as covered in Paragraphs E and F of this section). The allowable load on such piles shall be determined in accordance with the provisions of Paragraphs *H* and *I* provided it is 30 tons or less per single pile; and for loads exceeding 30 tons per single pile in accordance with the provisions of Paragraph *I* for load tests. The maximum allowable load on any single pile of this type shall not exceed that permitted by the limitation for material stresses, soil conditions, and other requirements of Sections C26–405.0, C26–405.1, and C26–405.2, but in no case shall the allowable load exceed 30 tons.

Where the points of a proposed foundation are underlaid by a stratum of compressible soil ranking below Class 10 (C26–377) then either:

(1) The piles shall be driven completely through such compressible stratum to satisfactory bearing capacities in underlying material of Class 9 or better.

(2) Or other effective measures shall be taken to reduce the magnitude and unequal character of the settlement to be expected as a result of the consolidation of such stratum under the stresses imposed by the foundation loads, in which case a report shall be submitted by a qualified licensed professional soil engineer to the superintendent establishing the effectiveness of such measures, based upon laboratory soil tests on undisturbed samples of the compressible soils of a satisfactory quality and upon foundation analyses to determine to the satisfaction of the superintendent that the probable total magnitude, distribution, and time rate of settlement to be expected for the proposed structure will not be excessive.

H. Pile Loads Evaluated by Formula. The following determination of the allowable pile load is to be used only where tests or experience have shown that formulas specified herein are applicable to the soil conditions as indicated by borings, and to the type of pile being considered. Where the existence of firm soil underlain by soil of poorer bearing values creates doubt as to the safe sustaining value of any pile, the superintendent may require that the site be investigated in accordance with the provisions of Paragraph I.

The allowable loads may be determined by the value of R obtained by one of the following formulas, provided that the piles with an average diameter or side of 8 in. or less are driven by a hammer which delivers a blow of at least 7000 ft-lb; that the piles with an average diameter or side greater than 8 in. and not more than 18 in. are driven by a hammer which delivers a blow of at least 15,000 ft-lb; and that piles with an average diameter or side of more than 18 in. are driven by a hammer which delivers a blow of at least 22,000 ft-lb. Double-acting hammers shall be operated at full rated speed, pressure, and stroke as shown in the manufacturers' catalogues. The minimum hammer blow for piles intended to carry 25 tons or more shall be 15,000 ft-lb.

For drop hammers: $R = \dfrac{2WH}{s + 1}.$

For single-acting hammers: $R = \dfrac{2WH}{s + 0.1}.$

For double-acting hammers: $R = \dfrac{2E}{s + 0.1}.$

R = allowable pile load—pounds.
W = weight of striking part—pounds.
H = effective height of fall—feet.
E = energy per blow—foot-pounds.
s = average penetration per blow—inches.

I. Determination of Bearing Value by Load Tests. When the allowable pile load is to be determined by load tests, these shall be made as described in the following. Such load tests shall be at the expense of the owner of the proposed structure, or of the person causing the piles to be installed. Before any load test is made, the proposed apparatus and structure to be used for the test shall be approved by the superintendent. All load tests shall be made under the supervision of the superintendent or his representative. A complete record of such load tests shall be filed with the department.

(1) *Uniform Conditions.* Areas of the foundation site, within which the subsurface soil conditions are substantially similar in character, shall be established by borings not less than as required by Section C26–376. Each such area shall be tested by driving at least three piles distributed over the area. Continuous records for the full depth of the penetration of the pile shall be kept of the blows per foot to drive the pile to the desired resistance. If the records of the driving resistance of these piles are not similar, or the driving resistance is not in reasonable agreement with the information obtained from the borings, or where piles designed to carry more than 30 tons each are to be installed in soils underlaid by strata of poorer bearing value, the superintendent may require additional piles to be driven for test purposes.

(2) *Allowable Pile Load by Test.* One of the three piles in each area of uniform conditions, but not less than two typical piles for the entire foundation of the building or group of buildings on the site nor less than one pile for each 15,000 sq ft of building area, shall be loaded by a method which will maintain constant load under

increasing settlement. The test load shall be twice the proposed load value of the pile. The test load shall be applied in seven increments equal to: $\frac{1}{2}$, $\frac{3}{4}$, 1, $1\frac{1}{4}$, $1\frac{1}{2}$, $1\frac{3}{4}$, and 2 times the proposed load. Readings of settlements and rebounds shall be referred to a constant elevation bench mark and shall be recorded to 1/1000 ft for increment or decrement of load. After the proposed working load has been applied and for each increment thereafter, the test load shall remain in place until there is no settlement in a 2-hr period. The total test load shall remain in place until settlement does not exceed 1/1000 ft in 48 hr. The total load shall be removed in decrements not exceeding one-fourth of the total test load with intervals of not less than 1 hr. The rebound shall be recorded after each decrement is removed. The maximum allowable pile load shall be one-half that which causes a net settlement of not more than 1/100 in. per ton of total test load or shall be one-half that which causes a gross settlement of 1 in., whichever is less.

(3) *Foundation Piles.* In the subsequent driving of the foundation piles for the structure, a pile shall be deemed to have a bearing value equal to that determined by the load test pile for that area of the foundation, when the foundation pile, using the same or equivalent make and model of pile hammer, and the same operation of the hammer with regard to speed, height of fall, stroke and pressure, and all other variable factors, shall develop equal or greater final resistance to driving than the load test pile. Where actual pile lengths vary more than 50 per cent from that of the test pile, the superintendent may require investigation to determine the adequacy of the piles.

(4) *Pile Groups.* Where the superintendent has reason to doubt the safe-load sustaining capacity of pile groups, he may require, at the expense of the owner, group load tests up to 150 per cent of the proposed group load.

J. Piles Installed by Jacking or Other Methods without Impact. The carrying capacity of a pile installed by jacking or other methods without impact shall be not more than 50 per cent of the load or force used to install the pile. The carrying capacity of piles installed by static forces shall be demonstrated by load tests, on not less than two piles selected by the superintendent, applied over a period of time sufficient to indicate that excessive settlement will not occur. Carrying capacities shall not exceed the allowable loads as provided in Section C26–405.2.

K. Underpinning Piles. Piles packed into position for permanent and for temporary underpinning shall be evaluated for safe-bearing capacity by the jacking pressures used. The working load of each temporary underpinning pile shall not exceed the total jacking pressures used to obtain the required penetration. The working load of each permanent underpinning pile shall not exceed two-thirds of the total jacking pressure used to obtain the required penetration if the load is held constant for 10 hr, or one-half of the total jacking pressure at final penetration, but in no case are the load values set forth in Section C26–405.2 to be exceeded.

INDEX

Abutments
  definition, 287
  design of, 296
  failures of, 297
  stability of, 299
  types of, 296
Active earth pressure, 1
Air locks, 233
Anchored bulkheads, 49
Angle of external friction, 3
  of internal friction, 2
  of repose, 2
  of visibility, 33
Artificial island method, 234
Auger borings, 70

Ball-and-socket type sheet piling, 44
Batter piles, 190
Bearing capacity of soils, 87
Berm, 209
Boring data, 72
Bottom seal
  in caissons, 235
  in single-wall cofferdams, 220
Boussinesq formula, 35
Bracing
  cellular cofferdams, 203
  single-wall cofferdams, 215
Breakwaters
  concrete blocks, 251
  crib, 252
  function of, 251
  rubble stone, 253
Bridge abutments, 296
Bridge piers, 287
Bouyancy, center of, 245

Caissons
  concrete, 231
  definition of, 230
  floating, 242
  open, 230
  pneumatic, 231
  rotating, 241
  steel, 231
  timber, 231
Cantilever sheet piling, 46
Cast-in-place piles
  shell type, 157
  shell-less, 159

Cellular cofferdams
  advantages of, 196
  circular type, 198
  cloverleaf type, 210
  diaphragm type, 198
  drainage of, 203
  on clay, 204
  tension in interlocks, 200
Center of rotation for pile groups, 170
Centrifugal force on pier, 291
Clay, 67
Cofferdams
  braced, 215
  self-sustaining, 196
  single-wall, 215
  in water, 219
Cohesion, 2
Cohesive soils, 67
Combined footings, 111
Combined pressures, 27
Consolidometer, 97
Coping, 287
Coulomb's equation, 6
Coulomb's theory, 10
Culmann's method, 18
Current pressure on piers, 292
Cutting edge for caissons, 236
Cutting off concrete piles, 145

Dead load for bridge piers, 290
Direction of earth pressure, 25
Distribution of earth pressure, 26
Docks, 263
Double-acting steam hammer, 150
Drainage of cofferdams, 203
Drilling for soil exploration, 72
Driving stresses in piles, 151
Drop hammer, 149
Dummy piles, 177

Earth pressure analogy, 1
Eccentric loads on footings, 121
Economical spacing of piers, 287
Elastic center method, 174
Embankment failures, 300
Engineering-News formula, 154
Equivalent point of support, 55
Excavation
  in caissons, 234
  in cofferdams, 220
Exploration of soils, 70

333